THE PRINCIPLES OF PHYSICAL OPTICS

AN HISTORICAL AND PHILOSOPHICAL TREATMENT

BY

ERNST MACH

TRANSLATED BY

JOHN S. ANDERSON, M.A., D.Sc., Ph.D.

AND

A. F. A. YOUNG, B.Sc., Ph.D.

WITH TEN PLATES AND 280 DIAGRAMS

DOVER PUBLICATIONS, INC.

This new Dover Edition is an unabridged republication
of the English translation first published in 1926.

Manufactured in the U. S. A.

TRANSLATORS' NOTE

I T is hoped that the following translation will be useful both to those interested in the philosophical aspects of Ernst Mach's work and to the student of physics.

In preparing this translation we have endeavoured as far as possible to keep to the plan of the German edition. For this reason we have retained the rather frequent use of italics in the text and have altered only a few of the symbols employed; a systematic revision of these has not been attempted, as it would have involved alterations in the lettering of the illustrations, many of which are reproductions from classical publications. We have also corrected several errors, principally algebraic, in the original and for the sake of clearness have added Fig. 269*a*.

J. S. A.
A. F. A. Y.

TEDDINGTON,
November, 1925

TO

DR. PAUL CARUS

AND

MESSRS. HEGELER

IN TOKEN OF FRIENDSHIP AND GRATITUDE

DR. PAUL CARUS,
La Salle,
Illinois, U.S.A.

MY ESTEEMED FRIEND,

I call to mind the time when the first numbers of the " Open Court " failed to reach me and there slowly sprang up between us a correspondence which greatly influenced my life. We met on common ground in our endeavour to remove from different branches of knowledge the restrictive barriers to progress. In consequence I became familiar with the educational work which your firm has accomplished to an ever-increasing extent. In this way you have attained to the only possible form of immortality.

It is not too much to say that only through your interest in my work and your masterly translations could I get into touch with a large circle of people and feel that I have not lived in vain. If my name should be frequently quoted, may this always be done with a remembrance of your name and that of Edward C. Hegeler.

Surrounded, perhaps for the last time, by the summer beauties of nature I send you and yours a farewell greeting.

Your old friend,
ERNST MACH

MUNICH,
July, 1913

PREFACE

IN this book I have set myself a task similar to that of the books on Mechanics and Heat, but the method of presentation corresponds mostly to that of the latter. I hope that I have laid bare, not without success, the origin of the general concepts of optics and the historical threads in their development, extricated from metaphysical ballast. Results of historical research have not, however, been accumulated here, and certain chapters, treated exhaustively in other quarters, are only cursorily surveyed.

I have endeavoured to show, from a critical and psychological standpoint, how the ideas concerning the nature of light have been moulded at the hands of prominent individual workers, what transformations these ideas have had to undergo on account of the revelation of new facts and by reason of the views associated with them, and how the general concepts of optics develop from these. This was also the basis of my lectures which began in a course on geometrical optics at the commencement of my work as a Privat Dozent at Prague. Such a presentation must, in the first place, be confined to bringing forward as clearly as possible the many salient facts and questions without special regard to the chronological sequence of the discoveries.

On account of my old age and illness I have decided, yielding to pressure from my publisher, but contrary to my usual practice, to hand over this part of the book to be printed,* while radiation, the decline of the emission theory of light, Maxwell's theory, together with relativity, will be briefly dealt with in a subsequent part. The questions and doubts arising from the study of these chapters formed the subject of tedious researches undertaken conjointly with my son, who has been my colleague for many years. It would have been desirable for the collaborated second part to have been published almost immediately, but I am compelled, in what may be my last opportunity, to cancel my contemplation of the relativity theory.

I gather from the publications which have reached me, and especially from my correspondence, that I am gradually becoming regarded as the forerunner of relativity. I am able even now to

---

* The printing was commenced in the summer of 1916, but at the wish of the author there were further experiments to be tried and completed. The delay in the publication of the present book is due to the long absence of the person to whom this task was entrusted, as a result of his mobilization during the same summer, and to a series of adverse circumstances resulting from the conditions of the times.

picture approximately what new expositions and interpretations many of the ideas expressed in my book on Mechanics will receive in the future from the point of view of relativity.

It was to be expected that philosophers and physicists should carry on a crusade against me, for, as I have repeatedly observed, I was merely an unprejudiced rambler, endowed with original ideas, in varied fields of knowledge. I must, however, as assuredly disclaim to be a forerunner of the relativists as I withhold from the atomistic belief of the present day.*

The reason why, and the extent to which, I discredit the present-day relativity theory, which I find to be growing more and more dogmatical, together with the particular reasons which have led me to such a view—the considerations based on, the physiology of the senses, the theoretical ideas, and above all the conceptions resulting from my experiments—must remain to be treated in the sequel.

The ever-increasing amount of thought devoted to the study of relativity will not, indeed, be lost ; it has already been both fruitful and of permanent value to mathematics. Will it, however, be able to maintain its position in the physical conception of the universe of some future period as a theory which has to find a place in a universe enlarged by a multitude of new ideas ? Will it prove to be more than a transitory inspiration in the history of this science ?

In conclusion I would like to recall the specially beneficial intercourse during the past decade with my late friend, Professor E. Reusch, of Tübingen, who introduced me to Dr. Steeg u. Reuter, and also the long-standing friendly assistance given to me in my work by the Viennese optician, Karl Fritsch-Prokesch. Dr. Rudolf Steinheil, of Munich, has, in the most unselfish manner, made possible our latest researches, for which I take this opportunity of heartily thanking him.

Thanks are due to Professor J. Plassmann, of Münster, and J. G. Hagen, S.J., of the Specola Vaticana, for the discovery of the long-sought picture of F. Grimaldi in the possession of Professor M. Rajna in the Observatory of the University of Bologna, of which Professor Majocchi, of the same University, has prepared a photograph. P. Christian Kiehl, S.J., of Vienna, and P. Kofler, of Rome, have constructed the block of Grimaldi's signature. I express my gratitude to each of the above for the trouble they have taken.

ERNST MACH

Munich-Vaterstetten
July, 1913

* " Scientia," Vol. 7, 4th year (1910), No. 14.

CONTENTS

LIST OF PLATES

THE PRINCIPLES OF PHYSICAL OPTICS

CHAPTER I

INTRODUCTION

1. BRIGHTNESS, darkness, light, and colour cannot be *described*. These sensations, experienced by people with normal sight, can only be *named*, that is, *designated* by means of a generally recognized arbitrary convention or one that suggests itself naturally.

A piece of copper, which in a dark room can only be *felt*, can also be *seen*, though of course only by a non-defective, open, eye directed towards it, in sunlight, in the neighbourhood of a burning lamp, or, if it is heated until it glows, in a dark room.

The appearance of the feature *red* in copper, therefore, depends on the concurrence of a variety of conditions which, for the sake of convenience and uniformity, are classified as *physical* and *physiological*.

The colour *red* can also appear under quite different physical conditions and on other objects, also when a galvanic current is passed through the eye, or when pressure is exerted on the eye, and, indeed, at times, without any *external* stimulus or presence of a body other than the organ of sight, as an *hallucination* (both in dreams and when awake).

Red can therefore be regarded as the terminal link of a chain of interrelated circumstances. The appearance of *red* presupposes *as a rule*, but not always nor necessarily, the existence of the *whole* chain.

With particular reference to the way in which the *feature* (red), which differentiates the *visible* from the merely *tangible* body, depends on the *last* (physiological) links of the chain, we call it a *light-sensation*.

The object which to us appears *red* can also be seen by *others*. It also brings about physical changes in its surroundings (see below). Presupposing the physiological conditions to be given as invariable, we may now regard the *red* also as a (physical) feature of the *behaviour* of the object in relation to other objects, or to the eye, etc. With respect to another object, for example, the red object exerts a reflex action.

A piece of chalk is *white* in the presence of a bright white flame, and *yellow* when near a sodium flame. The *white* and the *yellow* are in this case a physical feature of the behaviour of the flame, the feature determining the *white* or *yellow* of the chalk. The chalk and the flame which previously appeared white also, however, appear *yellow* when we take a dose of santonin. In this case we regard the *yellow* which we see, but others do not see, as determined *physiologically* by a condition appertaining to the more limited sensory complex of the body. Thus the *same* elements which we observe—white, yellow, red, etc.—are, according to circumstances, sometimes *physical*, sometimes *physiological*, sometimes *features* of bodies and of their behaviour towards other bodies, and sometimes *sensations*.

2. The sum total of the occurrences observable in common by all people with normal sight we shall call physical optical data (Tatsachen).* When investigating these, we pay no attention to the conditions present in the organ as being known, invariable, and given, but examine the relations of the occurrences *among themselves*. If, conversely, we pay attention to the dependence of the occurrences as observed by *individuals* on the conditions in their organs, we enter the field of *physiological optical data*. The circumstance that the *distinction* between these two *lines* of investigation has not always been sufficiently realized has often led to great confusion ; it has, for example, led such distinguished men as Goethe and Schopenhauer to ideas which were quite one-sided.

Moreover, it is obvious that in physical optical investigations a knowledge of the organ of vision is as useful as a knowledge of physical optical data is in physiological optical researches. In this book, therefore, the connexion between the two classes of data cannot be quite ignored, although the physical data form the particular object of our investigation.

3. The data of physical optics exhibit certain general and permanent characteristic *properties*, gradually elucidated during the historical development of optics, which correlate the data and draw attention to their points of similarity. We shall now give a résumé of these properties.

Certain objects, such as the sun, a flame, or glowing iron, are observed to be *visible* in themselves, whilst others, such as a piece of chalk, wood, (cold) copper, are visible only in the presence of the former. We call the first class of objects *self-luminous*, or, for short, *luminous*, the second class, *dark*. A dark body, then, *becomes luminous* in the neighbourhood of a luminous one, just as a piece of iron assumes magnetic properties in the neighbourhood of a magnet, or as a cold object is warmed by a hot one. The illuminated object can again *illuminate* a third (in itself dark) object by reflected light, and so on. We call the sum total of the physical relations between one object and another, determined by the feature of the visibility of the first object, the condition of *illumination*. The mechanism *imagined* to be involved, conditioned by the first object, is designated briefly as *light*.†

---

* The frequently used expressions optical *effects* (Erscheinungen) and optical phenomena (Phänomene) will be avoided in this connexion, because they have well-recognized metaphysical meanings. Where they do appear they will only be used to designate some fact observable by all.

† The above facts of experience are so axiomatic that an explicit account of them in historic sequence cannot be authenticated. On the other hand, quite erroneous conceptions of these relations are to be found often repeated in authoritative optical reference books (see below).

4. When the sun illuminates a misty atmosphere through a rift in the clouds, or shines over a roof into a dusty or smoky street, or through a hole in a window shutter into the dusty air of a dark room, the *rectilinear nature of the rays* is so obvious as not to escape the most casual observation. The phenomenon may be grasped more accurately as follows. If an extensive, opaque screen S containing an aperture O is placed between a luminous object A and a dark object B, then B can be illuminated by A only at points which lie on the line AO produced. A, B, and the cross-section of the aperture can be made very small without affecting the nature of the effect. Disregarding the spreading that takes place, the *ray* ultimately becomes a geometrical *straight line* and it is this *ideal ray* with which geometrical optics is concerned. The rectilinear property of the rays was well known to Euclid (300 B.C.), who made it the basis of a number of laws of perspective, which, however, he was unable to systematize.*

5. When the line of dust particles, illuminated by light passing through a small hole in the window shutter of a dark room, is examined, *another* property of the ray, *apart from its rectilinearity*, reveals itself. Let O be the small hole and B an illuminated object lying in the dark room. If an opaque object C is introduced in the path of the ray between O and B, the dust particles in the portion CB become invisible, but not those in the portion OC. Thus the physical state of the portions of the ray *nearer* to O *conditions* the reappearance of the same state in portions of the ray *farther* from O, but the contrary is not the case. Here the *one-sidedness* (polarity in the Maxwellian sense) manifests itself also as a continuous connexion (continuity) between the states at the different points of a ray. Wrong or inaccurate conceptions of this relation are allied to those mentioned above (footnote, p. 2).

6. Direct observation shows that a dark object becomes illuminated *immediately* a neighbouring self-luminous object is uncovered. Thus not only does the latter determine the illumination of the former, but also the conveyance of the attribute requires apparently no time. Objections to such a conception must appear on carefully considering even the data previously mentioned. Galileo conjectured that the propagation of the process of illumination has a very great velocity, but Römer (1644-1676) was the first to prove that the propagation of light from luminous objects is a function of time, and to measure its velocity. By this means the polarity and continuity of the ray as portrayed above could now receive a more exact definition, and the disclosure really gives us for the first time a full right to speak of light *processes*. Subsequent observers introduced the view that the velocity of propagation depends on the medium and on the colour of the light.

7. The undisturbed rectilinear propagation of light takes place only in a *physically homogeneous* transparent medium. At the boundary of two different media a ray undergoes division and deflection, giving rise to what are known as *reflection* and *refraction*. The equality of the

* In this connexion, see the detailed abstract in Wilde, "Geschichte der Optik," Berlin (1838), Vol. 1, pp. 10, etc.

angles of incidence and reflection was known to Euclid, who utilized this knowledge as the basis of a number of catopric laws which, however, are partly defective.* Hero expressed the law of reflection in an elegant mathematical form.

Although refraction was already known to Euclid † (300 B.C.), Descartes ‡ (1596-1650) was the first to give the correct quantitative form of the law of refraction. He held that, for a given pair of media, the ratio $\sin \alpha / \sin \beta = \mu$, the refractive index, is constant, where α, β denote the angles of incidence and refraction respectively.

There is another case in which light does not follow a simple rectilinear motion, namely, when it passes the edges of objects or through small slits. This is the phenomenon of *diffraction*, which was discovered by Grimaldi, and further investigated by Hooke, Newton, and others.

8. The *colour effects* which are associated with refraction have caused considerable difficulty. So long as it was thought that, for a given pair of media, the value of $\sin \alpha / \sin \beta$, or the index of refraction, was the same for every colour, attempts at an explanation of the phenomenon were unsuccessful. Such nearly always took the form of a representation of the colours as mixtures of light and darkness.

Descartes endeavoured to picture colour as analogous to musical tone. Marcus Marci (1595-1667) was of the opinion that the colours *originate in* refraction, and that the *degree* of *refraction* determines the colour. Grimaldi (1613-1663) held that light *possibly* consisted of a combination of coloured components. Newton (1642-1727) was the first to demolish all these vague conjectures, and as the result of his work the science of optics made a great advance. He showed (1666) that a great number of hitherto unintelligible facts immediately become explicable, if it is assumed that *there is an infinite number of kinds of light, different in colour, to which, for a given pair of media, there correspond as many different refractive indices.* Colour and refractive index are interdependent. §

9. Newton, however, advanced an important step farther than this in that he recognized the *periodicity* of light. The ground was prepared beforehand by Grimaldi, who, on observing the fringes in the shadow of a hair, was led to the idea that light depends upon a kind of wave motion. Newton observed the colours of very thin layers of air, and from the *periodic* variation of colour and brightness with continuously increasing thickness of layer elucidated the *periodic* nature of light. Considering it in conjunction with Römer's discovery, the periodicity must necessarily be regarded as relevant to *space* and *time*. The lengths of the periods, and their dependence on the colour and the refractive index, and therefore also on the medium, were determined by Newton. The ray, which had hitherto been regarded as uniformly constituted throughout, thus presented quite a number of new properties.‖

What Newton had overlooked, namely, that the colour phenomena

---

* Cf. Wilde, *loc. cit.*   † *Ibid.*   ‡ Cf. Descartes, " Dioptrique " (1637).
§ Cf. Newton's " Opticks " (1719).   ‖ *Ibid.*

referred to only occur when *two* rays combine, was discovered by Thomas Young.* In his principle of interference the periodic properties of the rays are regarded as *positive* and *negative* magnitudes capable of *algebraic summation.* For the view that the periodicity of light is not perfectly regular (as in the case of a vibrating tuning-fork), but is subject to frequent disturbances, we are indebted principally to Fresnel.

10. Newton † prepared the way for another great advance by recognizing that rays of light may exhibit different properties in different directions, that is, *polarization.* Huygens ‡ became acquainted with the phenomena in question in his observations on calcite, but was unable to give a complete explanation. A further study of them was first prosecuted by Malus,§ to whom new aspects presented themselves. Finally, Fresnel ‖ recognized an analogy between the periodic properties of a ray of light and geometrically additive distances in a *two-dimensional* space (a plane at right angles to the ray), and also the dependence of the properties on the direction in the (anisotropic) medium.

11. The fundamentals of physical optics may therefore be summarized as follows :—

(*a*) In a physically homogeneous space, light from a luminous object proceeds outwards in straight lines with a definite velocity (depending on the medium).

(*b*) At the boundary between two regions of space which are differently filled, reflection and refraction take place.

(*c*) For a given pair of media, the index of refraction is different for each colour.

(*d*) When light passes the edges of objects or through narrow slits, diffraction (i.e. a considerable deviation from rectilinear propagation) takes place.

(*e*) Light exhibits a periodicity in space and time (subject, however, to frequent disturbances). For a given medium, the length of the period depends on the colour.

(*f*) The periodic properties of a ray of light are representable geometrically only by distances drawn perpendicular to its direction.

These six propositions comprise properties exhibited by every physical optical phenomenon. Having once recognized them in one particular case, we find that they may be readily detected under different combinations, arrangements, and degrees of conspicuity in any other, so that the latter case appears to comprise something at least partially known and familiar. The rectilinear propagation of light is apparent with every shadow, and in each case of perspective, as something already known ; periodicity follows as a consequence of every interference experiment and, once acknowledged, enables us to understand any of the similar cases. The establishment of such general

* Cf. Young, " Lectures on Natural Philosophy " (1807), Lecture XXXIX, p. 364.
† Cf. Newton's " Opticks " (1719).
‡ Cf. Huygens, " Traité de la lumière," Leiden (1690).
§ Cf. Malus, " Memoires de physique et de chimie de la Société d'Arcueil," Vol. 2 (1809).
‖ Cf. A. Fresnel, " Œuvres complètes," Paris (1868), Vols. 1 and 2.

properties helps in the *elucidation* and leads to the discovery of known elements in new phenomena.

12. The above six propositions are evidently *descriptions ;* they are not, however, descriptions of a *single* case, but *comprehensive* descriptions of analogous cases. When they can be expressed in the hypothetical form " if the phenomenon responds to the reaction A, it will also respond to the reaction B," they comprehend all cases corresponding to the condition A and attribute to them the property B, and exclude all cases not corresponding to A. If I bring between a luminous object L and a dark one K an opaque screen with a hole O in it (reaction A), K will be illuminated only where the lines LO produced meet it (reaction B). If we superpose two rays from the same light source (reaction A), they alternately strengthen and weaken each other (reaction B). Such hypothetical propositions have a high practical and academic value in that they enable us mentally to associate with the given reaction A the anticipated reaction B and so to *supplement* the *phenomenon* with facts not included in what has already been observed.

13. From practical and academic standpoints it is desirable to discover propositions in which the reaction A implies a perfectly *unique* definition of the reaction B. Quite consistent with the desire for such propositions and the belief that these have been found is the fact that *new* experiences teach us the necessity of determining B not only by means of A but also by means of a *complement* C. The rectilinear propagation of light is demonstrated by experience : new experiences introduce refraction and reflection and limit rectilinear propagation to the case of homogeneous space : other experiences convey the notion of *diffraction* and limit the case of rectilinear propagation still further. The progress of science consists in a continual modification and restriction of propositions of the form indicated. The termination of this process is as little ascertainable as the termination of experience.

14. In the historical development of science a general survey of the phenomena is obtained only gradually. It may thus happen that quite new properties of the phenomena are discovered. It may, however, also happen that certain properties, assumed to be the *essential* ones, prove to be derivable from others, so that the latter are now evidently the *fundamental properties*, while the former are *derived* properties contained *in* the latter. If in this way the number of fundamentals necessary for the review of the phenomena decreases, this process is no less important than the discovery of new fundamentals, for the simplicity, uniformity, and economy of the review are substantially benefited.

In point of fact some of the above six fundamentals have become superfluous as such, since they prove to be simple derivations from the others. Huygens * showed that rectilinear propagation, reflection, and refraction are explicable from the finite rate of propagation of light with a velocity determined by the medium. Fresnel † perfected

---

* Cf. Huygens, " Traité de la lumière " (1690).
† Cf. Fresnel, " Œuvres," Vol. 1, " Théorie de la lumière," xviii, pp. 521, etc.

and completed Huygens' deduction by taking into account the periodicity and polarization of light and the dependence of both these properties, and of the velocity of propagation, on the direction in the medium. He found, indeed, that the laws of propagation as enunciated by Huygens do not hold unconditionally, but are only special cases of *diffraction*, that is, of a general behaviour which is likewise derivable from his fundamental laws.

15. Fresnel's investigation furnishes us with the following : *If the mechanism of light is imagined to have a periodicity in time, determined by the colour, and the features of the mechanism at a particular point in space and in time are supposed to be representable by geometrically additive distances in a two-dimensional space, the velocity of propagation being dependent both on the directions of these distances in the medium and on the time-periods, then a convenient review of the optical phenomena may be obtained with this aspect as starting-point.*

16. A systematic representation (theory) of a class of phenomena is perfect when a complete survey of all the phenomena possible to that class can be developed from the fundamental propositions, when no phenomenon arises to which there does not correspond a construction from the fundamental propositions and vice versa. How well the views of Fresnel comply with this requirement will appear in the following account.

17. With this *potential* power the value and efficacy of a theory are not, however, exhausted, for theory teaches us the manner in which reactions are inter-related. If we are acquainted with the reactions, we know potentially all there is to know. Practice and academic requirements demand that frequently, instead of commencing the labour of derivation afresh each time, the result should be ready at hand. Suppose that a reaction B depends on the reaction A and C . . . K depend on B. Frequently only the connexion between the first reaction A and the last reaction K is of practical or academic interest. In this case it is advantageous to have a store of such derived results or *theorems* upon which to draw. A good example of this type is afforded by the Gaussian dioptric laws. The interchange of laws which have a quite general potential value with those whose potential application is limited to special cases causes an account to assume a somewhat irregular character. As soon as the practical reasons for such an interchange have been realized, it is no longer a source of disturbance and logical and æsthetic tastes are satisfied.

CHAPTER II

THE RECTILINEAR PROPAGATION OF LIGHT

1. An impartial observer of the present day can have no doubt that the visibility of a dark object depends on the presence of a self-luminous one (this was known to Ptolemy in the second century A.D.), that the object so illuminated can by reflection illuminate another one, and so on, in short, that what we call light " proceeds from the illuminating body." If such objects were always sending out light and were visible only when one opened, and invisible when one closed, one's eyes, doubts might well arise with regard to this circumstance, as in fact, repeatedly happened in olden times. Epicurus * held the view that sight was caused by an emanation of pictures from the eye, but this could only have been due to an insufficient distinction between physical and physiological circumstances, to an overestimation of the latter, and to too strong an accentuation of the analogy between sight and feeling. Descartes, indeed, compared the man who sees with the blind man who feels his way with the help of two sticks. The strange view held by Damianus,† the son of Heliodor of Larissa, can, to a certain extent, be excused owing to the frequently-occurring examples of people being able to see in the dark and of the luminous eyes of animals. This has been proved, first in comparatively recent times by Gruithuisen ‡ and later with the help of beautiful and simple experiments by Brücke,§ to be due to external scattered light. The discovery in recent times of deep sea fish, which develop the light necessary for seeing by means of special, and to some extent voluntarily functioning, luminous organs, calls to mind the ancient view. The reconciliatory hypothesis of συναύγεια, the meeting of the rays from the object and from the eye, was put forward by Plato.‖ Aristotle ¶ doubted the old theory of emanation from the eye, and Alhazen ** was induced to oppose it definitely. In the case of Euclid and other mathematical writers, references to rays emanating from the eye can scarcely be looked upon literally, but rather in the geometrical sense in which we use the expression to-day with regard to perspective, the subject with which

---

* Cf. Wilde, *loc. cit.*, Vol. I, p. 2. † *Ibid.*, p. 61.
‡ Cf. F. v. P. Gruithuisen, " Beyträge zur Physiognomie und Autognosie," Munchen (1812).
§ Cf. E. Brücke, " Über das Leuchten der Augen bei Menschen," *Müllers' Archiv.* (1847).
‖ Cf. Wilde, *loc. cit.*, Vol. I, p. 2. ¶ *Ibid.*, p. 6. ** *Ibid.*, p. 70.

Euclid almost exclusively dealt. But even where, as in the case of Damianus,* an emanation, similar to sunlight, from the eye is undoubtedly meant, we must not charge the authors too much with this fallacy. The rays from the sun which appear and disappear with the sun are often enough clearly visible, but this is less the case with the rays from weaker sources of light. That rays are emitted also from illuminated objects cannot, however, be perceived by rough, unaided observation. To us the eye stands in the same physical relation to the visible object as the illuminated to the illuminating object.

With the ancient Greeks " Optics " meant the science of *sight*, which was originally limited almost entirely to the knowledge of the rectilinear propagation of light. The term " dioptrics " is not to be taken in the present-day sense. Hero's " Dioptra " † taught the use of the alidade sight and the solution of many geometrical and practical examples by this means. The term " catoptrics " is still used in connexion with mirrors, as in ancient times. We shall now discuss and compare the characteristic views of the ancients, since later in the book we shall only superficially return to individual points.

Euclid ‡ assumed that the rays emanating from the eye form a cone, whose apex lies in the eye and whose basal periphery passes through the boundaries of visible objects. The rays of sight, propagated rectilinearly, are represented to be such that they densely fill space, but have empty interstices between them. Now, in that it is assumed that only that object is seen on which a ray of sight falls, it is obvious that each optical image contains only a finite number of units. Each object disappears when it is so far away or so small that it falls in the space between neighbouring rays. This is a reasonable hypothesis which reminds one of the Faraday lines of force. It follows from these fundamental assumptions that the object appears higher which is seen by means of higher rays and that the same object is seen to be greater when near and smaller when far away, etc. There is extant a small book on the hypotheses of optics, by Damianus,§ the son of Heliodor of Larissa, in which the following are dealt with : (1) By means of an emanation from ourselves we affect the objects which we see ; (2) What emanates from us is light ; (3) This light moves in straight lines ; (4) This appears in the form of a cone ; (5) The cone in which the light moves is right-angled ; (6) The cone of sight is not uniformly filled with light ; (7) What we see is seen within a right angle or an acute angle ; (8) Thus things appear larger which are seen within a greater angle ; (9) We generally see by means of the light which surrounds the axis of the cone ; (10) The power of sight generally works in the forward direction ; (11) The apex of the cone lies within the pupil and forms the centre of a sphere, provided the surface of the pupil cuts off a quarter of it ;

* Cf. R. Schöne, " Damianos Schrift über Optik " (Greek and German), Berlin (1897).
† Hero's " Dioptra," edited by H. Schöne ; Hero's Works, Vol. 3, Teubner (1903).
‡ " Euclidis Optica," Heidelberg edition, Teubner (1895).
§ " Damianos Schrift über Optik " (Greek and German), edited by R. Schöne, Berlin (1897).

(12) We see what we see in that our ray of sight falls directly on the object, or is bent and thrown back, or passes through a medium and is thereby bent ; (13) The affinity between our eye and the sun ; (14) Our ray of sight forms equal angles at the point where it is bent (reflected) ; this is also true of the rays of sunlight.

The propositions 1, 3, 4, 6, and 8 correspond to Euclid's hypothesis. In 2 it is quite seriously asserted that light emanates from the eye ; 1, 7, and 11 explain the size of the field of view and 9 and 10 the clearness in the middle of the field and the direction in which objects are seen ; 12 and 14 deal with reflection and 13 compares the light from the eye with sunlight. In support of the emanation of light from the eye the luminous eyes of animals and vision at night time are considered. In the development of 3 emphasis is laid on the fact that light moves in straight lines in order to reach the visible object as quickly as possible, and on the other hand the cone of sight has a circular base in order to include as much as possible. The right-angled property of the cone of sight rays is deduced from the circumstance that an eye situated on the periphery of a circle sees the half of it. The right-angled cone is also, however, the most definite and is exhibited in nature. The light from the eye and from the sun behave in the same way as regards both reflection and instantaneous propagation. The sunlight which breaks through a cloud reaches us instantaneously and we immediately see the objects towards which we direct our vision. Proposition 14 is referred to in detail later. We see how Damianus partly built up his views from observation, partly founded them teleologically, and partly conceived of them as postulates, thus making sight intelligible. Experiences with regard to sight and especially more particularly observations with the alidade, which is indispensable to geometricians and astronomers, have had most to do with the foundation of the ancient conception of optics, the character of which can be most conveniently learnt from the lessons of Damianus. His geometrical knowledge is not very broad or deep. Sometimes he mistakes planimetric for stereometric ideas and dimensions.

2. Attention has already been drawn in the Introduction to the fact that the rectilinear spreading out of sunlight is so evident in a dusty or smoky atmosphere that it cannot possibly be overlooked. Having spent my youth on a great plain, I often saw how, when the setting sun cast its rays through rifts in the clouds, these rays, forming great circles in the heavens, coalesce again on the horizon at the opposite point from the sun as a perspective image of parallel bundles of rays on the spherical dome of the sky. If A is a luminous (or, in general, visible) object, O the eye, and B a dark (invisible) object, then A is not visible to the eye O as soon as B lies between A and O on the line AO. This also cannot escape the attention of the most careless observer. In fact, Euclid based numerous theorems of perspective on these experiences without, indeed, forming a connected system. We see, from the imperfect attempts of Aristotle * to explain the *round* image of the sun which is formed by sunlight passing into a dark

* Cf. Wilde, *loc. cit.*, Vol. 1, p. 128.

room through a small *angular* opening, how little the ancients knew how to begin with such a fruitful principle. Maurolycus * (1494-1577) was the first to explain this in that he thought of the production of cones having the sun as base and the points of the opening as apexes. Kepler found it still (1604) necessary, in this connexion, to make detailed considerations and experiments, which, it is true, leave nothing more to be desired as regards clearness. Kepler † set up a book, to a point of which he attached a thread, and, by passing the taut thread along the edge of a triangular opening in a screen, he traced a triangle on the wall. If the thread was attached successively to different points of the book the different, partially overlapping triangles on the wall gave the image of the book.

3. The laws of perspective represent the simplest deductions from the laws of the rectilinear propagation of light. A connected system of perspective, however, first resulted from the fundamental rule, which Leonardo da Vinci ‡ first formulated, namely, that one must think of the image plane as a transparent glass plate which is intersected by the rays which are drawn from the objects to the eye. If the image points are placed at these points of intersection the objects depicted in the image appear exactly as the real objects do when seen through the glass plate. In fact, according to this principle, one obtains a unique image. A. Dürer, in his " Unterweisung der Messung mit Zirkel und Richtscheit " (1525), develops the necessary constructions for perspective drawings. A more convenient treatment of these constructions is given by Lambert (" La perspective affranchie de l'embaras du plan géometral," Zurich (1759)).

The most important rules with regard to shadows are similarly derived from the rectilinear propagation of light. Leonardo da Vinci (1452-1519) has very thoroughly dealt with these in his " Trattato della pittura," and so has Kircher (1601-1680) in his " Ars magna lucis et umbrae," Rome, 1646. The light distribution in shadows can naturally be obtained only in conjunction with a knowledge of photometry, the development of which began much later.

4. G. B. Porta (1536-1615), in his " Magia naturalis " (1558), has described a surprising experiment which illustrates the rectilinear propagation of light. In a dark room, provided with a small hole in the window shutter, there appears on the white wall opposite the opening an inverted, coloured, perspective image of the illuminated objects outside the room. This is a phenomenon which makes a really magical impression on anyone seeing it for the first time. One can understand the phenomenon on considering that each external, coloured point a sends out light in all directions, of which a small portion passes through the hole O and falls on a point a' of the wall as a coloured reflection, where aOa' is a straight line. The phenomenon, therefore, depends upon a limiting of the reflections by the shutter. On increasing

* Cf. Maurolycus, " Photismi de lumine et umbra," Venet (1575).
† Cf. Kepler, " Ad Vitellonem Paralipomena, quibus astronomiæ pars optica traditur," Francofurti (1604), p. 50.
‡ Cf. Leonardo da Vinci, " Über die Malerei," German edition by Ludwig, p. 70. According to others the principle originated with Pietro dal Borgo.

the size of the hole the appearance becomes brighter, but more diffuse, the image becoming less sharp. The experiment is also important from a theoretical point of view ; for the first time it shows undoubtedly that light proceeds rectilinearily also from illuminated objects. Of necessity the ancient conception had to be entirely obliterated and, in fact, the way leading to a new quantitative conception of the eye and its receptive function was prepared.

Although it was shown by Poggendorff * that this so-called " camera obscura " of Porta was already known to Leonardo da Vinci (1519), and in the Commentary by Cesariano on Vitruvius (Como, 1521) its discovery is ascribed to the Benedictine monk Dom Panunce, Porta was, indeed, the first to make it generally known in his frequently-published book. In the 1589 edition of his " Magia " Porta describes an improvement of the " camera obscura " which consisted in placing a lens in a larger hole in the window shutter. It is, however, doubtful whether this improvement is due to Porta himself.

Porta considered the eye as a dark chamber, but he ascribed to the lens the rôle of the white screen ; this error was first remedied by Kepler. Porta also drew attention to the convenience of using his " camera obscura " for observation of eclipses of the sun. With regard to the image of a concave mirror, by means of which he reflected or focussed not only light, but also heat, cold, and sound, his knowledge is of recognized value. Many characteristics of lenses were also known to him.

The eye of the nautilus is a " camera obscura " (without a lens). The round bright specks in the shadow of a tree or of a thin fabric may be considered as " camera obscura " images of the sun. In the case of an eclipse of the sun these images become crescent-shaped.

Porta's book contains a mixture of sense and nonsense, with a well-marked preponderance of the latter. It is an excellent example of what has elsewhere † been said with regard to the sense of the miraculous, and a glance at the same shows us the unscientific and uncritical mode of thought in these times. The titles of some of the chapters may be quoted here : " de mirabilium rerum causis " ; " de variis animalibus gignendis " ; " de gemmarum adulteriis " ; " de mulierum cosmetice " ; " de extrahendis rerum essentiis " ; " de catoptricis imaginibus." The concluding chapter is called " Chaos " —a suitable title for the whole book.

5. Kepler, in his work " Paralipomena ad Vitellionem," which appeared in 1604, makes really valuable applications of the knowledge of the rectilinear propagation of light. A glance through this work is highly instructive, not only with regard to optics, but also with regard to the history of the time. The whole scientific mode of thought in these times, corrupted as it was by theology and scholastic divinity, is evident in this book, and at frequently recurring intervals there are glimpses of Kepler's genius. The efficacy of his genius was, however,

* Cf. Poggendorff, *Brogr. liter. Handwörterbuch*, Vol. 2, p. 505.
† E. Mach, " Die Prinzipien der Wärmelehre," p. 367

to become greatly damped, for dogmas were further encouraged in Germany in the course of the Thirty Years' War.

In a wonderful way Kepler * begins by working out that the sphere, in its inseparable combination of centre, radius, and surface, may be a representation of the Trinity. He then, in several propositions, analyses the characteristics of light. From each luminous point an infinite number of rays travel out to infinity. The propagation takes place *instantaneously*,† because light has neither mass nor weight, the moving force, therefore, bearing an infinite relationship to these. During its propagation the ray suffers no longitudinal expansion, for it is nothing else than the motion of light. The rays, however, are more concentrated near the centre than farther out. The strengths or concentrations of the light at different distances from the centre are related to each other, therefore, inversely as the spherical surfaces described round the centre.‡ Light is not prevented by solid bodies from spreading out, since it is not a body itself ; for a body has three dimensions, but light, which spreads out on the surface, has only two. On the other hand, light is affected by the boundaries of bodies which also have only two dimensions, and are, therefore, similar in kind. Colour is the light enclosed in a transparent material. A substance is non-transparent which has many (reflecting) surfaces, or is very dense, or has much colour. The rays of light do not illuminate, colour, or hinder each other. Heat is peculiar to light. The stars also exert a heating effect in proportion to their luminous power. Black bodies, which take up more light, are more easily heated. Then come the already-mentioned investigations into the consequences of the recti-linear propagation of light, observations on astronomical refraction, and other matters to which reference will be made later.

6. Kepler's reference to photometry long remained isolated and unused. Bouguer and Lambert were the first to lay the foundations of scientific photometry. Bouguer described his methods first in his " Essai d'optique sur la gradation de la lumière," Paris (1729). His complete work, " Traité d'optique," Paris (1760), appeared after his death. If two neighbouring pieces of the same kind of paper, each illuminated normally by a source of light, appear equally bright, Bouguer states, according to Kepler's principle, that the intensities of the light sources are proportional to the squares of their distances. By means of this experiment he finds that the eye can estimate correctly only to $\frac{1}{64}$ of the intensity of illumination. Bouguer's method of determining the reflection losses in mirrors is ingenious. It is illus-trated diagrammatically in Fig. 1, where P, P' represent two pieces of paper and L is a source of light, the position of which is adjusted until P', seen direct, and P, seen reflected in the mirror S, appear *equally* bright. According to Kepler's principle one can estimate how much more strongly P is illuminated than P', and hence what loss the light from P has suffered by reflection at S. An analogous experiment is applicable to the determination of the loss of light by transmission through transparent bodies. If we allow sunlight to pass through

* Kepler, *loc. cit.*, p. 6.   † *Ibid.*, p. 9.   ‡ *Ibid.*, p. 10.

two unequal openings into a dark chamber, one beam falling direct on the wall and the other after reflection by a mirror, we find that only 1/nth part of the light is reflected by the mirror, if the opening for the latter beam has to be n times that of the former in order to make both patches of light equally bright.   The intensities of illumination at the foci of similar lenses can be equalized by covering the lenses with opaque *sectors*, if the sources of light are unequal.   This gives a further method, by means of which Bouguer proved, for example, that the sun is darker at the edge than in the middle, while for the moon the opposite is the case.   By means of a concave glass he diminished the light from the sun in order to compare it in a dark chamber with that of a candle, and then to compare the latter with the light from the moon.   The light from the sun proved to be 300,000 times as strong as that of the full moon.   With the help of this ingenious and neatly applied experimental method Bouguer was able to carry out a large number of measurements.   At a slope of 15°, according to his results, 628 out of 1000 rays—as he put it—are reflected by a glass mirror, and 561 by a metal mirror.   At large angles of incidence water reflects $\frac{3}{4}$, and at normal incidence $\frac{1}{55}$, of the direct light.   Since equal thicknesses of semi-transparent bodies absorb the same proportion of the incident light, the intensity of the transmitted light diminishes according to a geometrical progression with the number of equal thicknesses passed through. The intensity of sunlight 311 feet below the sea is equal to that of the full moon at the surface.   The air is 4600 times as transparent as sea water.   The light which is reflected in different directions from matt surfaces is *different* according to the nature of the surface (matt silver, plaster of Paris, Dutch paper).

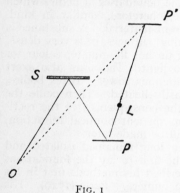

Fig. 1

7. Lambert's " Photometria" appeared in 1760 also.   Whilst Bouguer was primarily a good experimenter who was clever at knowing how to apply various means to many individual determinations, Lambert concerned himself more with critically investigating his fundamental principles and building them up into a mathematical system.

Lambert mentions at the very beginning that for the measurement of light intensity no instrument analogous to the thermometer is known, although the eye with its pupil reaction makes clear the possibility of such an instrument.   In light measurements we are quite dependent on the eye, which, however, according to the light conditions, is subject to various illusions.   In order to determine these illusions and to take them into account, the photometric principles ought to be known to us beforehand.   We must, therefore, according to Lambert, guard ourselves carefully against arguing in a logical circle.

If nothing more is expected from the eye than that it should estimate *equality* of brightness between two neighbouring objects which can be seen simultaneously (i.e. with the same pupil opening), there is an approximately correct physical fact underlying this estimation. In comparing different light intensities the question is, therefore, to vary these intensities according to known laws so that they become *equal*, and the eye has only to judge this equality. The three principles which Lambert advances are as follows :—

(1) The intensity of illumination increases in proportion to the number of candles (equal light sources) which illuminate a surface.

(2) It varies inversely as the square of the distance of the light source from the illuminated surface.

(3) It varies as the sine of the angle of inclination.

Lambert considered these three principles, not as *newly established*, but as already known. In fact, if one is not too critical, the first principle appears self-evident ; the second is mentioned by Kepler. One finds qualitative addenda to the second and third principles in

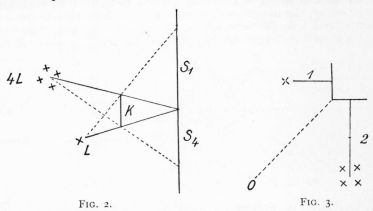

FIG. 2.   FIG. 3.

Leonardo da Vinci's book on painting (German edition by Ludwig, Vienna (1882) p. 308). Leonardo deals with the third on the analogy of oblique impact. What he says requires only to be thought of correctly in a quantitative sense in order to be brought into Lambert's form.

8. If it is assumed that *one* of these laws is given, the others can be proved by experiments, such, for example, as the following : Two contiguous shadows, S_1, S_4, of an opaque object K (Fig. 2) are thrown on a wall by a source of light L and a combination of four equal sources 4 L. Each shadow is illuminated by the other source. If the shadows are equally bright, the quadruple source is twice as far away from the wall as the single one. If one assumes with Kepler that Principle 2 is correct, this experiment shows the correctness of Principle 1.

The experiment is more impressive if carried out in the way indicated in Fig. 3, where O represents the position of the observer. Lambert's experiment corresponds to the photometer used much later by Rumford ; the experiment of Fig. 3 embodies Ritchie's photometer.

By assuming Principle 1 it is also possible to prove Principle 3, or vice versa, by means of an arrangement such as is diagrammatically shown in Fig. 4. Lambert deals with all three principles as being known; they are, in fact, expressed or implied (as in the case of Principle 3) by Bouguer also. Lambert lays stress only on their critical investigation and holds that not one alone in itself, but the association of all three, can be proved by experiment, if one of them is assumed to be valid.

9. From what has been said it is clear why Lambert defines his principles as he did, in that he ignores the conception of quantity of light and bases everything on that of intensity of illumination, a thing that can be observed. The intensity of illumination of a surface element, according to Lambert's idea, can be expressed as

$$\frac{\cos i \cdot \cos i' \cdot I}{r^2},$$

where i is the angle which the rays from the illuminating body make with the normal to the illuminating surface element, i' is the angle of incidence on the illuminated element, r is the distance between the elements, and I is the intensity of illumination for unit values of $\cos i$, $\cos i'$, and r, from which the (specific) illuminating power of the

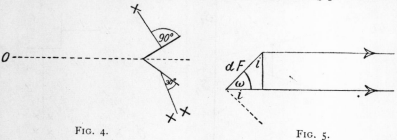

FIG. 4.   FIG. 5.

luminous element per unit surface is evident. By multiplying the above expression by df and df', the illuminating and illuminated elements of surface, what may be designated as the *quantity* of light sent from the first to the second element is obtained. Of the incident light only a fraction α, which depends on the nature of the surface, is radiated back. The value of α is connected with Lambert's idea of albedo.

With regard to the significance of i, the *angle of emission* or the angle which the emergent rays make with the normal to the illuminating surface, Lambert's conception is opposed to that of Euler,[*] who assumes that a luminous element illuminates equally strongly (in proportion to its surface) in all directions. Lambert, however, mentions that the sun appears as bright at its edge as in the middle. Thus the rays (Fig. 5) which reach the eye from oblique elements of the surface are *not denser* than those from elements normal to the line of sight. Each element, therefore, illuminates only in proportion to its apparent size—the element df in proportion to $df \sin \omega$ or, according to modern notation, $df \cos i$.

* Euler, *Mémoires de l'Académie de Berlin* (1750), p. 280.

PLATE I

G. B. PORTA

(1536-1615)

In this respect Bouguer's examples and also modern observations do not agree with Lambert's conception, and we may still be entitled to question whether Lambert has not too quickly generalized the result of his observation on the sun. The fundamental principle, however, that similar illuminating surfaces illuminate an element only in proportion to their apparent sizes as seen from the element, is useful for the simplification of Lambert's calculations and has become very valuable. According to this conception there is no difficulty in expressing in formulæ the illumination of given surfaces by any form of illuminating surface of equal apparent brightness.

10. With the aid of his fundamental principles, Lambert investigates theoretically and experimentally the intensity of illumination of images formed by lenses and mirrors, and the diminution of light that takes place in the passage through semi-transparent bodies. He gives theories of twilight, and of the light intensity of the moon's phases and the planets, and investigates the strengths of the colours in the light scattered by coloured objects.

Lambert's work has, in any case, become the basis for the modern theoretical and experimental researches of A. Beer, Steinheil, Seidel, Zöllner, Seeliger, and others.

11. We will now endeavour to get a closer insight into the first phase of development of the photometric conception. We see how the light from a flame, on passing through an opening in a screen, illuminates a piece of paper. If we remove the paper to a greater distance, the illuminated surface becomes greater, but the illumination becomes weaker. If, however, we introduce a convex lens, the light is again collected on a smaller surface, which it illuminates more strongly. The impression is instinctively formed that, in spite of the variations which take place with the light, something or other *remains invariable*. The name light, indeed, points to a *substantial* conception and one must not fail to appreciate that this (conception) lies at the base of Kepler's ingenuous representation of the inverse square law. In spite of Kepler's assurance to the contrary, light may be considered as a quantity which diminishes in surface density when spread out on a larger surface and increases in density when collected, just as in the case of a cloud of dust, a drizzle, or a coat of paint. Without this tacitly assumed conception, Kepler's inverse square law of intensity has *no meaning whatever ;* in particular Kepler had no physical means of *measuring* light intensity, and the sensation of brightness in itself is not measurable. The genesis of the idea is explained by the natural tendency towards the substantial conception, the observation of the diminution in illumination accompanying the spreading out of light, and the consideration of the rays which, so to speak, indicate how *something* has come from elsewhere.

12. Let us assume that we had a physical measure of illumination strength, a photoscope or photometer, similar to the thermoscope or thermometer, and that to begin with an arbitrary scale is given to the instrument. The endeavour would then be quantitatively to render the instinctive idea more precise, and we would suspect that for a given source of light the product of surface and strength of illumination

remains *constant* as the light spreads out over greater and greater surfaces. We can measure the surfaces and, if the arbitrary photometric scale conforms to this conjecture, we have discovered an important conception. We call this product *quantity of light*. If the scale does *not* fit in with this conjecture we shall either abandon the idea, or, if it is too valuable to us, or even too congenial, we shall modify the scale in such a way that it does agree, that is, we shall suitably define the strength or intensity of illumination.

In fact, the latter happened in a clear way in the case of Lambert. The eye itself is, indeed, a photoscope. Unfortunately, however, we cannot assign to it a visible and constant scale. We can only distinguish *stronger* illumination from *weaker* without being able to assign a relative measure, and we can in particular estimate the *equality* of the illumination. When now Lambert establishes one of his three laws, he, in fact, formulates an *arbitrary definition* of strength of illumination or light intensity. In this connexion it must be remarked that the second and third laws are identical, for both say that corresponding to double density of the rays the strength of illumination is doubled. If it is assumed that the different rays do not disturb each other, a thing that, of course, only experience can demonstrate, the first law, according to which *n* similar candles give *n* times the strength of illumination of one, contains the definition of illumination strength in terms of ray density. But also without this assumption the first definition could be *arbitrarily* formulated. Since, in form, it is very simple and obvious, Lambert appears to forget for a moment that this definition is also *arbitrary*, for he says : " Then, since different rays of light do not disturb each other, the piece of paper *must obviously* increase in brightness by as many degrees as new candles are added."

13. If we consider Lambert's three laws in the manner indicated, we shall not be surprised to find that they agree with each other (logically), since they express one and the same definition. Expressed in physical terms these laws tell us that we shall always see the same body equally bright, so long as *the density of the illuminating rays is the same*. This, however, is a *physical* experience which the *definition* cannot foretell. The definition becomes usable and the concept of *quantity of light* becomes tenable in a physical sense only in so far as this expectation is really verified by all direct and indirect quantitative, photometric determinations. For if we apply a definition to *nature*, we must see whether it fits and whether nature will correspond to it. The observed intensity of illumination could, indeed, depend upon quite other conditions than the density of the rays. By way of explanation one may compare what has elsewhere * been said with regard to the definitions of temperature, quantity of heat, and mechanical mass.

The idea of ray density reminds one of the Euclidean fiction of rays of sight. It has already been mentioned that there exists a relationship with the idea of lines of force.

* E. Mach, " Die Prinzipien der Wärmelehre," 2nd ed., p. 40 ; " Die Mechanik in ihrer Entwicklung," 7th ed., p. 211.

14. So long as we have at our disposal no physical photoscope we must base each measurement on the subjectively observed intensity of illumination of a given surface. A certain intensity of illumination of a given surface may serve as the *unit*. The *intensity* of the light source which by normal illumination of that surface at unit distance exhibits this intensity of illumination may be taken as the *unit of light intensity*. Since, however, the recognition of the same intensity of illumination is very uncertain after the lapse of time and after variations, not easily controllable, in the physiological conditions of the eye, and since it is much easier to control and keep constant the physical conditions of the light source, it has been found convenient to reverse the situation. One defines a *given light source* as the *unit of light intensity* and the intensity of illumination of a given surface, normally illuminated at unit distance by that source, as the *unit of illumination intensity*. Nevertheless the *illumination intensity* as defined above remains the basis of all measurements.

The calculations are very simple, so long as the light source can be considered as a point or a very small sphere radiating equally in all

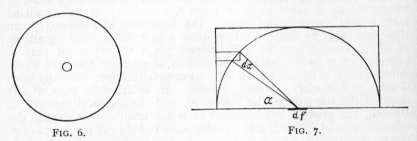

FIG. 6.   FIG. 7.

directions. If we assume that such a light source radiates unit *quantity* of light, we can receive this on the surface 4π of a hollow sphere (Fig. 6) of unit radius described about the light source as centre. Then by normal radiation at unit distance there falls on each unit of surface a *quantity* of light $1/4\pi$. The converse relation is obvious, if one prefers to look upon the latter quantity of light as the unit.

15. As a matter of fact accurate and absolute practical determinations will require *more complicated* stipulations with regard to the *units*, for most light sources are bodies bounded by luminous surfaces, the elements of which radiate in different directions in proportion to the sine of the angle of emission, if Lambert's law holds generally, or which perhaps behave in different cases according to more complicated laws, if Lambert's law should not be true. Assuming Lambert's law, let us place the surface element df in a plane and form, with df as centre, a hemisphere (Fig. 7) which intercepts all the radiation. Then we find from the figure that

$$i \cdot df \cdot 2\pi \int_0^{\pi/2} \sin a \cdot \cos a \cdot da = i \cdot df \cdot \pi \int_0^{\pi/2} \sin 2a \cdot da = i \cdot \pi \cdot df.$$

We could call i the specific illuminating power of the element and say that for unit surface and unit specific illuminating power the total radiated *quantity* of light π escapes. In *one* direction the quantity of light radiated from such an element would be infinitely small. All rays, however, between the angles of emission a_1 and a_2 would give the quantity of light

$$\pi \int_{a_1}^{a_2} \sin 2a \, . \, da.$$

We need not, however, enter into further details here.

We know nowadays that an illuminating body in consequence of its illumination loses energy, but not mass. A surface of 1 sq. cm., for example, receives in *each* second approximately $56 \, . \, 10^{-8}$ gramme calories or 23·5 ergs from the normally incident *illuminating* rays from a sperm oil candle, situated at a distance of 1 m., which burns 8·2 grammes of sperm oil per hour (Thomsen, Tumlirz). We have here, therefore, the possibility, which did not exist in Lambert's time, of measuring in absolute physical units the quantity of light emitted from a light source in unit time. The definitions in photometry can thus nowadays be determined on quite a new basis. The equalizing of illumination intensities still, indeed, plays an important part in practical photometry, but the method of observation has been made more sensitive by means of the spectrophotometer, the ingenious devices of Lummer, and other means. In addition we have at our disposal the thermopile, the bolometer, and the chemical methods of Bunsen, the gradual improvement of which enables us to make the measurement of visible radiation independent of the eye just as thermometric methods have made us independent of the sensation on the skin in observation of heat.

16. Great difficulties stood in the way of our knowledge of the rate of propagation of light. Damianus,* the son of Heliodor of Larissa, who wrote *after* Ptolemy, still believed in the instantaneous propagation of light. As already mentioned, Kepler held the same view, and Descartes † also advocated it. On the other hand, Francis Bacon, Baron Verulam (1561-1626) ‡ compared the propagation of light with that of sound, and Galileo assumed that it has a very great velocity, but O. Römer was the first to determine its velocity.

We need not be surprised at these various views. The simplest observations rather indicate an instantaneous propagation of light. The sudden illumination of a large neighbourhood by lightning during a thunderstorm at night, whereby the light passes in an immeasurably short period of time through quite different distances from the position of the flash to the individual points of the neighbourhood and thence to the eye, tends, in fact, to indicate an instantaneous propagation, or

* Cf. Wilde, *loc. cit.*, Vol. 1, p. 62.

† Cf. Descartes, " Dioptrices," Chap. I. The instantaneous motion of light is compared with the *simultaneous* motion of both ends of a stick.

‡ Cf. Wilde, *loc. cit.*, Vol. 1, p. 137.

at least a very great velocity of propagation. Such observations have no doubt played an important part in the development of these views, even if the foundation of the generalizations is often very vague and clumsy. Damianus meant that the propagation of light is instantaneous because at the same moment as the sun breaks through a cloud the light reaches us. Since, however, we cannot see the breaking through of the sun before the light reaches us, nothing naturally follows from this argument. According to Damianus we also see the heavens as soon as we look upwards. It is just as wonderful that we can hear the music from a distant orchestra as soon as the ears are uncovered. There is, in general, only one interpretation, if one assumes that light is emitted from the eye. Damianus also endeavoured, quite unsuccessfully, to form a theoretical basis for his views derived from observation. In order that light may reach objects as *quickly as possible*, it must be propagated in a straight line. But why a *straight* line in the case of instantaneous propagation ?

In writings dealing with physics in ancient times the logical structure is very loose and cannot be compared with that of the mathematical works. Thus one would not expect Euclid's " Optics " from the author of the " Elements." Philological criticism has, however, decided that the work is genuine. Mention has already been made of Kepler's argument with regard to instantaneous propagation.

17. Galileo * made the first definite proposal to determine experimentally the velocity of light. He suggested training two observers A, B with screened lanterns in such a way that when A uncovered his lantern, B would immediately uncover his. Galileo expected that, if the observers were placed at a great distance from each other at night time, A would see B's lantern at a moment measurably later than when he uncovered his own lantern. With a distance of less than a mile an experiment furnished a negative result, but Galileo suggested observation by means of telescopes over a distance of 8 or 10 miles. Later on an experiment set up under more favourable circumstances by the Academy of Cimento also proved unsuccessful. Galileo believed he could observe the commencement, progress, and end of the flash, and deduced that the propagation of light occupies time, but is very rapid.

18. Descartes † was of the opinion that light depends on a pressure which is propagated instantaneously, and he thought of it as being similar to the pressure in a liquid—not a very fortunate analogy. He also attempted to prove his assumptions by experiments and he was the first to think of trying these experiments in astronomical space, an idea of appreciable service. This idea was reintroduced by Huygens ‡ in an improved form together with critical remarks, as follows :—

" Let A (Fig. 8) be the position of the sun and BD a portion of the earth's yearly orbit. ABC is a straight line which, I assume, meets the circular orbit CD of the moon in C. If now light requires time, for example an hour, to traverse the space between the earth and the moon,

---

* Cf. Galileo, Discorsi. First Day. Ostwald's edition, No. 11, p. 39.
† Cf. Descartes, *loc. cit.*, Chap I.
‡ Cf. Huygens, " Traité de la lumière " (1690), p. 5.

it follows that, when the earth reaches B, the shadow or diminution of light which it causes has *not yet* reached the point C, but arrives there *one hour later*. Thus, reckoning from the instant when the earth *was* at B, the moon arriving at C will itself be darkened one hour later, but this darkening or light diminution will only reach the earth after another hour. Let us assume that in the two hours the earth has reached the position E. When now the earth is at E one will see the darkened moon at C, which position it left one hour before, and at the same time one will see the sun at A. Since the sun is *fixed*, as I assume with Copernicus, and light is propagated in straight lines, it must always appear where it *is*. But, someone says, it has always been observed that the eclipsed moon appears at the point of the ecliptic directly opposite to that of the sun, whereas according to the above argument it would appear behind this position by an amount corresponding to the angle GEC, which is the supplement of the angle AEC. This, therefore, contradicts fact, since the angle GEC would be quite appreciable, amounting to about 33 degrees.

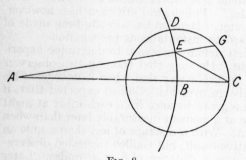

"One must, however, remember that in the above argument the velocity of light has been assumed to be such that it requires one hour to travel from here to the moon. If one assumes that the necessary period is one minute the angle GEC will clearly be only 33 minutes, and for a period of 10 seconds the angle will be not quite 6 minutes. But it is not easy in observations of the moon's eclipse to be sure of this angle, and it is therefore not permissible from this to conclude that the propagation of light is *instantaneous*."

Fig. 8.

19. O. Römer * and Cassini, at the Paris Observatory, observed, in 1675, the eclipses of the first satellite of Jupiter. Their periods exhibited peculiar inequalities, and Römer perceived that these depended on the distance of the earth from Jupiter. For the minimum and maximum values of this distance, that is, for positions of the earth for which its distance from Jupiter was altering very slowly, one could observe the entrance of the first satellite into the shadow of Jupiter, or its exit, and thus deduce its orbital period. When, however, the earth moved away from Jupiter, the calculated revolutions of the satellite appeared to occur later, and on the other hand to occur earlier when the earth was approaching Jupiter ; the mean value of the orbital period was the same as for the minimum and maximum distances of Jupiter. The differences in time were only observed after

---

* Cf. Du Hamel, *Academ. scientiarum regiæ historia* (1700), pp. 155, 194 ; *Histoire de l'Académie pro* 1676 (issued in 1733), p. 140 ; *Mémoires de l'Académie*, Vol. 10 (1730), p. 399.

many revolutions, because of their small amount and of the uncertainty of observation (since the satellite does not appear and disappear suddenly). Römer, having eliminated other causes, attributed the retardation in question to the extra time required by the light to traverse the longer path from Jupiter. He estimated the time required to traverse the semi-diameter of the earth's orbit as 11 minutes and deduced that the velocity of light is 48203 lines per second. For the time which Römer determined as 11 minutes, Horrebow gave the value 14 minutes 7 seconds; Cassini, 14 minutes 10 seconds; Newton, 7 minutes 30 seconds; Delambre, 8 minutes 13 seconds; and Arago, 8 minutes 16 seconds. According to modern determinations the diameter of the earth's orbit is 307 million kilometres and the time taken by light to travel this distance 16 minutes 26 seconds, thus giving as the velocity of light 311,000 kilometres per second.

20. In order to make Römer's ideas quite clear, let us think of the revolving sails of a wind-mill. At a constant distance from an observer the revolution of the sails appears to be just as quick as it actually is. If, however, the observer moves very quickly away, the revolution must appear slower, because the light from each successive position reaches him later. The period of revolution apparently depends upon the relative velocity with regard to the observer. The principle thus expressed differs from the well-known Doppler's principle only in its application.

Although Römer's idea appears quite clear to us nowadays, it by no means met with general acceptance immediately. Even Cassini, who to begin wi.h agreed with Römer, soon abandoned the correct view. To a certain extent this is not surprising, for the results obtained by different observers agreed only approximately. Once attention had been directed by Descartes to astronomical phenomena, Galileo's idea of a measurable finite velocity of light took root, and Römer's observations could no longer remain unfruitful. Galileo, whose attemps at a terrestrial measurement of the velocity of light failed, had, indeed, in Jupiter's satellites, discovered the regularly covered and uncovered lanterns with which the measurement, according to his scheme, succeeded astronomically. The circumstance that the *outer* satellites were not convenient for this purpose, on account of their slower motion and the consequent greater uncertainty of the results, admittedly hindered the speedy recognition of Römer's discovery.

21. In 1727 Römer's conception received remarkable confirmation from Bradley * (1692-1762), who wished to determine the parallaxes of the fixed stars by utilizing the motion of the earth in its orbit. He chose a star in the constellation of the Dragon and noticed, in fact, a displacement, which was, however, in the opposite direction to what would be expected from the earth's motion. Bradley's attempts to explain this displacement by instrumental errors, nutation, and alterations in the plumb line were fruitless. Observations on other stars showed that all stars in the course of a year exhibit periodic

* *Phil. Trans. Roy. Soc.* (1727-1728), p. 637.

displacements of a similar kind. A star at the pole of the ecliptic appears in the course of a year to describe a circle of diameter 40·5 seconds. Stars in the plane of the ecliptic apparently oscillate in a straight line between two points separated by an angular distance of 40·5 seconds. Stars which are elevated above the plane of the ecliptic move in ellipses whose major axes amount to 40·5 seconds and whose minor axes increase to the value 40·5 seconds when they approach the pole of the ecliptic. A star has the greatest displacement, not when the earth's motion in the line of sight is a maximum (on the contrary, the star's displacement is then zero), but when the earth's velocity perpendicular to the line of sight is a maximum, and is in the *same sense* as the earth's velocity. Bradley perceived that such displacements could not be parallactic.

The explanation was found by Bradley who, while crossing the Thames, observed the combined action of the motions of the wind and the ship on the ship's flag. He then thought of a combination of light motion with that of the earth. If a " particle of light " moves from A to B (Fig. 9) while the eye moves from C to B, the axis of an observing telescope must take up the position CA so that the light from A reaches the point B when the axis has gone from CA to the parallel position BA'. The tangent of the " *angle of aberration* " a is given by $\tan a = \dfrac{CB}{AB} = \dfrac{w}{v}$, where w is the earth's velocity perpendicular to the line of sight and v is the velocity of light. In fact, all the phenomena observed by Bradley can be explained by this means. Bradley concluded from his data that light takes 8 minutes 12 seconds to traverse the semi-diameter of the earth's orbit, which is, in fact, a very good value. According to Bradley *all* the fixed stars give this velocity.

22. In the case of all astronomical determinations of the velocity of light the diameter of the earth's orbit, which is deduced from the somewhat inaccurately known parallax of the sun, plays an important rôle. Thus the value of the velocity of light differs according to the value adopted for the sun's parallax. Conversely, therefore, direct determinations of the velocity of light can be used to check the value of the sun's parallax. Such determinations on a terrestrial scale were stimulated by Arago and have repeatedly been carried out.

Wheatstone * endeavoured by means of a new and ingenious experimental arrangement to determine the velocity of propagation of an electric discharge. He observed in a rapidly revolving mirror the images of several neighbouring sparks from the discharge of a Leyden jar, the spark gaps being separated by very long conductors, and estimated the time difference of the sparks from the relative displacement of the spark images. From an abstract of Wheatstone's work Arago obtained the idea of applying an analogous method to decide the fundamental question whether in refraction the velocity of light increases towards the normal, according to the emission theory, or decreases, as one must expect from the wave theory. Although the

---

* *Phil. Trans. Roy. Soc.* (1834).

Fresnel-Arago interference experiments agreed with the latter conception, a new direct proof would be very valuable.   Arago * thought of
approximately the following arrangement, which he communicated to
the Academy in 1838.   In a vertical line GG, parallel to the axis of
rotation of the mirror SS (Fig. 10) two sparks simultaneously spring
across the gaps I and II.   The beams of light 1 and 2 from these
sparks fall on the rapidly revolving mirror (1000 revs. per sec.), and the

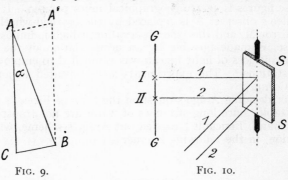

FIG. 9.   FIG. 10.

sparks are seen in the mirror, one vertically above the other.   If,
however, 1 is passed through water and 2 through air, 1 suffers a displacement in the direction of rotation of the mirror, owing to the
longer time taken by the light to pass through water, if the wave
theory is correct.   Arago not only discussed his scheme quantitatively
from the point of view of the possibility of carrying it out, but also
actually constructed mirror apparatus capable of revolving with high
velocity.   His discussions undoubtedly exerted an influence on the

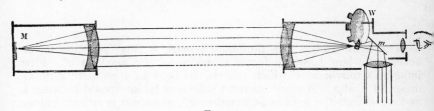

FIG. 11.

quite unique experiments which Fizeau and Foucault actually carried
out.

23.   The principle of Fizeau's method † is as follows.   A beam of
light is reflected by a plane parallel glass plate *m* (Fig. 11), and allowed
to pass between the teeth of a toothed-wheel W.   After travelling
through a great distance it is reflected back along its original path by
a mirror M, and passes between the same teeth and through the glass

* " Œuvres complètes de F. Arago," Paris, 7 (1865), 569.
† *Ann. de Chim. et Phys.*, Vol. 29 (1849) ; Arago, " Astronomie populaire," Paris,
4 (1857), p. 418.

plate. If the wheel is rotated at a quick enough speed the returning beam does not pass between the teeth, and an observer who looks at the mirror through the edge of the wheel then sees it dark. This happens when a tooth reaches the position of a space while the light travels through the distance WM and back again. Fizeau's wheel had 720 teeth, the distance WM was 8633 m., and the darkening occurred when the wheel was making 12·6 revs. per sec. The velocity derived from these figures is 42,219 geographical miles per sec. It is evident that Galileo's observer A is replaced by the toothed-wheel W, and B by the mirror M, and that the observation, which is impossible in the single case, is made possible by an accumulation of the effect. In order to avoid loss of light Fizeau was compelled to employ telescopes at both stations.* The experiments were repeated in an improved form by Cornu.†

24. For deciding Arago's question the form of Fizeau's experiment is not suitable, since long stretches of water are not transparent. On the other hand, Foucault ‡ carried out Arago's scheme, with a useful modification, in the following manner :—

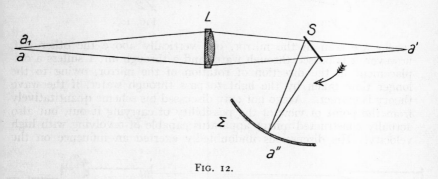

FIG. 12.

The light from a fine illuminated mark a (Fig. 12) falls on an achromatic lens L, which forms an image of the mark at a'. First imagine a mirror at a' which reflects the light back so as to form an image of a' at a. A plane mirror S may now be interposed between L and a', so that the light is deflected to a'', whence it is reflected along its path by a mirror Σ so as to form an image at a. This happens so long as S is *at rest*. It also happens if S rotates so slowly that the light leaves S and reaches it again after reflection at Σ while S is sensibly at the same position. If, however, the mirror S rotates so quickly that it changes its position appreciably while the light traverses the path Sa''S, the returning light forms a new image a_1 *close to a*. In order to make a_1 sufficiently bright, Foucault employed at a'' a concave mirror Σ, whose centre of curvature lay at S. Thus, in practice, the light returned to a_1 during an appreciable fraction of a revolution of S, and

* *Compt. Rend.* (1849).   † *Ibid.*, Vol. 76, p. 338.
‡ Cf. Foucault, " Recueil des travaux scientifiques," Paris (1878), p. 173 ; *Compt. Rend.*, 30 (1850), 551.

not only for *one* position of S.   The velocity of light can be deduced from the displacement aa_1, the distance $S\Sigma$, and the speed of rotation of S.   If a portion of the light in the path $S\Sigma S$ is allowed to pass through water, a second, *more strongly* displaced image of the mark is obtained close to *a* ;   this corresponds with the conception of the wave theory. In Foucault's experiments the distance $S\Sigma$ was 4 m., and the mirror S made 800 revs. per sec.   Foucault himself remarked that the principle of his method was the observation of the fixed image of a moving image.

25. It is clear that Foucault's method cannot be applied to *great* distances, for, owing to the alteration of the direction of the light and to the dimensions of the mirror Σ that can be used, the intensity of the light decreases very rapidly with increase in $S\Sigma$.   Jaumann,* therefore, proposed to rotate, not the *direction* of the light, but the *plane* of polarization.   If plane polarized light is allowed to pass through a half-wave plate which is rotating in its own plane, the emergent light is plane polarized, the planes of polarization of the incident and emergent beams being symmetrical with respect to the principal section of the plate.   The plane of polarization of the emergent beam thus rotates in the same direction as the half-wave plate, and with double its velocity.

26. It may be observed that in all methods of determining the velocity of light from that of Römer onwards the same fundamental ideas recur.   The first idea is the periodic covering and uncovering of a lantern.   This occurs with Römer and also with Fizeau.   The second idea consists in the accumulation of the effect by repetition ;   with Römer this was applied with respect to time, with Fizeau and his successors, with respect to the intensity.   The third idea consists in the combination of a known with an unknown component of motion in order to determine the latter by means of the effect of the combined action.   It may be said that this idea is applied in all methods, but it was consciously and intentionally introduced for the first time by Wheatstone and Arago.

* Cf. Jaumann, *Sitzb. d. Wiener Akad. math.-nat. Kl.* (3rd Dec., 1891).

CHAPTER III

REFLECTION AND REFRACTION

1. THAT the equality of the angles of incidence and reflection was known to Euclid can be gathered from his " Catoptrics." He does not indeed formulate the law of reflection as a principle immediately derivable from experience, but deduces it from some observations of the positions, relative to the eye, of an object and its image in a plane mirror, and of the disappearance of the image when certain portions of the mirror are screened. " Each visible object is seen in a direct line of vision ; " " heights and depths appear in plane (horizontal) mirrors to be interchanged ; " and so on. It is scarcely credible that the equality of the angles of incidence and reflection should not at times have been immediately forced upon his attention on observing the reflection of sunlight by water surfaces, metal mirrors in dark rooms, etc. Considering, however, that Euclid worked with the invisible, hypothetical rays corresponding to sunlight, it is clear that his deductions could not have been otherwise. Everything that Euclid gives in this connexion is mentioned incidentally, and is quite imperfect and inexact in comparison with the treatment given in his writings on geometry. In particular, the focus of a concave mirror is wrongly given ; Kepler also erred in this respect.

According to Damianus, Hero of Alexandria (second century A.D.) expressed the law of reflection in an excellent form. In explanation of Law 14 (cf. p. 10), Damianus says : " For the mechanic Hero in his ' Catoptrics ' has proved that the bent (reflected) straight lines which form two equal angles are shorter than those which are bent (reflected) at unequal angles at the same straight line (mirror surface) towards the same end points. After he has proved this, however, he says that if the nature of our ray of vision did not permit of aimless wandering, the ray would be bent (reflected) at equal angles." * As already mentioned, it is not quite clear whether the teleological conception refers to a minimum of time, or space, or perhaps both. Further, the proof quoted from Hero's " Catoptrics " (which corresponds with that given in Ptolemy's " liber de speculis," † Chapters II, III) traces the rectilinear motion back to a similar violence (violentia) to that of an object thrown. Moreover, reflection, and in conse-

---

* R. Schöne, " Damianos," p. 21.
† C. Ptolemy, " liber de speculis in Hero's works," edited by W. Schmidt, Teubner, 1900, Vol. 2, Part 1, pp. 321, 323, 325.

quence (rationaliter, λογῳ),* the equality of the angles of incidence and reflection, must be explained by such a slinging action (*ibid.*, Chap. IV). The teleological conception has, indeed, a comprehensible meaning only in the case of a finite constant velocity of light. Thus we see the difficulty of the rudimentary method of ingenuously and indiscriminately seizing on all ideas, in themselves mutually incompatible, which appear to simplify the conception or the comprehension of the phenomena. We shall not discuss here the Hero-Ptolemy mirror devices, which have no scientific value but present an interesting study from technical and social points of view.

Alhazen (1100 A.D.), doubtless following Ptolemy, was the first to state that the incident and reflected rays lie in a *plane perpendicular to* the reflecting plane ; this was the first *complete* presentation of the law of reflection.

2. Naturally, the discovery of the law of refraction presented much greater difficulties. Euclid, in his " Catoptrics," describes the following experiment : " If an object is thrown into a vessel and the latter is removed to such a distance that the object can no longer be seen, it will become visible at the same distance if water is poured into the vessel." There is no mention here of a quantitative determination. The quotation is, moreover, looked upon as having been inserted later.

Ptolemy (second century A.D.) knew that a ray of light on entering a denser medium approaches the normal and on passing out into a less dense medium recedes from the normal. He also made visual measurements in quite a clear way with the help of a graduated vertical circle which was half immersed in water, and carried at the centre a small pin, and on the periphery two movable indicators. He drew up refraction tables for every 10° up to 80°. According to his view, the *ratio* of the angle of incidence (α) to the angle of refraction (β) remains constant $\left(\dfrac{\alpha}{\beta} = \text{const.} \right)$ for the same pair of media. His observations, indeed, correspond in no way to this law.†

Alhazen understood that Ptolemy's law of proportionality does *not* hold for the *complete* quadrant, and he improved the expression for the law of refraction by adding that the incident and refracted rays lie in one plane *at right angles to* the plane separating the media. Alhazen also knew that a ray crossing the interface between two media, when reversed, retraced its original path. This important fact might be designated the *reciprocal law*.

Vitello (c. 1270 A.D.) prepared tables of refraction for combinations of air, water, and glass. In the tables for refraction from the denser to the less dense medium he made mistakes owing to a wrong application of the reciprocal law.

3. Kepler ("Ad Vitellonum Paralipomena ") made an intensive study of refraction, and sought to illustrate the results of his researches by means of quite wonderful physical considerations. The divergence

---

* R. Schöne, " Damianos," p. 4.

† G. Govi, " L'ottica di Claudio Tolomeo da Eugenio Ammiraglio di Sicilia-scrittore del secolo XII—ridotta in latino sovra la traduzione araba di un testo greco imperfetto," pubblicata da G. Govi, Torino, 1885, Sermo quintus, p. 142.

of a beam of light and its *tendency to scatter* are diminished on passing into a denser, more resisting medium—hence the rays approach the normal.* Bright light and faint light are equally strongly refracted. If α and β are the angles of incidence and refraction respectively, in the present-day sense, Kepler calls $\alpha - \beta$ the angle of refraction. He contests (p. 111 of the original edition) the statement that the ratio $\alpha : \alpha - \beta$, or what amounts to the same thing, the ratio $\alpha : \beta$ as Ptolemy assumed, is *constant*. He imagines rather that $\alpha - \beta$ is composed of two parts, one proportional to α and the other proportional to sec. β. The actual refraction relations are much better demonstrated in this way. For air and glass, for example, $\alpha : \beta = 3 : 2$ or $\alpha : \alpha - \beta = 3 : 1$ for small angles. For $\alpha = 90°$, however, $\alpha - \beta$ is not $30°$, as it should be according to Ptolemy's assumption, but according to Kepler, $48°$. Nevertheless, Kepler himself felt the artificiality of his conception.

4. Kepler, however, stands on a much higher scientific plane in his work " Dioptrice," published in 1611. He begins this with suitable and simple experiments, illustrated in Fig. 13.

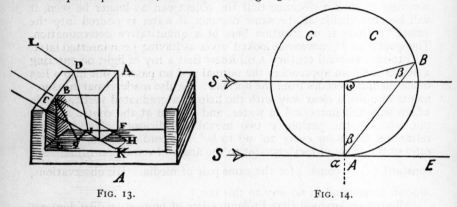

FIG. 13.   FIG. 14.

Sunlight passing the edge B goes partly through the glass cube and partly to the side of it, and forms on the graduated base of the board A two shadows, HK and IG, from which α and β or $\alpha - \beta$ can be deduced.

Another beautiful experiment of Kepler is the following. A glass cylinder CC (Fig. 14) is so mounted that rays from the sun fall on it in a direction perpendicular to the axis ; this can easily be checked by means of a small hole bored through the cylinder normal to its axis, or by mounting an alidade on the cylinder. If now an opaque pointer is moved round the circumference of the cylinder, the ray which grazes the cylinder at A is refracted along AB. Thus for $\alpha = 90°$ we have $2\beta + \omega = 180°$, or $\beta = 90° - \dfrac{\omega}{2}$. Kepler's so-called angle of refraction, $\alpha - \beta = \dfrac{\omega}{2}$ is half the angle subtended at the centre by the arc AB.

* P. 15 of the original edition, which contains a manuscript dedication by Kepler, and is in the possession of the University library at Prague.

For angles of incidence (a) up to 30°, Kepler makes the angle of refraction $a - \beta = \dfrac{a}{3}$ or $\beta = \dfrac{2}{3} a$. The largest value of the angle β which was obtained from the experiments with glass for $a = 90°$ was 42°, the smallest value of $a - \beta$ thus being 48°. Since Kepler, then, held that a and β *simultaneously* increase, decrease, and become zero, or, as we might put it, that the *incident* and *refracted* rays *simultaneously rotate in the same sense about the point of* incidence, he furnished a complete survey of all possible cases of refraction from air into glass. All rays incident above the glass surface GG (Fig. 15) at the point O fill the angle of a hemisphere, but after refraction into the glass they fill the smaller solid angle corresponding to the plane angle MOM ($= 2 \times 42°$). Since Kepler considered that to each ray above GG there corresponds *one* ray below GG, and vice versa, according to

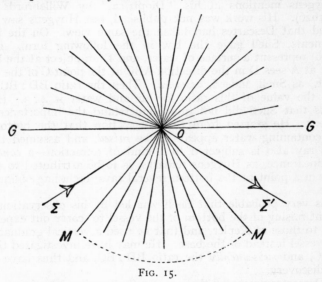

FIG. 15.

Alhazen's *reciprocal law*, to each ray in the space MOM there corresponds *one* ray of the *whole* ray complex above GG, he was of necessity confronted with the question, *what* happens to a ray, such as $\varSigma$, which is incident at O *in the glass* outside the MOM ? He came to the conclusion that such a ray in general does not pass out into the air, and cannot therefore be refracted, but is *only reflected*. In this way Kepler discovered the phenomenon of *total reflection*.

5. No less noteworthy than this important discovery is the *method* by which it was reached. The *reciprocal law* may easily be generalized and referred back to the easily observable fact that when one eye E_1, by means of any number of reflections and refractions, sees another eye E_2 conversely, E_1 can be seen by E_2. This results in a *simplified survey* of the subject, in that two optical cases, deducible from each other, are combined in *one*. The *continuous tracing through* of the

incident ray for all possible angles of incidence, and the intuitive tracing of the corresponding refracted rays form a further *simplification* and *improvement* of the survey. By means of this survey our attention is directed to a *gap* in our knowledge. The ray Σ must exhibit a *special* behaviour *different* from that hitherto known. Kepler's hasty conclusion that the ray Σ is *only reflected* has, of course, not yet been justified *logically*. The ray might possibly behave according to some other new law. We must, for the present, hold that only *experiment* can here decide *how* it behaves. This must be added as a necessary supplement to the consideration that has been outlined, at least at this stage of our knowledge.* The method of discovering gaps in our knowledge by means of comprehensive surveys of a subject is of quite general heuristic importance.

6. The correct quantitative form of the law of refraction was found, as Huygens mentions in his " Dioptrica," by Willebrord Snellius (1591-1626). His work was not published, but Huygens saw it, and assumed that Descartes had taken the same view. On the basis of experiments, Snell gave the law in the following form. Let BE (Fig. 16) represent a surface of water, and D an object at the bottom. An eye at A sees D in the direction ABC at the point C of the vertical line DE, as Snell, indeed, *assumed*. Then the ratio BD : BC is *constant ;* the value of this ratio for air and water is 4 : 3. Huygens remarks that Snell did not quite understand the importance of his discovery. He started from the observation that the bottom of a vessel containing water appears to be *raised*, and assumed that the *vertical* ray also is subjected to a kind of refraction—a *contraction*. This appearance, as Huygens remarks, is to be attributed to the fact that from a point at the bottom several rays, including oblique ones, diverge.

It is very probable that Snell was led by his observation of the apparent raising of the bottom of the vessel to carry out experiments similar to those of Kepler, and that he used a vertical graduated wall of the vessel instead of the base. He may have investigated the ratio ED : EC, and *subsequently* the ratio BD : BC, and thus have arrived at his discovery.

7. Descartes presented the law of refraction in a new form. In the plane which contains the incident and refracted rays, he describes a circle with the centre at the point B (Fig. 17), where the rays meet the surface of separation. He then states that the ratio BC : BE, or as we would put it now, $\sin \alpha : \sin \beta$, remains *constant*.

The attempt of Descartes to prove this law *theoretically* is a terrible example of the *pedantic* method of demonstration. Although to him light is a pressure which propagates itself instantaneously, he intro-

---

* Those who know the exact law of refraction must not come to the conclusion given in many text-books : If $\sin \beta = \dfrac{\sin \alpha}{n}$ and $n < 1$, it follows that, when $\sin \alpha > n$, $\sin \beta > 1$, an impossible value, hence there is no refraction but only reflection. On the contrary, it only follows that the formula or the construction does not represent this case any more, and that special investigation must be made as to what happens in this case.

PLATE 11

Nil dat, quod nihil est!

Jo: Kepler

1600.

duces the picture of a moving ball in order to explain reflection and refraction. A ball moves along AB. On reaching B the horizontal component of its velocity remains unchanged, but the vertical component increases by a half. The ball will now move through a distance equal to AB in two-thirds of the time which it formerly took to traverse AB; in this period the horizontal component of its path will be $BE = \frac{2}{3} BC$. This, however, would also happen if the ball at B were to meet a body in which it would move half as " easily " again as in the air. Descartes does not find it strange that light meets with less resistance in a harder medium than in a softer one like air, for a ball when thrown against a soft object loses more velocity than when thrown against a hard object. The simpler case of reflection is treated in a still more unintelligible and unscientific manner.

After actually reading these discussions in Chapter II of Descartes' " Dioptrices," it will scarcely be assumed, even apart from the statement of Huygens, that Descartes discovered the law of refraction. It

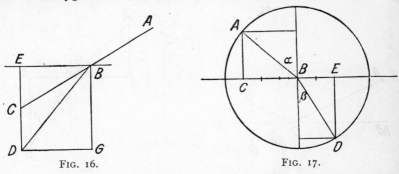

FIG. 16.　　　　　　FIG. 17.

was easy for him as an applied geometrician to bring Snell's law into a *new* form, and as a pupil of the Jesuits to " establish " this form. Descartes, however, had too little of the disposition or the ways of a scientist to discover the law by observation, and to examine it carefully from a theoretical point of view. The suppression of the previous work of Snell should not be too strongly censured in view of the customs of those times. Descartes, by founding the study of analytical geometry, exerted a strong influence on the reaction against pedantic philosophy and physics. He also gave a considerable impetus to the study of physiology and psychology. This same individual, however, who would question everything that was unknown, was also subservient to all the pedantic ideas. He, who would set aside all obscure qualities from physics and reduce everything to quantity and motion, produced a system of physics full of wonderful hypotheses, which Leibnitz rightly termed a beautiful romance. Physics at that time was the most unsuitable realm for a mind so essentially deductive. That mediæval and modern ideas were in marked opposition in the case of Descartes cannot perhaps be better illustrated than by the fact that in order to solve one question he undertook a pilgrimage to Loretto.

8. Descartes' deductions, although they exerted a very stimulating influence, were strongly contested even by his contemporaries, who could not understand, in particular, how light on passing through a plane parallel plate resumes its original direction and regains the corresponding velocity. Fermat gave an interesting turn to these discussions by copying Hero's form of the law of reflection for the purpose of understanding the law of refraction.

According to Hero, light on being reflected at the plane mirror MN (Fig. 18) moves between the initial point A and the final point B via the point D in such a way that the path ADB is shorter than any other path which passes through any other point of the plane. It is obvious that the path from A to B' (the mirror image of B) is *straight* and *of the same length* as ADB.

This method of considering the problem cannot be directly applied to the case of refraction; indeed the *shortest* path across the refracting surface would be *straight*. Fermat, however, discovered an analogous method of considering refraction. Let A (Fig. 19) be the

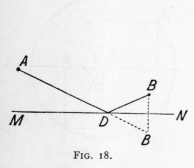

FIG. 18.

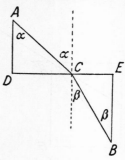

FIG. 19.

initial point and B the end point of a beam of light refracted at the surface DE. Then, according to Fermat, the light chooses the path through the point C which involves the *shortest time*. Let us denote the perpendicular distances AD and BE from the refracting plane by h_1 and h_2 respectively, DE by e, and DC by x. If the velocities of light above and below DE are v_1 and v_2 respectively, then, according to Fermat,

$$\frac{AC}{v_1} + \frac{CB}{v_2} = \frac{\sqrt{h_1^2 + x^2}}{v_1} + \frac{\sqrt{h_2^2 + (e-x)^2}}{v_2} = \text{a minimum} = M.$$

Thus

$$\frac{dM}{dx} = 0$$

or

$$\frac{x}{v_1\sqrt{h_1^2 + x^2}} - \frac{e-x}{v_2\sqrt{h_2^2 + (e-x)^2}} = 0,$$

that is,

$$\frac{\sin \alpha}{v_1} - \frac{\sin \beta}{v_2} = 0,$$

or

$$\frac{\sin \alpha}{\sin \beta} = \frac{v_1}{v_2} = \mu.$$

It is evident that Fermat's condition is identical with the law of refraction, and it defines the refractive index (μ) in terms of the velocities of propagation. With regard to the dimensions of the velocities we must make the opposite assumption to that of Descartes. If we put $v_1 = v_2$, we immediately obtain Hero's case, which is therefore a special case of Fermat's proposition.

Fermat's conception greatly stimulated J. Bernoulli in founding the calculus of variations, and it occurs again later in a modified form.

9. Let us compare the expressions of Snell and Descartes for the law of refraction. Snell finds (Fig. 20) the ratio—

$$\frac{OS'}{OS} = \frac{\operatorname{cosec} \beta}{\operatorname{cosec} \alpha} = \text{const.} = \mu,$$

the index of refraction.

This ratio, however, is also given by

$$\frac{S'P}{QR} = \frac{ST}{QR} = \frac{\sin \alpha}{\sin \beta} = \mu.$$

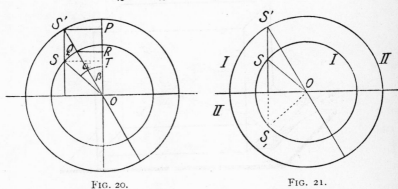

FIG. 20.   FIG. 21.

The latter expression, that of Descartes, is therefore identical with Snell's law.

Contrary to what is frequently asserted, Snell's conception is much more convenient as regards *construction* than that of Descartes. If several rays in the same normal plane are incident at the point O (Fig. 21) of the boundary surface between the two media, it is only necessary to construct in that plane two concentric circles, with O as centre, the ratio of the radii being equal to that of the velocities in the two media, that is, equal to the refractive index. If a ray incident in the first medium cuts the first circle at S, by drawing a normal through S, one immediately finds the point S' where the corresponding ray in the second medium cuts the second circle, and vice versa. For each new ray only one new normal is required, whereas with Descartes conception a much more detailed construction must be repeated each time. If the point S is allowed to travel along the periphery of the first circle, or S' along that of the second circle, we obtain a complete survey of all possible cases of refraction, including the limiting case of total reflection, beyond which no point is obtained for the refracted ray. Snell's construction, however, also gives the ray reflected in the same medium by producing the normal so as to cut the corresponding circle twice (as at S_1 for the first medium).*

If, instead of an approximate construction for the paths of the rays, an *exact* calculation is desired, Descartes' formula $\dfrac{\sin \alpha}{\sin \beta} = \mu$ will be found more convenient. The fact that the incident and refracted rays on *the same* side of the normal form unequal angles with it, while the incident and reflected rays lie *symmetrically* on *either* side of it, shows that *reflection* may be considered as a special case of refraction for which $\mu = -1$. For this case, $\dfrac{\sin \alpha}{\sin (-\alpha)} = -1$. Snell's construction includes this case and it is used by Gauss in his researches on dioptrics.

10. Let us consider a few ways of illustrating these facts. A

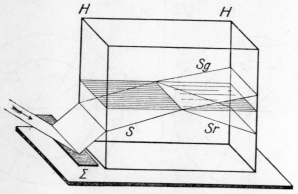

Fig. 22.

rectangular cell (Fig. 22) made of glass plates, the wall HH consisting of blackened metal, may be used. The lower half of this cell is filled with a weak solution of eosin in water, or some other fluorescing liquid, and the upper half with smoke, and the cell is covered with a glass plate. If we allow a beam of light, preferably after passing through a horizontal slit, to be reflected from a mirror Σ into the cell, the rectilinear propagation of light is at once illustrated in the fluorescing liquid or the smoky air, and the three beams S, Sr, and Sg are seen. On passing from the air into the liquid the beam is refracted towards the normal. Reflection takes place on passing from the air into the liquid, and also on passing from the liquid into the air. In the latter case, total reflection is shown by increasing the angle which the beam S makes with the normal. It is convenient to mount the mirror Σ on an adjustable arm which can be rotated about a pivot attached to

* See the detailed discussion of these relations in Mach's "Leitfaden der Physik," 2nd edition, p. 116.

the wall HH. The reciprocal law can be demonstrated by causing the reflected or the refracted ray to retrace its path with the aid of a mirror.

11. The following apparatus is also very convenient for these demonstrations. A cast-iron stand A (Fig. 23) carries a cylindrical glass vessel B, one side of which is closed by an iron plate C provided with an axle D at its centre ; the other side is formed by a glass plate E, which can be unscrewed. A piece of metal *eed*, with two adjustable mirrors *a* and *c'*, is rotatable about the axle D. The vessel B is provided at the top with two holes, through one of which liquid can be poured in, while the other allows the air to escape. At the foot of the vessel there is a hole, closed by a screwed plug, by means of which the liquid can be drawn off again. The vessel can conveniently be cleaned when the glass plate E is removed. A funnel for pouring in the liquid and a bent tube for blowing in tobacco smoke complete the outfit.

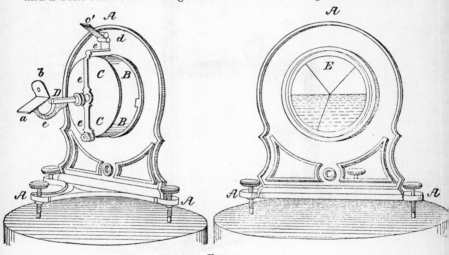

FIG. 23.

The apparatus is used as follows. The vessel B is half-filled with eosin (or a solution of quinine sulphate) and half with smoke. The mirror *a* is first adjusted in such a way that images seen in it do not move when the piece of metal *eed* is rotated about the axis D ; the mirror is then normal to the axis of rotation. The apparatus is now adjusted until the light which comes from a heliostat through a small hole is reflected by the mirror *a* back on to the hole ; the beam of light is then parallel to the axis. A larger beam of light is now allowed to fall on the mirror *a*, which is rotated until the light passes through the hole *b* to the mirror *c'*, and is reflected through the gap *e* to the centre of the vessel B. By rotating *ee* any desired angle of incidence may be obtained. The complete path of the incident, refracted, and reflected beams is visible through the plate E. The case of total reflection is particularly striking.

12. Fermat's principle can be expressed in a different way than that given above. If light in any medium M traverses the path w, in a vacuum, it would traverse in the same time another path w'. This path, which, following Huygens, we will call the *optical path*, is given by $w' = \mu w$, where μ is the refractive index of the medium M referred to a vacuum. According to Fermat, the refractive index of one medium with respect to another is obtained by dividing the velocity in the latter by that in the former.* If then light passes from A (see Fig. 19) through C to B in minimum time, the corresponding optical path is also a minimum. Thus $\mu_1 AC + \mu_2 CB$ is a minimum, or

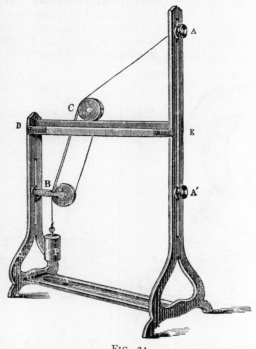

F I G . 24.

$AC + \dfrac{\mu_2}{\mu_1} CB$, that is, $AC + \mu CB$ is a minimum, where μ_1, μ_2 are respectively the refractive indices of the first and second media, and μ is the refractive index of the second medium with respect to the first.

We may describe here an apparatus which serves to illustrate Fermat's principle. A pulley C (Fig. 24) can move along a double rail DE. A cord is fixed at A and passed over C, then round the fixed pulley B, again round C and over B, and a weight is hung on the end. The equilibrium condition is now that $AC + 3BC$ is a minimum,

---

* As will be seen later, this is the present-day view.

the condition which would hold for the optical path if the velocity of light above DE were three times as great as that below DE. As a matter of fact, the pulley C takes up a position such that $\dfrac{\sin \text{EAC}}{\sin \text{DBC}} = 3$.

It is obvious how the cord must be wound in order to illustrate the case of any other refractive index. In order to obtain good results with the experiment, the pulleys C and B must consist of as many independent disks, rotatable about the same axis, as there are cords wound round them, since each disk rotates with a different velocity. In order to illustrate the law of reflection, the cord is simply wound from A over C and B.

13. To the experienced reader the geometrical interdependence of the incident, reflected, and refracted rays will be quite clear from the constructions already described. By considering the points of construction as *movable*, it is possible to obtain a survey of all cases and to picture the movements which take place when the incident, reflected, or refracted ray, or the surface separating the media, is rotated. Those who are not so experienced can do this with the aid of the simple working models described elsewhere.* It will easily be observed that the incident and refracted rays rotate simultaneously in the *same* sense, whilst the incident and reflected rays rotate in *opposite* senses. To an incident ray S there corresponds a reflected ray S′, while S is the reflected ray corresponding to S′ considered as an incident ray. To an incident ray S in the first medium there corresponds a refracted ray S_2 in the second medium, but to the ray S_2 incident in the first medium there corresponds, not S, but another ray S_3 in the second medium. The *reciprocal law*, to which reference has frequently been made, holds for the incident and reflected rays as well as for the incident and refracted rays. An incident ray, however, is split up into two rays at the bounding surface, each of which when reversed on itself retraces the same path, but the reflected ray gives rise to a *new refracted ray*, which in turn forms a *new* reflected ray on reversal.

14. The investigation of refraction provides an excellent and instructive example of the manner in which scientific knowledge gradually develops. Euclid merely made qualitative observations. Each of the later investigators, making use of the knowledge of his predecessors, made only a small step forward, and it was about 2000 years after Euclid's time before a *correct, quantitative* form of the law was reached by Descartes. The *theoretical interpretation* of the law, however, only begins with Fermat and Huygens, and reaches fruition in Foucault's experiments in recent times.

The grouping together of cases of refraction in the form of tables by Ptolemy, Alhazen, Vitello, and Kepler is equivalent to the collection of descriptions of single cases. Ptolemy's attempt to express the law $\dfrac{a}{\beta} = \text{const.}$ comprises the endeavour to replace the tables by a simple *rule for establishing them*, and thus to describe the facts *comprehensively*.

* Cf. Mach, " Leitfaden der Physik."

The expressions put forward by Snell and Descartes comprise *imitations* of refraction by means of geometrical constructions, and with the formula $\dfrac{\sin a}{\sin \beta} = \mu$ the description of cases of refraction is reduced to descriptions of geometrical relations contained in complete goniometrical tables. Apart from Descartes' faulty attempt, the explanation of these complicated facts in simple terms is lacking. Reference will be made later to this process.

The study of refraction has received a great impetus from the requirements of astronomers with regard to atmospheric refraction, and later from the practical and scientific interest in the construction of optical instruments.

CHAPTER IV

THE EARLY KNOWLEDGE OF VISION

THE earliest investigators must have been convinced that knowledge of the *organ of vision* would be of importance in connexion with the investigation of physical optical data, and in consequence we find that the beginnings of physical optical researches are closely bound up with physiological optical researches. Nevertheless, discussions as to whether the eye was of a " fiery " or " watery " character were of *no value* to physics. In Euclid's case we can see how very greatly the ignorance with regard to the organ of vision hindered physical investigations, for it undoubtedly prevented him from developing a clear conception of an optical image and correctly determining the positions of images even in simple cases.

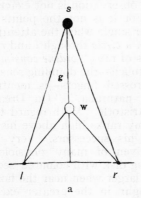 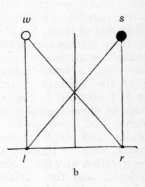

FIG. 25.

There can be no longer any doubt that Ptolemy * considered " illumination " necessary in order to see any object. He discusses the differences in the organs of sense with respect to the nature of their perception, and investigates the conditions under which one sees single and double images with both eyes.

His experiments, to which he was led by attentive observation and the use of the sight vane, were carried out very neatly and practically. Let *l* and *r* (Fig. 25a) represent the left and right eyes respectively, *g* a horizontal straight line drawn perpendicular to *lr* through its mid-point, and *w* and *s* white and black cylinders with vertical axes. If

* G. Govi, " L'ottica di C. Tolemeo," Turin (1885).

both eyes are directed towards *s*, it appears simply *in front ;* in addition, however, there appears to the right a white cylinder which disappears on covering the left eye, and to the left a white cylinder which disappears on covering the right eye. Similarly, the black cylinder is seen doubled when the attention is fixed on the white cylinder. Let us now consider the case shown in Fig. 25b, where *w* and *s* are horizontally in front of *l* and *r* respectively. If the axis of the left eye is directed towards *w*, and that of the right eye towards *s*, a *grey* cylinder is seen, and in addition to the right a black cylinder which disappears on covering the left eye, and to the left a white cylinder which disappears on covering the right eye. If a straight line is drawn through the observed point parallel to *lr*, and a number of points are marked on it, one sees, according to Ptolemy, single images of these simultaneously with the point observed. " Illæ quidem, quæ aspiciunter per radios ordine consimiles, etsi fuerint duo, videntur quasi in uno loco ; si vero non aspiciuntur per radios ordine consimiles, etsi fuerit una, videtur quasi in duobus locis." * (" Those objects, which are observed by means of similar and similarly oriented rays, appear in one place, although there may be two of them ; if, however, they are not observed by means of similar and similarly oriented rays, even if there is only one object, it will appear in two positions.") Here Ptolemy expresses correctly the law of simple vision by means of identical (corresponding) rays of vision, although the fundamental observation is not exact, and the geometrical expression not clear. For it is not the points of a *straight line* parallel to *lr* which all appear single when the attention is directed to one of them, but the points of a *circle* through *l* and *r*, and only for these are the corresponding pairs of rays " *ordine consimiles.*" The analogous experience in the sense of touch—the doubling sensation when one feels a small sphere with crossed fingers—is mentioned in one of the writings, called " parva naturalia," " On Dreams," Chapter II,† ascribed to the school of Aristotle. With regard to his knowledge of physiological optics, Ptolemy ranks high above his contemporaries, and even above many of his successors. Very good descriptions and explanations were given of many physiological phenomena, such as those of the rotating disk with coloured sectors. Also the question why the moon appears larger when near the horizon is considered, and the explanation sought in the greater exertion required in elevating the direction of vision.‡

The first anatomical description of the eye was given by Alhazen ; his nomenclature is still in use at the present day. He considered, however, that the crystalline lens is the real organ of vision, into which the sensation is conducted. The junction of the images in the common visual nerve results in single vision with two eyes. The effect of imagination and fatigue on the interpretation of an optical image is fully discussed. The moon appears larger when near the horizon

---

* *Loc. cit.*, p. 70.

† Translated into German by J. Müller, " Über die phantastischen Gesichtserscheinungen," Coblentz (1826), p. 107.

‡ Cf. O. Zoth, " Über den Einfluss der Blickrichtung auf die scheinbare Grösse der Gestirne, u.s.w.," *Pflüger's Archiv*, Vol. 78 (1899).

because we estimate its distance as being greater (for a constant angle of vision) on account of the large number of intervening objects in the landscape.

Porta also considered that the sensation lies in the crystalline lens, although he was quite familiar with the property which lenses have of forming images. Maurolycus * was the first to consider the crystalline lens as a lens, upon the curvature of which long- and short-sightedness depend ; he also mentions spectacles. He did not, however, know the position of images in the eye, nor the requisite condition for acute vision.

Kepler † was the first to give complete explanations of the functions of the eye. He describes the eye anatomically, and explains his statements by means of a plate. He explains the process of vision by demonstrating clearly for the first time the action of the crystalline lens, making use of Porta's experience of images formed in the air by lenses, and of his own experiments with spherical glass vessels filled with water. All points of the field of view produce cones of rays whose common base is the surface of the pupil. All these cones of rays are refracted by the crystalline lens in such a way that they converge again, and their apexes fall on the retina. The axes of all cones intersect at the centre of the crystalline lens with the result that an *inverted* image of the field of view is formed on the retina. According to Kepler, this diminished, inverted image should actually be visible if the outer cuticles were removed. The rays of a cone intersect in the case of short-sighted eyes in front of, and in the case of long-sighted eyes behind, the retina. In both cases the want of sharpness in the image is due to the fact that corresponding to an *object point* there is not an *image point*, but a circle of light. Since normal eyes can see clearly both near and distant objects, Kepler very praiseworthily guesses the existence of *accommodation*, the optical variability of the eye, but naturally he could not decide as to its mechanism. It was only possible to deduce this mechanism two and a half centuries later.

Kepler's treatment of the question why we see objects erect in spite of the inverted images on the retina is not so masterly. He overlooked the fact that such a problem cannot arise with one who pays attention *only* to the images without being able to compare them with the " objects," and that it only arises in the brain of a physicist who erroneously carries a physical problem into the region of psychology. Kepler holds that the image must be inverted because the passive must be opposed to the active ; here we have again the pedantic outlook ! Kepler's service to science, however, is not to be discounted owing to this error, inasmuch as this question has been discussed in the most astonishing manner for centuries, even up to recent times. Kepler very ingeniously discusses the deviation of the crystalline lens from spherical form and the consequent advantages, and in realization of his remarks considers the application in dioptric instruments of hyperboloidal instead of spherical surfaces.

---

* " Photismi de lumine et umbra " (1575).
† " Paralipomena ad Vitellonem " (1604), Chap. IV, " De modo visionis "

In Chapter III of the " Paralipomena," Kepler says : " The position of the *image* is the point at which the rays drawn from *both* eyes through the point of reflection or refraction coincide." He thus considers the point of intersection of the rays which reach the eyes as the *image*. By this conception he avoids the vagueness and uncertainty of the ancient geometricians. In the same chapter it is asserted that we estimate the distance of an object by *unconsciously* making use of the triangle whose base is the distance between the eyes and whose sides are the lines of vision drawn to the object.

These statements are amplified and explained by the nineteenth " optical axiom " in the " Dioptrice," which Kepler expresses in the following manner : " The position of an object is estimated from the direction in which the ray of sight *originally* emerges from the eye, no matter how this direction may be altered by refraction in its path between the eye and the object. For the eye *cannot detect* what happens to the rays outside itself in intervening media, but *assumes* that these proceed in the original direction." This view had also been held by Ptolemy.

The statements which have been quoted include the *important* and *physically correct* assertion that the perception by one or both eyes is fully *determined* by the directions of the ray elements immediately before entering the eyes, since the further course of the rays in the eye is exclusively given thereby. If, however, these ray elements behave geometrically *as if* they came in straight lines from points of a certain object, with respect to the eye they will act in place of this illuminating object, and release the *same* sensations as it would, that is, their real or apparent point of intersection will form an *image* of the object. Kepler here confuses two questions—(1) to what retinal points of one or both eyes do given illuminating points in space send their light ; and (2) what space representation is stipulated by the stimulation of certain retinal points ? The first question is a *physical* one. If we answer the second question by saying that the real or apparent apex of a bundle of rays behaves optically like an illuminating point, we have by no means solved the question, but have only declared two physical cases to be physiologically equivalent in value. This natural confusion on the part of Kepler has introduced into physiology and psychology a state of bias which has exerted an influence even up to recent times in the study of the projection of sensations outwards, and in the study of the erection of the inverted retinal image, that is, of the so-called *direction lines*. This prejudice was first removed recently by Panum and Hering on the basis of the views of J. Müller.

The harm these biassed views in physiological optics have caused, and how they may be removed, can be seen in the literature of the subject. Mention will be made here only of the points which are of importance to the physicist. The physiological perception of space, especially as regards sight and touch, is given to each individual, being for the most part inborn. On the other hand, the quantitative sense of magnitude is the result of the combined sensory, kinetic, and intellectual activities of men, and of the combined *experience* concerning the interrelation of objects gained by spatial comparison. No system of geometry can be obtained from observations of the vision space alone. If the geometrical arrangement of objects and of a pair of eyes is given, we can immediately construct, as Ptolemy and Kepler did, the complex of the rays of vision or of the retinal images. Doubtless one can also conversely determine from the images the arrangement of the objects, though with disproportionately less accuracy in the case of more distant objects. In fact, photogrammetry solves a problem analogous to this converse one. It may thus be understood why Ptolemy, Këpler, and others amid the fervour of their discoveries ascribe to the eye the power of solving this converse problem, although nevertheless their attitude is quite a wrong one.

Such an investigation gives no information concerning the *physiological* action of the retinal images. The eye directed towards its perceptions is not conscious of geometry; in fact, geometrical concepts find no application to these perceptions, and have no sense in connexion with them. The sense of sight has only to do with the *relative* arrangement of visible objects, and depends on objects which are always present, such as the nose, eyebrows, etc. When, therefore, Ptolemy * says with regard to the intersection of the axes of the eyes with an object : " Videbitur ergo haec res *una*, et in ipso loco *quo* est " (" One will see this object *single* and at the position *where it is* "), he can only mean that we simply see the object looked at *where* we see it in the field of view. We cannot speak of an accurate, *quantitative*, geometrical fixing of the position according to direction and distance.†

A few examples will suffice to show that the projection or direction lines do *not* have the significance ascribed to them by all the ancient and some of the modern investigators. Observation with one eye makes this clear. If the left eye is closed and any object is observed with the right eye, it appears to move downwards when the right eye is moved upwards by gently pressing it with the finger. In this case the line of direction remains the same, but the image is moved to a higher position on the retina. Thus it is not the line of direction, but the stimulated position of the retina which determines position in the field of view. The case when both eyes are used will make this still clearer. If an object is viewed with both eyes, a light finger pressure, which displaces or distorts one eye, immediately causes the formation of a double image, even although the lines of direction still intersect at the same points of the object. If the double image is got rid of by an arrangement of prisms, as is often done in the case of pathological double images, a *single* object is again seen, although the corresponding lines of direction frequently intersect no longer. Here again we are concerned with the stimulation of corresponding portions of the retina. If the stereoscopic picture of an object is cut and the two parts are separated, then with binocular vision the parts are seen *in front* as a solid object, even in the case of considerable *divergence* of the axes of

---

* G. Govi, " L'ottica di C. Tolemeo," p. 69.

† This does not exclude the fact that with *experience* one can acquire great *dexterity* in spatial estimations, and can approximately solve the above-mentioned converse proposition without instrumental aid.

the eyes ; the lines of direction intersect *behind* the back of the observer On looking for about 20 or 30 seconds at the centre of a disk which consists of four equal sectors, alternately very bright red and green, and then at a mark on a uniform neutral background, the cross-like boundary of the after image always appears to coincide with the point of observation. If one eye is displaced by a finger or the fixation is relaxed, the mark appears doubled, but not the boundary of the after image. Here again the portions of the retina, and not the lines of direction, are the decisive factors. If the attention is fixed, with symmetrical convergence of the axes of the eyes, on a mark on a windowpane, the mark is seen in the median plane, and at the same time behind it in the same median plane those objects to the right and left of it which lie on the axes of both eyes.

Descartes, in his " Dioptrice," continues Kepler's investigations. In Chapter 1 he mentions the great improvements in the construction of optical instruments, and refers to the consequent advancement of our knowledge of nature and to the interest inherent in the question as to the nature of light. Since he does not know the true nature of light he must content himself with assumptions which could be made use of just in the same way as in astronomy the truth might finally be discovered with the help of wrong hypotheses.

He considers light to be a very quick motion which takes place through the air and other transparent substances situated between the visible objects and the eye. As a blind man by movements of a stick can discern the positions, forms, and substances of objects, so the man endowed with sight moves with the aid of this light-motion, which can also proceed from the eye (even in the dark). Chapter 3 contains the description of the eye, and Chapter 4 a comparison of the various senses. In Chapter 5 Descartes proves the existence of an image in the eye, as indicated by Kepler, by placing an eye, from which the opaque cuticle had been removed, in a hole in a windowshutter and receiving the image on a piece of thin paper laid on the retina. According to Schott,* Scheiner had already carried out such an experiment in 1625. Descartes, however, also discusses the effect of the size of the pupil on the brightness and sharpness of the image, imitates accommodation by means of pressure on the eye, and explains the formation of a retinal image by means of Porta's experiments with lenses.

In Chapter 6 (" De Visione ") all perceptions of the senses are traced back to movements. Colours and tones are compared ; it is known, however, that the latter depend on movements. Descartes explains that the sensation of light in particular is due to movement by instancing the phenomena which occur when the eye is struck ; he also compares these with the blinding images obtained after glancing at the sun. In order to explain how images are seen erect, single, and double, he refers again to the blind man with two sticks, and to the experiment of Aristotle with crossed fingers. The immediate source of the perception lies, not in the organs of sense, but in the brain, and thus by move-

---

* Schott, " Magia universalis " (1657).

ments there hallucinations, dreams, etc., can originate. These movements, which give rise to the perception, have no resemblance to the objects which the imagination depicts. Mention is made of illusions, caused by prisms and lenses, with regard to direction and size, and of Alhazen's problem of the size of the moon when near the horizon. Nothing of importance is here added to Alhazen's and Kepler's ideas. The following Chapters (7 to 10) deal with the perfection of sight by means of optical instruments.

Kepler's view that the retina is the perceptive part of the eye was frequently contested until in recent times it was established as a physiological fact. The opposition originated with Mariotte (d. 1648), who endeavoured to investigate whether the light falling on the portion of the eye where the nerves enter is perceived to be brighter or weaker. He looked at a point on a board with his right eye, his left eye being closed, and placed another object about 2 feet to the right and somewhat lower down so that, according to the anatomical relationships of the eye, its image would fall on the point where the nerves enter the eye. To his astonishment he found that at a distance of about 9 feet he could not see this object. He concluded that the retina is *not* the perceptive portion of the eye, but ascribed this function to the choroid.* By using Mariotte's method, Pecquet was able to make an image of the full moon disappear. Picard, by keeping both eyes open and crossing the axes of vision, was able to arrange an object in the field of view in such a way that it became invisible.† In another part of his writings ‡ Mariotte expresses views which remind one of J. Müller's theory of specific energies.

So far as the questions which have been considered here are concerned, the most important advance in *physical optics* is marked by the point of view taken by Kepler in his " Dioptrice "

* From the data given by Mariotte's experiment, it follows that the ray which corresponds to the blind spot makes an angle of about 13° with the axis of vision. This angle varies with individuals ; a similar rough experiment with my own eye gave an angle of about 15°.

† " Œuvres de E. Mariotte," The Hague (1740), p. 496.

‡ " Sur la nature des couleurs," p. 196.

CHAPTER V

THE DEVELOPMENT OF DIOPTRICS

1. IT is a remarkable fact that the optical instruments—spectacles, the microscope, and the telescope—appeared *before* the theoretical development of dioptrics. We must regard these inventions as the result of good fortune. The *necessity* of *understanding* and improving these devices caused the evolution of scientific dioptrics, which began with Kepler. Interest in these instruments was largely stimulated by the great discoveries of the astronomers (Galileo, Huygens, Cassini, and others) by means of the telescope, and of the anatomists (Leeuwenhoek, Malpighi, Swammerdam, and others) by means of the microscope. Quite large branches of optics, such as Newton's theories of colour and dispersion, owe their origin primarily to this interest. We constantly see here the beneficial effect of the mutual reaction of technique and science.

If, however, it is now assumed that *accidental* experiences combined with *practical* interest can bring about various discoveries, there must first, indeed, have been suitable *objects* with which these fortunate observations could be made. *Lenses* or objects similar to lenses—to whatever purposes they may have been put—must have been in existence before the *telescope* could be discovered. This is an irrefutable postulate. In fact, this view is confirmed by historical investigations which undoubtedly establish the existence of such objects in classical times. The continuity of ancient and modern civilization was indeed prodigiously affected, but by no means broken, by the great events connected with the migration of peoples in the fourth to sixth centuries A.D., and again by the Black Death in the fourteenth century, and the consequent upheaval of economic conditions. The Crusades, on the other hand, greatly broadened the European outlook and stimulated industry, opening out new paths by which the results of the ancient civilization indirectly returned to the peoples of the West. In this connexion one must especially take into consideration the penetration of Arabian civilization into Spain. Later (1453), we have the migration of the Greeks who were expelled from Constantinople by the Turks, and carried with them their literary treasures.

It is no mere accident that towards the end of the thirteenth century a number of apparently new and important inventions make their appearance ; gunpowder is discovered, and the compass and spectacles are introduced. About the middle of the fifteenth century the first printed books appear, and voyages are undertaken which, resulting in the discovery of America and of the sea passage to India, give rise to important developments. Europe is seized with a hitherto unexpected impetus in the realms of science and discovery, and with a marvellous confidence in its own possibilities. Copernicus, Stevin, Gilbert, Kepler, Galileo, and Descartes appear and strike out new paths for themselves.

Optics especially received considerable stimulus from art. In this connexion first place must be given to Leonardo da Vinci, who observed optical phenomena from an artist's point of view, and, by means of his work on perspective, intensity of illumination, shade, and colour, greatly advanced the study of physical optics.

For reasons which have been described elsewhere,* we find in the history of each science a period in which it is treated with great secrecy and bears an alchemistic or magical character. At such a time the chief interest in mechanics is the construction of automatic models imitating living creatures or the discovery of perpetual motion, while in chemistry the transmutation of metals into gold is all-important, and so on. We must, therefore, not be astonished when we find optical phenomena described in such a book as Porta's " Natural Magic." It would not be far wrong to assume that the knowledge of many optical discoveries was confined to, and kept secret by, a few people before it was made known publicly. Many vague descriptions in the writings of Porta and Roger Bacon (1216-1294) may thus be explained without having to assume that they were wholly fabricated and contained nothing corresponding to fact. I can quite well recall how, as a boy of ten, I was playing with a lens and was greatly amazed at accidentally seeing on a wall the image of trees in the garden, although I did not in the least understand the cause of it. The more wonderful such a phenomenon appears, the stronger is the impetus to investigate the matter further, and the greater is the tendency to keep the results secret, especially if their publication should entail danger, as the fate of Roger Bacon amply proves. It will be conceded that under such conditions a description when it was attempted might be vague and indefinite. The magic lantern is first described in 1671 by A. Kircher (1601-1680), but already in the biography of Benvenuto Cellini (1500-1571) we find mention of a frightful appearance which can scarcely have been obtained except by some similar arrangement. Thus many an optical mystery may have long been kept secret until some courageous individual found its explanation and made it public.

In addition to the *tendency* of individuals to keep unusual knowledge to themselves, the next greatest drawback to the spread of scientific discoveries was the *danger* threatening the possessors of such knowledge. The appalling folly of belief in witchcraft and magic, and the power of the Church, which for centuries condemned free investigation of every kind, combined to bring this about. The first burning for witchcraft took place at Toulouse in 1275, while the organized persecution of witches began after the publication of the book called " Malleus maleficarum " in 1489. The Inquisition was already

* E. Mach, "Prinzipien der Wärmelehre," pp. 367, etc.

established in 1199. One can scarcely credit the brutal, barbarous, and disgraceful conditions in Europe which permitted a trial for witch-craft in 1782, and a trial by Inquisition as late as 1852.

2. The concave mirror and its most striking characteristics were known to the ancients. Euclid was familiar with these, although he treated them in a faulty manner. The appearances to be seen with polished metal objects and the covers of vessels were too self-evident to escape observation. The knowledge of burning glasses is also re-ferred to in various places. Strepsiades, in Aristophanes' " Clouds," refers to the annulling of a promissory note by burning off the letters with the help of a glass. We need not be surprised that the remarks of Pliny on such subjects are somewhat vague and strange, for he was by no means a critical author. We must not, however, assume that these remarks are wholly fabricated, for Pliny (Book 36, Chap. 67) says : " If one exposes to the sun glass spheres filled with water they produce so much heat that one can set clothes on fire with it ; " and (Book 37, Chap. 10) : " I find that some physicians hold the view that there is nothing better for burning bodies than a glass sphere placed in the path of rays from the sun." With regard to Pliny's reference (Book 37, Chap. 16) to Nero's emerald, it is difficult to decide whether this served as a mirror or a lens or for some other purpose.

Through the kindness of my colleague, Professor R. v. Schneider, I had the opportunity of examining a lens which had been found in a Roman grave in Mayence. On the surface it is laminated and irri-descent, and consequently quite opaque. The measurement of its diameter (5·5 cm.), its axial thickness (5·9 mm.), and its marginal thickness (1·8 mm.), gave as a result a focal length of between 18 and 19 cm., assuming a refractive index of 1·5. This lens could serve equally well as a *reading glass* or a *burning glass*. If it is undoubtedly of Roman origin, as it appears to be, it furnishes more conclusive evidence than the combined quotations from various authors.

Lessing, in his historical letters (No. 45), which give one an unpleasant impression on account of their meagre information and their aim to cast an aspersion on Klotz wherever possible, denies the existence of magnifying glasses among the ancients. He holds that the ancients had keener vision than we, but this view can scarcely be held by present-day scientists. The microscopically accurate work exhibited in old cameos seems rather to indicate the use of magnifying glasses. The magnifying action of spherical glass vessels filled with water, and of ancient plano-convex glass knobs, many examples of which are to be found in museums, can easily be seen. It is, indeed, probable that this property was turned to good account, and that more convenient magnifying glasses were produced. The meagre scientific disposition of the Romans, which was satisfied with collections of curiosities such as that of Pliny, makes it conceivable that, in spite of the practical use of lenses and magnifying glasses in the workshop, authors knew very little about them.

It may be noted that in addition to the ancient glass lenses here mentioned, the discovery of which is recorded in the " Archälogisch-epigraphischen Mitteilungen," Vol. 3, p. 151, other lenses have been found—for example, in England a bi-convex glass,* in Pompeii a plano-convex one, and in the Palace of Assurnazirhabal at Nimrod a bad example of a quartz lens (discovered by Layard).† For interesting data with regard to the Roman glass industry and similar subjects, see J. Marquardt, " Das Privatleben der Römer," Leipzig (1886), Vol. 2.

If we assume that lenses existed and were used in ancient Græco-Roman times, it is rather astonishing that Ptolemy makes no mention of them, and that when Alhazen speaks of the optical magnification caused by the larger segment of a glass sphere, on the plane side of which the object under observation is placed, he does so in quite a clumsy and inexperienced manner. We can understand the position, however, when we consider that both authors deal with optics only in the interest of astronomy, referring to refraction only on account of atmospheric refraction, and that in those days lenses were of no practical value to astronomers. In any case, what could people have said about lenses when they knew so little of their practical application, and had done so little to establish the theory of their action ?

3. According to the sources of information collected by Wilde,‡ the use of eye-glasses or spectacles is first spoken of towards the end of the thirteenth century (1299). According to an epitaph in Florence (1317), it appears that the inventor was Salvino degli Armati, and that Brother Alexander de Spina (d. 1313), a Pisa monk, copied his idea and spread the knowledge of spectacles. My colleague, R. Heinzel, informs me that in the " Mariengrüssen " of the brothers Hans, about the middle of the fourteenth century (V. 5129), reading with the aid of spectacles is referred to as a sign of old age ; this agrees very well with the above statements. I have been told by Dr. T. v. Frimmel that an eye-glass can be seen in a picture of the Giotto school in the Figdor Gallery at Vienna, and that in his opinion the picture must have been painted about the year 1350. According to a letter from Prof. F. Wickhoff, a magnifying glass appears in Raphael's portrait of Leo X (1518) ; the Pope is examining miniature handwriting with its aid.§ An eye-glass appears in the votive picture (dated 1436) of Canon van der Paele, copied by pupils of Quinten Messys, from the painting by Jan van Eyck. From 1521 onwards, according to Wickhoff, the appearance of an eye-glass in pictures is more common.

If we assume that the use of the (ancient) reading glass never quite died out, it is conceivable that the increased amount of reading and writing of itself led to the idea of using more conveniently mounted double glasses, i.e. spectacles. It is rather remarkable that spectacles made from smoky quartz were known in China in the thirteenth century, as Dr. Kühnert informs me. According to the same authority, the Chinese imported the smoky quartz from Malacca. It is thus conceivable that the knowledge of spectacles was carried far and wide from the common source by travellers. In the description ‖ of the

* *Journ. Brit. Arch. Assoc.*, Vol. 11, p. 144.
† Perrot et Chipiez, " Histoire de l'art dans l'antiquité," Vol. 2, p. 718.
‡ Wilde, " Geschichte der Optik," Vol. 1, pp. 94, etc.
§ Cf. L. Geiger, " Renaissance und Humanisnus," Berlin (1882), p. 284
‖ Marco Polo, " De regionibus orientalibus " (1671).

travels of Marco Polo, who explored almost the whole of Asia in the twelfth century, I found, however, no reference to the use of spectacles. The greater demand for, and supply of, lenses also increased the opportunities for new experience ; the real images formed by lenses were observed, the camera obscura discovered, and possibly also the magic lantern *before* the time of Kircher. Is it not possible also that the idea occurred to some one to observe with the help of a magnifying or other glass the small real image formed by a lens ? Is it not natural to assume that in this way the telescope and microscope were invented ? Is it likely that chance *alone* was the cause ?

4. We shall not repeat here all that Wilde * found from documents with regard to the invention of the telescope and the microscope, nor shall we relate the well-known legends about it. According to Wilde, Zacharias Joannides of Middelburg invented the telescope in 1590. Wilde cites Guilelmus Borelius as having stated that previous to that date the spectacle-maker Hans (i.e. Joannes) and his son Zacharias had also invented the microscope. Borelius himself saw one in 1619, and described its outer form and its action. These telescopes and microscopes probably were constructed with one convex and one concave lens. Franciscus Fontana claimed in 1618 to have invented the microscope with two convex lenses.

It is known that Galileo endeavoured to construct a telescope in accordance with the descriptions which he had received of the invention of the telescope in Holland (1609). He succeeded in his attempt with the help of two lenses, one convex and the other concave, which he mounted in the leaden tube of an organ-pipe. Soon afterwards, however, he constructed more perfect telescopes of greater magnification, and astonished the world with those great astronomical discoveries which are described in " Sidereus nuncius," Venice (1610).

5. Huygens † held the view that only a superhuman genius could have invented the telescope on the basis of theoretical considerations, but that the frequent use of spectacles and lenses of various shapes over a period of 300 years contributed to its chance invention. On the contrary, it is remarkable that this did not occur earlier. I think that similar observations *were* perhaps made previously, but were not understood and were kept secret. We know, in fact, that at the beginning of the seventeenth century an attempt was made to sell a telescope at a high price on condition that the buyer promised to keep the invention secret.‡

The scientific impetus produced by the great discoveries made with the telescope can be gauged from the enthusiastic manner in which Huygens in the " Dioptrica " speaks of these discoveries. He describes how Galileo was able to see the mountains and valleys of the moon, to observe sun-spots and determine the rotation of the sun, to discover Jupiter's satellites and the phases of Venus, to resolve the Milky Way into stars, and to establish the differences in apparent diameter of the planets and fixed stars. He mentions further how

---

* Wilde, " Geschichte der Optik," Vol. 1, pp. 138, etc.
† Huygens, " Dioptrica, de telescopiis."   ‡ Wilde, *loc. cit.*, Vol. 1, p. 150.

Galileo, on account of the imperfection of his telescope, considered Saturn to be a triple star, while he himself, being provided with better means, observed the ring of Saturn and one satellite, to which Cassini, being still better provided, added other two satellites. What great pleasure, he considers, it would have been to the ancient astronomers had they lived to see such discoveries, and what explanations we may expect to obtain by further improvements in these instruments ! One realizes what a tremendous impetus theoretical optics must have received from such results of research.

6. In his " Dioptrice," which occupies only eighty pages, Kepler * established the fundamental scientific principles of dioptrics. By means of very simple considerations of an elementary geometrical nature, at times only qualitative, he ascertained the characteristics of lenses and lens combinations.

Let the central ray of a parallel bundle of rays coincide with a radius of a spherical glass surface, and let the portion of the surface on which the rays fall be so small that the greatest angle of incidence does not exceed 30°. Since in this case, on passing from air to glass, the angle of deviation can be taken as equal to one-third of the angle of incidence, it is easy to show that the focal distance in the glass is three times the radius of curvature of the refracting surface. In a similar way a bundle of rays emerging into the air from *one* spherical glass surface is investigated. For an equi-bi-convex glass lens the distance of the focus of an incident parallel bundle is equal to the radius of curvature of each surface.

It is then shown that the focus of the rays behind the lens moves away to the distance as the point from which the rays originate approaches the lens. There follow here statements with regard to the inverted real images formed by lenses and their sizes in relation to that of the object, the experimental determination of focal lengths and radii of curvature, the action of burning glasses, the application of lenses to illumination, and suggestions as to the estimation of distance by means of lenses.

The insight thus obtained is applied to the explanation of the eye ; the advantages of the hyperbolic meridian section of the crystalline lens are mentioned. " Sight is the sensation of retinal stimulation." Spectacles are also explained.

Then comes an investigation of the cases in which the eye, on looking through one or two convex lenses, sees the object erect, inverted, reduced, or magnified, according to the positions of the lenses. Erect and inverted projection with the aid of several lenses is discussed. These observations form the first foundation for the theory of optical instruments.

In an equally simple manner the combination of a convex with a concave lens to form a telescope is investigated, and the effect of curvature and position of the lenses is discussed. By means of a convex and a concave lens a larger inverted image can be projected than with the former alone. The magnification, which Kepler estimates

* Kepler, " Dioptrice, Augustae Vindelicorum " (1611).

in the manner still used of looking at the image with one eye and at the object direct with the other, depends, as he proves, on the relation of the curvature of both lenses. His discussions with regard to the combination of convex lenses have stimulated the construction of astronomical and terrestrial telescopes, which were first manufactured by Scheiner (1613) and Rheita.

7. Descartes, in his "Dioptrices," Chapter 8, considers the action of lenses of elliptical or hyperbolic section, which he says are superior to those of circular section, but he arrives at no useful result of practical or scientific interest.

Huygens,* after remarking that Kepler's researches, in spite of the great advances they contained, still required to be improved, says in reference to Descartes, "Neque illo felicier fuit Cartesius, imo ut vere dicam a via potius aberravit in his, quae de ratione et effectu telescopii demonstranda susceperat. Quod vix credibile de tanto Viro, tamque in his rebus versato, tamen dicendum fuit, ne quis frustra ea intelligere laboret, e quibus nulla sana sententia elici potest." As a matter of fact, it remained for Huygens to raise dioptrics to a higher level.

8. Huygens found himself in a much more favourable position than Kepler. He knew the exact law of refraction, $\frac{\sin \alpha}{\sin \beta} = \mu$, and was able to judge *to what*

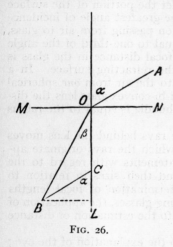

FIG. 26.

extent Kepler's approximate law $\frac{\alpha}{\beta} = \mu$ was valid. He was thus able, not only to formulate more general statements, but also to investigate the *aberrations* of lenses. His deductions, like those of Kepler, are of an elementary geometrical nature, thus necessitating the consideration of many special cases. Let a ray AO (Fig. 26) be incident on the boundary surface MN of a denser medium, and let it follow the path OB in this medium. If from any point B a line BC is drawn parallel to OA, then OB : CB = sin α : sin β, or $\frac{OB}{CB} = \mu$. The case is simplified when the lines OB, CB nearly coincide with the normal OL.

If a parallel beam of light falls centrally on the convex spherical surface of a transparent medium (Fig. 27), and if the radius of curvature CA = r, and the focal distance AQ = p, then $\frac{AQ}{CQ} = \mu$, as can easily be seen from the above principle. The shorter focal distance of the marginal rays follows at once.

* Huygens, "Opuscular postuma. Dioptrica Lugduni Batavorum " (1703).

For a parallel beam incident in a transparent medium on a convex bounding surface (Fig. 28), the relation $\frac{CQ}{AQ} = \mu$ also holds.

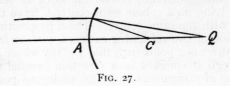

FIG. 27.

The measurement of the focal distance of a plano-convex lens, on the plane surface of which a parallel beam falls normally (Fig. 29), thus gives the index of refraction of the material of the lens, if the radius

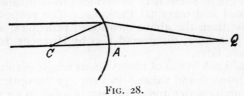

FIG. 28.

of curvature of the convex surface is known. Huygens gives an analogous relation for the focal line of a transparent cylinder.

If a beam of light emerging from the point D (Fig. 30) falls on the

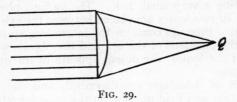

FIG. 29.

convex surface A of a transparent medium and converges to the point S, and if R is the point from which rays must emerge in order to form a

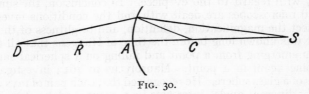

FIG. 30.

parallel beam after refraction, Huygens finds that DR : DA = DC : DS, an equation which differs only in form from the one now used—

$$\frac{1}{u} + \frac{\mu}{v} = \frac{\mu - 1}{r}.$$

9. In considering the case of a bundle of rays making an angle with the beam previously considered, it is only necessary to confine the attention to the central ray in order to prove that, if the object distance is the same, the image distance is also the same as before. Thus all luminous points lying on a sphere with centre C have their images on a second sphere with the same centre. These propositions are applied to the combination of two refracting surfaces, viz., to *lenses*.

In each lens there is a point such that the ray whose path inside the lens passes through it emerges in a direction parallel to the incident ray. In the case of a meniscus lens, the analogous point lies outside the lens substance.

The aberrations of lenses which enter into consideration when Kepler's approximation is disregarded arise from their spherical form. Another aberration is dependent on colour dispersion.

The focal length of a lens may be deduced from its aperture and the difference in axial and marginal thickness. The propositions in this connexion follow from the above-mentioned principles, and also from quite different principles, discovered also by Huygens, to which reference will be made later.

10. Huygens' book is full of observations which even at the present day are still of interest and value. In Prop. 33 the optical relations of the human eye under water and of the eye of a fish in air are discussed, and the construction of submarine spectacles is given. Then follows the analysis of the two forms of telescope, attention being paid to accommodation. In connexion with the explanation of spectacles, it is mentioned that defective accommodation can be compensated by a diaphragm having a very small hole. The various phenomena which occur when one or two lenses are placed between the eye and the object are investigated. Prop. 40 contains the interesting statement that, by interchanging the positions of the eye and the object, without altering the positions of the lenses, the object appears to the eye to be of the same size as before.

Many forms of telescope are described, and the dependence of their magnification and field of view on the focal lengths of the lenses is investigated. Mention is next made of spherical and chromatic aberrations, and the effect of the aperture and focal length on these aberrations. Huygens made very great improvements in the telescope, especially with regard to the eyepiece. In conclusion, the simple and compound microscopes are dealt with and the conditions investigated which affect the magnification, definition, and brightness of the image.

11. It was known long before the time of Huygens that all the rays of a beam emerging from a point and falling on a spherical surface do *not* combine again in a point. Maurolycus in 1613 investigated the focal lines of a glass sphere. He recognized that each pair of rays incident at slightly different angles intersects in a point, and he described the image formed by all such points as a cone with curved sides. Huygens, in 1678, was the first to give the correct sequence of the intersections (the focal lines) in the case of a concave spherical mirror. Tschirnhausen,* in the investigation of these focal lines, made mistakes,

---

* Tschirnhausen, " Acta eruditorum " (1682).

to which de la Hire drew attention.   Johann and Jacob Bernoulli and the Marquis de l'Hôpital dealt with the focal lines formed by reflection and refraction.

12. Investigations with regard to the focal lengths of mirrors and lenses were also carried out by Huygens.   The work of Kepler in this connexion has already been mentioned.   Cavalieri, in 1647, gave a rule which is valid for all lenses ;   this he deduced from detailed consideration of many special cases.   J. Barrow treated the matter similarly in 1674.   E. Halley * was the first to draw attention to the advantages of using the principle of algebraic signs, and thus including many special cases in one general case.   His formula holds for the focal lengths of all lenses and mirrors.   W. Browne gave in the appendix of his English edition of D. Gregory's " Optics " (1735) the now customary formula

$$\frac{1}{u} + \frac{1}{v} = (\mu - 1)\left(\frac{1}{r_1} + \frac{1}{r_2}\right),$$

which in the case of mirrors assumes the form

$$\frac{1}{u} + \frac{1}{v} = \frac{1}{f}.$$

These were based on Halley's work.   R. Smith † was the first to apply the method of constructing the image of a point object by means of an unrefracted central ray and a ray which is parallel to the axis and is refracted through the focus.

13. L. Euler ‡ deals with the general questions in dioptrics which relate to the aberrations of one or several lenses, apparent size, brightness, definition, and field of view.   His method of attack is based on quantitative geometrical considerations, use being made of the approximate formula $\sin \phi = \phi - \frac{1}{6} \phi^3$.   The second part of his work deals with telescopes, and the third part with microscopes.   We shall not consider these investigations here, as they are predominantly of *technical* value.

The development of dioptrics has been described above only in so far as it is of importance to the considerations which follow.   A very complete bibliography dealing with the subject in ancient times is to be found in Dove's " Repert. d. Physik," Vol. 2, Berlin (1837).

14. We will refer once again to the peculiar character of the science of dioptrics.   The knowledge of the laws of reflection and refraction *alone* enables us, without the aid of any other proposition whatever, to visualize the paths of rays which fall on any form of reflecting or refracting surface.   There is, however, no practical or scientific interest in considering all possible cases of this nature.   On the other hand, it is evident that spherical reflecting and refracting surfaces, and such combinations of them as have all the centres of curvature

* E. Halley, *Phil. Trans. Roy. Soc.* (Nov., 1693).
† R. Smith, " System of Optics," Cambridge (1738).
‡ L. Euler, " Dioptricae pars prima," Petropoli (1769).

collinear, lend themselves to many technical applications, and that they often become useful in undertaking purely scientific observations of an optical nature. Further, it is evident that in these cases the *approximate* knowledge of the paths of rays slightly inclined to the axis is more important and interesting than the *exact* knowledge of the behaviour of particular rays. We are therefore not content with establishing the laws of reflection and refraction, and saving the further labour of considering the special case, when it occurs, or with investigating all possible individual cases—a process which is not interesting and cannot be carried out in practice. It is better to consider those cases of spherical surfaces which frequently occur in practice and in scientific work, determine their characteristics *once for all*, and record them in the form of special propositions ready for use. This is an example of the *economic* function of science referred to elsewhere.

During the evolution of dioptrics a general system gradually developed which is also of advantage for the solution of future problems. It is advisable, therefore, to keep in mind the following fundamental propositions, on which it is based :—

(*a*) Each ray is independent of the others.

(*b*) Its characteristics are determined only by direction and position.

(*c*) Each point of the ray has special characteristics.

(*d*) Each ray possesses all the characteristics determined by its points.

(*e*) The ray is independent of the point of view adopted by the investigator.

(*f*) It combines all characteristics which can be discovered by different methods of observation.

15. We will now discuss more fully the parts of dioptrics which will be applied to other problems. The historical sequence will be retained, so that the elements of knowledge and motives of investigation introduced by Kepler, Huygens, and others, will easily be recognized. In this connexion we must above all remember that the properties possessed by lenses of forming images, concentrating the light from the sun in a " point," and so on were known before an endeavour was made to explain these properties theoretically by means of refraction. The whole process has, therefore, the nature of an *explanation* of something remarkable and complicated by means of something more common and simple. The *method* gained by this attempt at explanation, moreover, enables one forthwith to see *more,* both qualitatively and quantitatively, than is possible by rough observation.

16. In Fig. 31 a mass of glass (right) is separated from the air (left) by a portion MN of a spherical surface, a section through the centre C of which lies in the plane of the paper. The ray AC coincides with the normal CS, and passes across the bounding surface undeviated. The ray AM makes an angle $u = \phi + \psi$ with the normal CM, and is refracted in the direction MA', which makes an angle $v = \psi - \chi$, so that $\sin u = \mu \sin v$, or, for small angles of incidence, $u = \mu v$.

Let us assume that ψ, and therefore the arc m, is small. If we double or treble the values of ϕ and m, we also double or treble the values of ψ, of $u = \phi + \psi$, of $v = u/\mu$, and of $\chi = \psi - v$. The rays from A which cut off arcs $2m$ and $3m$ are refracted in directions making angles 2χ and 3χ with the central ray, and therefore coincide at the same point A'.

On account of the smallness of the angles we may in general put

$$\phi + \psi = \mu(\psi - \chi) \qquad . \qquad . \qquad . \qquad . \quad (1)$$

Expressing the arc m, whose curvature we neglect, in terms of the radius r and the distances a and α, we obtain $\phi = m/a$, $\psi = m/r$, $\chi = m/\alpha$. Thus equation (1) becomes

$$\frac{1}{a} + \frac{\mu}{b} = \frac{\mu - 1}{r} \qquad . \qquad . \qquad . \qquad . \quad (2)$$

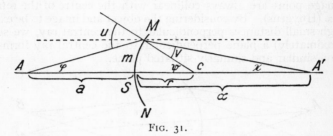

FIG. 31.

The arc m, if it is small, thus disappears from the equation (2), i.e. the (homocentric) rays which emerge from the point A of the central ray re-combine (homocentrically) at the point A'. Thus a fundamental characteristic of spherical refracting surfaces, the *homocentric law*, on which the formation of *images* by lenses depends, is explained by Kepler's approximate law of refraction. The point A' appears to an eye which receives the rays emerging from it like the self-luminous point A ; it is the *image* of A.

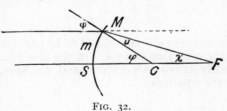

FIG. 32.

If the point A is infinitely distant (Fig. 32), the incident rays are parallel and refraction takes place according to the equation

$$\phi = \mu u = \mu(\phi - \chi), \text{ or } \chi = \frac{\mu - 1}{\mu} \ \phi,$$

that is, if m is small, the focal distance SF $= \dfrac{\mu r}{\mu - 1}$. For glass ($\mu = 3/2$) the focal length, according to Kepler, is $3r$, or, in general, according to

Huygens, $\dfrac{SF}{CF} = \mu$. From equation (2) it follows that, when $a = \infty$, the focal length in the medium of refractive index μ is given by $f_2 = \dfrac{\mu r}{\mu - 1}$ and, when $a = \infty$, the focal length in air is given by $f_1 = \dfrac{r}{\mu - 1}$.

17. If the whole bundle of rays diverging from A and converging to A′ is rotated about C (Fig. 33), so that A and A′ move towards B and B′ respectively, we observe that all object points lying on the surface of a sphere having C as centre give image points which also lie on a spherical surface concentric with the former. An object point and its corresponding image point are always collinear with the centre of the refracting surface (Huygens). By considering the object and image to be extended through small distances perpendicular to the central ray, we see that (approximately) a plane perpendicular to the central ray forms as its image a similar and similarly situated plane.

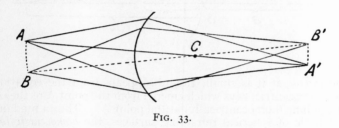

FIG. 33.

18. If reflection is considered as a special case of refraction for which $\mu = -1$, equation (2) gives for a convex spherical mirror

$$\frac{1}{a} + \frac{1}{a} = \frac{2}{r} \quad . \qquad . \qquad . \qquad . \qquad . \quad (3)$$

where the image distance a is considered to be positive when the image lies in front of the reflecting surface. In the case of a concave mirror, r is conventionally taken as negative, and we have, since the focal length $r/2 = f$, the equation

$$\frac{1}{a} + \frac{1}{a} = \frac{1}{f} \quad . \qquad . \qquad . \qquad . \qquad . \quad (4)$$

which, for $1/f = 0$, includes the characteristics of a plane mirror (Halley, Browne).

19. In practical optics spherical refracting surfaces are generally to be found in pairs, each pair enclosing a medium optically denser than air, and forming a so-called lens. We shall here assume that the points S, S′ (Fig. 34) lie very close to one another, so that we can neglect the thickness and consider the lens as being infinitely thin. The line joining the two centres of curvature C, C′ is the axis of the

lens. If the first surface (left) were alone present, we should have the equation

$$\frac{1}{a} + \frac{\mu}{a} = \frac{\mu - 1}{r_1} \qquad . \qquad . \qquad . \qquad (5)$$

where $SC = r_1$. If the second surface, bounded on the left by glass and on the right by air, were alone present, we should have

$$\frac{1}{b} + \frac{\mu}{\beta} = \frac{\frac{1}{\mu} - 1}{r_2} \qquad . \qquad . \qquad . \qquad (6)$$

where $S'C' = r_2$ and b, β are the distances of the object and image respectively from S'.

Since now the negative image distance for the first surface is equal to the object distance for the second surface, i.e. $1/b = -1/a$, we find, on taking the value of a from (5) and substituting in (6), that

$$\frac{1}{a} + \frac{1}{\beta} = (\mu - 1)\left(\frac{1}{r_1} - \frac{1}{r_2}\right).$$

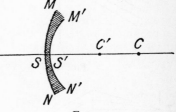

FIG. 34.

where a and β are the object and image distances respectively for the *whole* lens. For the sake of uniformity we may call the latter a. We thus obtain

$$\frac{1}{a} + \frac{1}{a} = \frac{1}{f} \qquad . \qquad . \qquad . \qquad . \qquad (7)$$

for all lenses, where

$$\frac{1}{f} = (\mu - 1)\left(\frac{1}{r_1} + \frac{1}{r_2}\right),$$

if we consider the radius of an air-glass (glass-air) surface as *positive* when the surface is convex (concave) to the incident light, and vice versa (Halley, Browne).

It follows that $a = f$ for $a = \infty$ and $a = f$ for $b = \infty$. The two focal lengths of a lens are equal and not *different* as in the case of *one* spherical refracting surface.

20. Thus the properties of a lens are deducible by a double application of the laws for spherical refracting surfaces. Apart from the equality of the two focal lengths, the characteristic of a lens corresponds exactly to that of *one* spherical refracting surface : homocentric bundles of rays with small angles of incidence remain homocentric after refraction. The rays of a beam incident parallel to the axis coincide at the *second* focus, while rays which after refraction are parallel to the axis originate from the *first* focus. We designate the planes perpendicular to the axis through the two foci the first and second focal planes. Each infinitely distant luminous point forms an image in the second focal plane, while each luminous point in the first focal plane gives rise after refraction to a parallel beam of rays.

21. Let a parallel beam of light from a very distant point be incident on the lens L (Fig. 35). Since the ray which passes through F_1 could equally well belong to a beam diverging from F_1, it is parallel to the axis after refraction, and cuts the second focal plane at S, which is

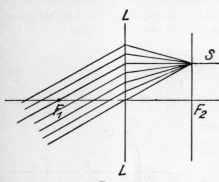

therefore the focus of the whole beam. A beam of light diverging from a point T (Fig. 36) of the first focal plane becomes parallel after refraction. The ray through T parallel to the axis could, however, belong to a beam of rays parallel to the axis; it therefore passes through F_2, and all the other rays of the beam are parallel to this direction after refraction. (This method of construction originated with R. Smith.)

FIG. 35.

In order to construct the path of a ray AM (Fig. 37) lying in a plane through the axis of a lens LL, we can consider the ray as belonging to a parallel beam, and construct the parallel ray through F_1, which gives the point S through which the refracted ray must pass, or we can think of the ray AM as be-

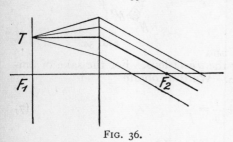

FIG. 36.

longing to the point T, and construct the ray which leaves T in the direction parallel to the axis, and this ray after refraction again gives the direction of the refracted ray in question.

According to both constructions the ray SO (Fig. 38), which passes

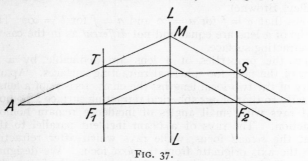

FIG. 37.

through the centre of an infinitely thin lens, is undeviated, as is at once obvious; this also holds approximately for a lens of moderate thickness.

In order to construct the image A' of a luminous point A (Fig. 39), we remember that all the rays emerging from A combine homocentrically at A'. All that is necessary for the construction, therefore, is a pair of rays, such as AL and AF_1, or AL and AO, or AO and AF_1.

22. According to Kepler, a ray refracted into glass revolves in the same direction as the incident ray, and with two-thirds its velocity, if the angle of incidence is *small*. If the ray again emerges into air almost normally, he states that the emergent ray moves in the same direction and with the same velocity as the incident ray. For a lens, therefore, the incident and emergent rays revolve in the same direction and by the same amount. This enables one to realize the relation of image to object. This method of considering

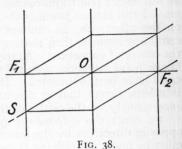

FIG. 38.

the problem could also be made use of in establishing a more complete theory.

If the point A (Fig. 40) moves towards the lens (→), and the rays from A are always supposed to meet the lens at the same points, the

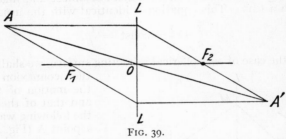

FIG. 39.

above principle shows that the emergent rays suffer a displacement in the same direction (→). Similarly, if the point A moves downwards (↓), A' moves upwards (↑) if A and A' lie on different sides of the lens, and downwards (↓) if they both lie on the same side of the lens. Thus

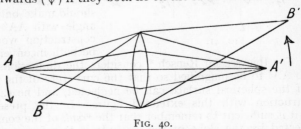

FIG. 40.

a displacement of A to B results in a displacement of the image A' to B'. The components of the motion of object and image parallel to the axis are therefore always *in the same sense*. In dealing with lenses it is of great assistance to bear this principle in mind.

There is no difficulty in making use of Kepler's method of consideration for picturing the general behaviour of object and image, for a *single* refracting surface as well as for a lens. If light from an infinite distance is incident on a piece of glass bounded by a convex surface, the image is formed at the second focus, and it moves towards infinity as the object point approaches the first focus. As the object point is moved still farther towards the surface, the image goes over to infinity on the other side, and moves after the object, overtaking it on the refracting surface, then passing it and eventually coinciding with it at the centre of curvature. As the object point moves off to infinity, the image point advances only up to the second focus. Thus all possible cases have been exhausted. The process is the same for an infinitely thin lens, except that in this case the object and image coincide only *once*, namely, at the centre of the lens.

23. Since the *reflected* ray ($\mu = -1$) and the incident ray move in opposite directions by the same amount, it is clear what modifications must be made in applying the considerations to the case of mirrors.

The method of investigation above described leads very simply to the equation

$$\frac{da}{a^2} = -\frac{d\alpha}{\alpha^2} \qquad . \qquad . \qquad . \qquad . \qquad . \qquad (8)$$

for the changes in a and α, the distances of object and image respectively from a lens. This equation is identical with the usual one

$$\frac{1}{a} + \frac{1}{\alpha} = \text{const.} = \frac{1}{f}.$$

24. In the case of *one* spherical refracting surface, we shall illustrate

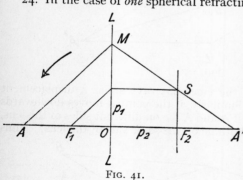

FIG. 41.

the connexion between the motion of the image and that of the object in the following way. From a point A (Fig. 41) on the axis we draw the ray AM and construct the image A′ by means of the line MSA′, as before. Strictly speaking, the ray AM should make only a small angle with AA′, but the construction would then be both inconvenient and inexact. For this reason Reusch * considers the dimensions perpendicular to AA′ to be magnified so that the curvature of the meridian section of the spherical surface can be neglected, and he carries out the construction with this extended figure. In the present case, however, it is sufficient to remember that the *result* of the construction is *not* affected by the slope of the ray. It is therefore permissible,

---

* Reusch, " Konstruktionen zur Lehre von den Haupt-und Brennpunkten eines Linsensystems " (1870); also " Theorie der Zylinderlinsen " (1868).

where the *result* is the only thing that matters, to allow the ray to make a large angle, for example, 45°, with the axis AA'. In such a case, OM = OA, that is, the ray drawn through the corner S of the rectangle whose sides are p_1, p_2, cuts LL at a distance from O which is equal to the object distance and the axis AA' at a distance equal to that of the image. If this ray MA' is rotated about S as centre, all possible cases are obtained. If the points are marked and LL is rotated in the direction indicated until it coincides with AA', *two* projected rows of points are obtained from the bundle of rays through S. The same holds for every neighbouring central ray. It is evident that the *object space* (embracing all object points) is a *projection* with regard to the image space (embracing image points), and that it lies in *perspective* with regard to the centre of curvature. On each central ray there lie projected rows of points covering each other. The centre of curvature corresponds to itself (as double point), and each point of the spherical refracting surface corresponds to itself. This is evident from an *optical* point of view, just as it can be seen by rotating the ray MA' in the figure. The focal plane F_2 of the image space corresponds to the infinitely distant plane of the object space, and the focal plane F_1 of the object space corresponds to the infinitely distant plane of the image space. If A is the object, A' the image, S the point where the central ray cuts the spherical surface, and C the centre of curvature, then the relation $\dfrac{CA}{SA} : \dfrac{CA'}{SA'} = \mu$ holds. Möbius,* by means of considerations of a different type, was the first to deduce this relation.

25. In the case of a spherical mirror the *opposite* movements of object and image follow from an analogous geometrical construction. Instead of the two points F_1, F_2 there is here only one point F (Fig. 42). The straight line through P cuts SA at the object distance and SA' at the image distance. By rotating SA' in the direction of the arrow until it coincides with SA the projective relationship of object and image spaces is obtained for the mirror. The double ratio mentioned above has the value — 1 for this case.†

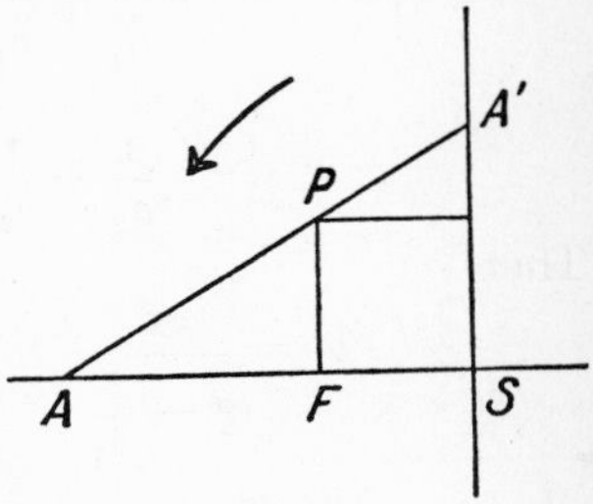

FIG. 42.

In the case of a spherical refracting surface the *dioptric* image of an object point A is an image point A'. If this point A' is now considered as an object point in space, called B, the corresponding image point is a point in space B', which differs from A. If, however, A is an

---

* Möbius, *Ber. d. k. Sächs. Ges. d. Wiss.* (1855), p. 8.

† The quantitative relation between object distance and image distance is the same for a lens as for a spherical mirror, except that the movements of object and image are in the same sense for a lens. It may be mentioned here that the idea underlying Figs. 41 and 42 can be applied to the construction of the focal length of a lens, if *one* corresponding pair of values of a and α is given. This is done by inscribing a square in the triangle AA'S (Fig. 42)—for a spherical surface a rectangle whose sides are in the ratio 1 : μ must be inscribed.

object point and A′ its catoptric image, then A is the image corresponding to A′ considered as an object point. The relation of object space to image space is described as one of *involution*. It is evident that this behaviour is due to the differences in the laws of refraction and reflection. To each straight line there corresponds a different line, according as the former is considered as an incident or refracted ray, but only one and the same line, when the former is considered as an incident or reflected ray. The reciprocal law, which presumes a reversal of the *sense* of the light motion, naturally does not contradict this.

26. It was natural to extend the laws obtained for *one* spherical surface or *one* lens to a system of any number of surfaces or lenses. Attempts to do this in the case of lenses had already been made by Cotes,* Euler,† Lagrange,‡ and Piola.§ The same subject was investigated fundamentally by Möbius, who, however, in his paper entitled " Über die Haupteigenschaften eines Systems von (unendlich dünnen) Linsengläsern," ‖ also made use of the arguments of the older writers. The authors before Möbius principally attempt to find a method of computation for solving those examples which contain no inherent difficulties. Möbius, on the other hand, draws attention to the analogies which exist in the behaviour of a *single* lens and a *system* of lenses. In his analytical treatment he makes use of continued fractions and the method of computation which Euler ¶ devised for them. The method of arrangement in continued fractions is quite simple. For example, if two lenses have powers ** g_1, g_2, object distances a_1, a_2, image distances b_1, b_2, and separation h_1, the following equations hold :—

$$\frac{1}{a_1} + \frac{1}{b_1} = g_1,$$

$$b_1 + a_2 = h_1.$$

$$\frac{1}{a_2} + \frac{1}{b_2} = g_2,$$

Then

$$b_1 = \cfrac{1}{g - \cfrac{1}{a_1}}$$

$$b_2 = \cfrac{1}{g_2 - \cfrac{1}{a_2}} = \cfrac{1}{g_2 - \cfrac{1}{h_1 - b_1}} = \cfrac{1}{g_2 - \cfrac{1}{h_1 - \cfrac{1}{g_1 - \cfrac{1}{a_2}}}}.$$

* Cf. R. Smith, " System of Optics," Book 2, Chap. 5.
† Euler, *Mem. de l'Acad. de Berlin* (1757, 1761).
‡ Lagrange, *ibid.* (1778, 1803).
§ Piola, " Mailänder Ephemeriden " (1822).
‖ Möbius, *Crelles Journ.*, Vol. 5, p. 113.
¶ Euler, *Nov. Comment. Acad. Petrop.*, Vol. 9.
** Power = reciprocal of focal length. Tr.

Of the analogies to which Möbius referred, the following may first be mentioned. For a *single* lens the well-known equation

$$\frac{1}{u} + \frac{1}{v} = \frac{1}{f}$$

holds, and this can be written in the form

$$(u - f)(v - f) = f^2,$$

or,

$$x \cdot x' = f^2,$$

if the distances of the object and image from the respective foci are designated by x and x'.

For a *system* of lenses there are analogously two foci, and the geometrical mean of the distances of the object and image from these points is likewise *constant*, so that it can be called the *focal length* of the system.

To an object at a distance of twice the focal length from a *single* lens there corresponds an *inverted* image of *equal size*. An object *on* the surface of a lens (where object and image coincide) has an *erect* image of *equal size*. Similarly, for a *system* of lenses there is a point A for the object corresponding to which the image at a point A′ is *equal* and *inverted*, and also a point B corresponding to which the image at a point B′ is *equal* and *erect*. The pairs of points A, A′, and B, B′, are situated at distances equal to the focal length away from the foci, but in opposite directions. The points B, B′ were later designated by Gauss *principal points*.

27. The treatment by Gauss * is still more general. He considered analytically the case of a system of coaxial refracting surfaces. Although the case of lenses (of finite thickness) is the main theme, the more general case of a succession of quite different refracting media is not excluded. The treatment is greatly simplified by special substitutions, to the choice of which he was apparently guided by his knowledge of the analogies between a single lens and a system of lenses, but which appear to the reader rather arbitrary ; the constructions resulting from the treatment are very practical. C. Neumann † attempted to give a simpler presentation of Gaussian dioptrics. The first clear presentation of the subject, however, appears to me to have been given by the projective relations of object space and image space discovered by Möbius. These will now be briefly considered with the partial aid of C. Neumann's method of investigation, the long calculations associated with it being, however, avoided.

28. In the above-mentioned paper of 1778, Lagrange introduced the idea of *conjugate* elements. If p is an object point and p' its image point with respect to a refracting surface or a system of such surfaces, then p and p' are *conjugate points*. If S is an incident ray and S′ is the corresponding ray after refraction, then S and S′ are conjugate

* Gauss, " Dioptrische Untersuchungen " (1843).
† " Die Haupt-und Brennpunkte eines zentrischen Systems sphärisch brechenden Flächen " (1866).

rays. According to the *homocentric law*, which holds to the well-known approximation, *all* rays which intersect at p will after refraction again intersect at p'. Owing to the *independence* of the rays in a bundle of rays, *each* point of a ray can be considered as the origin of that ray—a conception of which R. Smith had already made frequent use.

On this assumption the two following relations hold :—

1. If a ray S passes through the points p_1, p_2, the *conjugate* ray S' passes through the points p_1', p_2', which are conjugate to p_1, p_2.

2. If two rays, S_1, S_2, intersect at the point p, the conjugate rays S_1', S_2' intersect at the point p', which is conjugate to p.

It may further be recalled that at each refraction at a spherical surface the object point p and image point p' always lie on the same central ray. It follows that to a system of object points lying in a plane perpendicular to the central ray there corresponds a *similar* system of image points (also lying in a plane perpendicular to the central ray) which is *perspectively* related to the first system with respect to the centre of curvature. The image system is erect or inverted, and the middle point is an outer or inner point of similarity, according as

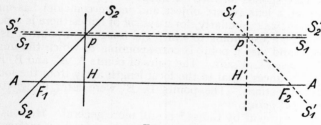

FIG. 43.

the two systems lie on the same side or on opposite sides of the centre of curvature. These relations hold to the well-known approximation.

29. In dealing with a *coaxial* system of spherical refracting surfaces, the centres of curvature of which all lie on the same straight line, the *axis*, the above considerations show that a system of points lying in a plane normal to the axis will, after the rays have passed through all the surfaces, give rise to a system such that the object and image are similar, and are situated *perspectively* with regard to a point on the axis.

Let AA (Fig. 43) be the axis of a *coaxial* system and S_1S_1 an incident ray parallel to the axis. After passage through all the surfaces *in the plane* of S_1S_1 and AA, there will correspond to this ray a conjugate ray $S_1'S_1'$, which *in general* will make a *different* angle with the axis, and will therefore cut the axis in some point F_2. On account of the *homocentric property*, however, all rays incident parallel to the axis will eventually intersect at F_2. F_2 is the (second) *focus* of the system.

If now the *same* ray parallel to the axis, and designated $S_2'S_2'$, is considered as emerging from the system, there corresponds to it an *incident* ray S_2S_2 in the same plane which in general makes a different angle with the axis and cuts it at F_1. *All* rays proceeding from F_1, then, emerge *parallel to the axis.* F_1 is the (first) *focus* of the system.

If S_1S_1, S_2S_2 are two incident rays which intersect at p, it follows that the point of intersection p' of the two conjugate rays $S_1'S_1'$, $S_2'S_2'$ is conjugate to p. Thus p' is the image of p and, according to what has been said, the whole system of points in the plane through p' normal to the axis is the image of the similarly situated system of

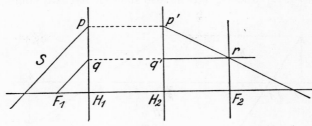

FIG. 44.

points through p. On account of the perspective relation, however, the system through p' is the *erect, equal-sized* image of the system through p, and both lie perspectively with regard to the infinitely distant point of the axis. The two planes H, H' are called, according to Gauss, the *principal planes*, and their intersections with the axis the *principal points*.

30. Having obtained this view of the problem, and having determined once for all by construction, computation, or experiment the

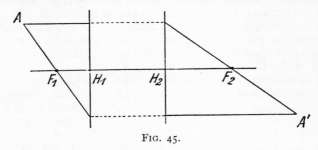

FIG. 45.

principal points and foci of a dioptric system, all further constructions follow very simply. It is not necessary to construct the path of each ray through the system, for the emergent ray corresponding to each incident ray can be determined without troubling about its actual path in the system.

Let S (Fig. 44), an incident ray lying in a plane through the axis, cut the principal plane H_1 at the point p; it may be considered as one of a parallel bundle of rays. The parallel ray through F_1 passes through q and the conjugate point q', and then travels parallel to the axis, cutting the focal plane F_2 at the point r. The ray S passes through p', the point conjugate to p, and likewise passes through r. According to Gauss the construction is simplified if it is remembered that the ray S cuts the focal planes at distances from the axis whose sum is equal to the distance from the axis of the point where it cuts the plane H_1.

The image A′ (Fig. 45) of a point A can be obtained by choosing from the rays which leave A the one which is parallel to the axis and the one which passes through F_1.

As is evident from the above, Möbius had already referred to the points F_1, F_2, H_1, and H_2, but he also showed that two points, L_1, L_2

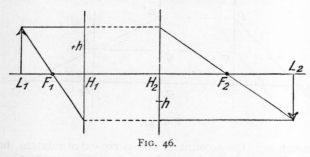

FIG. 46.

(Fig. 46), exist such that an object at L_1 forms an equal, but inverted, image at L_2. For a *single* lens or a *single* spherical surface, this happens when the object and image lie on opposite sides of the lens or spherical surface at distances equal to double the focal length ; this follows immediately from the formulæ. The case of a coaxial system can be proved in an analogous manner. Let us assume that an object point is distant $+ h$ from the axis, but its *position* is not known. We construct the *incident* ray parallel to the axis at a distance $+ h$, and the emergent ray parallel to the axis at a distance $- h$. This enables us to determine the points L_1, L_2, which are at distances from the foci F_1, F_2 equal to double the focal lengths, measured in the opposite directions to H_1, H_2.

31. It is evident that the behaviour of a coaxial system is similar to a *single* refraction at *one* spherical surface or *one* lens, *combined* with

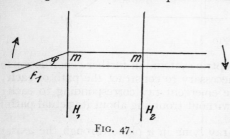

FIG. 47.

a *displacement* along the axis by an amount equal to the *separation of the principal planes*. If the system has unequal focal lengths, it is similar to a *single* surface, while if it has equal focal lengths it is similar to a lens. It is now obvious that the two focal lengths of a system are *equal* if the first and last media are the *same*, but that the first and second focal lengths are to one another as $1 : \mu$ if μ is the refractive index of the *last* medium with respect to the *first*. This can easily be shown by using Kepler's method of considering the problem.

Let a ray which comes from the first focus (Fig. 47) make a very small angle with the axis, and cut the principal plane H_1 a very short distance m from the axis ; this ray proceeds parallel to the axis at a distance m from it. If the ray is now rotated through an angle ϕ in the direction of the arrows until it is parallel to the axis, the point where it cuts H_1 being kept fixed, then the emergent ray rotates in the same direction, but only through the angle ϕ/μ, the point where it cuts H_2 remaining fixed. The second focal length is therefore $f_2 = \mu f_1$. When the first and last media are the same, $f_2 = f_1$. In the former case, equation (8) on page 64 would become

$$\frac{da}{a^2} = -\,\mu\,\frac{da}{a^2}.$$

32. In addition to the *fundamental* or *cardinal* points of a coaxial system, discovered by Möbius and Gauss, Listing * has supplied two new points, the *nodal points*. Their introduction follows from the further development of the analogy between a refracting surface and a coaxial system. In both cases there are two foci. The rôle of the refracting surface is distributed between the two principal planes, so that the refracting surface has, so to speak, been split into two. It is natural to inquire whether the rôle of the centre of the lens is not likewise filled in some way in a system. Since in this case everything can be reduced to one refraction and a displacement, it is to be expected that to the centre of the lens there will correspond *two* points through which the incident and emergent rays will pass parallel to each other.

Let us consider a ray of *given* direction but of unknown position. We can begin the construction by drawing the parallel ray u (Fig. 48) through F_1. The ray of unknown position will pass through the point P in the focal plane F_2 and, since the whole bundle of parallel rays converge at P, there will be one ray v which emerges parallel to u. If we trace this ray backwards we obtain the parallel incident ray w.

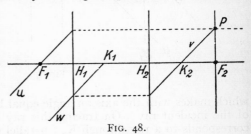

FIG. 48.

Thus the incident ray w, which when continued cuts the axis at K_1, will emerge in a parallel direction through K_2. Since, now, the result of the construction, namely, the determination of the points K_1, K_2, is quite independent of the *direction* of the incident ray, it follows that the *nodal points* K_1, K_2 possess the characteristic that each incident ray passing through the first emerges from the second in a parallel direction. These points therefore fill the rôle of the centre of the lens. They lie each on the same side of the corresponding principal plane at the same distance $H_1 K_1 = H_2 K_2 = f_2 - f_1$, that is, the difference of the two focal lengths. If the first and last media are the same, that is $f_2 - f_1 = 0$, the nodal points coincide with the principal points, just as with an infinitely thin lens the apex assumes the rôle of the centre of the lens.

As the points L_1 and L_2 of Fig. 46 exhibit characteristics opposite to those of the principal points H_1 and H_2, Toepler called them *negative* principal points ; we may therefore designate them by the symbols H_{-1} and H_{-2}. The question may now be asked whether there is a pair of points which fulfil an analogous, but possibly modified, rôle to that of the nodal points K_1, K_2. Let us consider again an incident ray u (Fig. 49), of given direction but unknown position, and find the emergent ray which cuts the axis at an equal angle, but in the opposite sense. We commence the construction by drawing through F a ray parallel to the given direction. This ray, as also the whole bundle of parallel rays, passes eventually through the point P_2 in the focal plane F_2. Of the rays emerging from the image P_2 there is one, namely, P_2K_{-2},

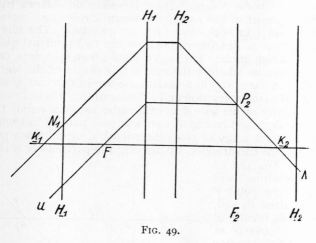

FIG. 49.

which makes with the axis an angle equal but of opposite sign to that of the incident ray. On tracing this ray backwards we find that it corresponds to a ray through K_{-1} parallel to u. The points K_{-1} and K_{-2}, whose positions are independent of the angle of incidence used in the construction, were called by Toepler negative nodal points. The distance of K_{-1} from the plane H_1, and similarly that of K_{-2} from the plane H_2, is equal to $f_2 + f_1$. The distance of K_{-1} from the plane H_{-1}, and similarly that of K_{-2} from the plane H_{-2}, is equal to $f_2 - f_1$. The symmetry on which the whole construction depends is quite obvious. If $f_2 = f_1$, K_{-1} coincides with H_{-1} and K_{-2} with H_{-2}.

33. If we consider a coaxial system through which only rays making small angles with the axis pass, the object and image spaces with respect to the first surface are related both projectively and perspectively. This image space acts as the object space for the second surface, and it also is related projectively and perspectively with regard to the image space for this surface. This holds throughout the system,

the ratio mentioned on page 70 changing its value according to the relative refractive indices for each refraction. The first object space is related to the last image space projectively, but not perspectively, because the refracting surfaces are not coincident. Thus the two spaces which are related projectively are displaced from the perspective position by an axial shift equal to the distance between the principal planes of the whole system.

In a lecture on geometrical optics in 1870 I pointed out, without knowing of Möbius' paper, that the Gaussian dioptrics leads to relations which can most simply and naturally be looked upon as projective. I was led to this view by a study of Steiner's geometry and a remark of Ch. Paulus, but refrained from a full publication of my views after the papers of Toepler * and Lippich † had appeared, and confined myself to a short statement in Carl's " Repertorium," Vol. 7, p. 262. I was particularly glad of this later, as I found that Möbius had already given all the necessary details.‡

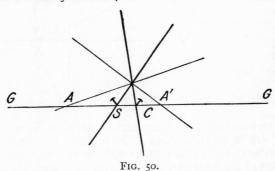

FIG. 50.

The positions of object and image and their projective relation (cf. Fig. 41) can be illustrated on the axis itself by drawing GG (Fig. 50), fixing pins at the points S (the apex of the refracting surface) and C (the centre of curvature), and laying over this a fixed network of four wires, as shown. So long as the wires S and C are made to touch their respective pins, the intersections of the wires A and A' with GG give respectively the positions of an object and its image in a spherical surface. If the wires A and A' bisect the angles between the other two wires, we have the case of a mirror ; the value of the ratio mentioned on page 70 is then − 1. In this *geometrical* illustration the wires do not require to pass through the points S, C ; they may be allowed to touch the pins on one side or on the other.

34. Lagrange, in the above-mentioned paper of 1803, and Möbius, in his work of 1830, define the *telescope* as an optical system in which the two focal lengths are infinitely great. It is obvious that in this

* Toepler, *Pogg. Ann.*, 142 (1871).

† Lippich, *Mitt. d. naturw. Vereins du Graz* (1871).

‡ Cf. also Hankel, " Elemente d. projektivischen Geometrie," Leipzig (1875), pp. 146, etc. ; also the reference by Czapski, in Winkelmann's " Handbuch der Physik," Breslau (1894), Vol. 2, to the work of Abbe on this subject.

case the above constructions are not applicable. The complete system can, however, be divided into two portions, each of which has finite focal lengths, and can therefore be treated in the above-mentioned way. The second focal plane of the first portion (the objective system) then coincides with the first focal plane of the second portion (the eyepiece system).

35. In experiments with dioptric systems it is essential to ensure that a point of the image space corresponds to each point of the object

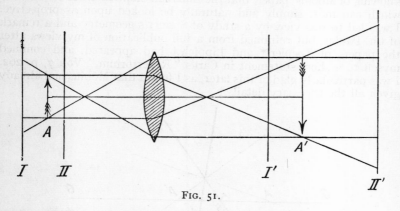

FIG. 51.

space, and further that the object and image move in the same sense. Let A (Fig. 51) be an object and A' its image. If a screen is brought into the position of the latter, there corresponds to each point of the object a point of the image on the screen, since A and A' are conjugate. In addition, however, if the screen is moved to another position, such as I' or II', images are obtained, not indeed of the object, but of the complexes of ray intersections in the conjugate planes I and II.

If this is remembered, it is not difficult to understand phenomena which might otherwise appear rather extraordinary. Suppose, for example, that a bright luminous object, such as a candle flame, is observed through a small hole in a screen CC (Fig. 52) with the aid of a magnifying glass LL. If the lens and eye are so placed that the plane E_1E_1, which is conjugate to the retina, lies between CC and LL, an *inverted* image of the flame is seen ; if, however, the conjugate plane occupies the position E_2E_2, an *erect* image of the flame is seen, and if the plane coincides with CC the illuminated hole is seen. The flame can be removed to a considerable distance from the screen. All the rays which are unable to pass through the hole are excluded from

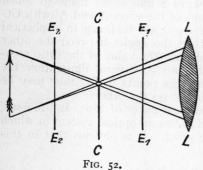

FIG. 52.

taking part in the formation of the image. Grey,* the well-known electrician, on observing an analogous phenomenon, thought that it was due to a concave mirror action of the small hole !

36. A survey of the development of dioptrics enables us to make the following remarks :—

1. The approximate solution of the problems which have arisen in practical dioptrics under simplified and intentionally idealized conditions has been particularly successful both in theory and practice. The more exact solution has resulted in the form of corrections to the approximate solution.

2. It has been found useful to investigate the most common cases *once for all*, and to record the result of the investigation for further use in the form of laws.

3. By comparing the simpler with the more complicated cases analogies between the two have been discovered.

L_1 L_2

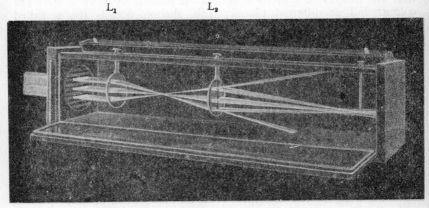

FIG. 53.

4. By making use of these analogies it has been found superfluous to repeat all the intermediate investigations in each case of a complicated system. These can be *omitted* after having been carried through *once*, since they produce a direct relation between the first object space and the last image space. The process thus involves an *economy* of effort.

37. The properties of lenses may be demonstrated by means of the apparatus shown in Fig. 53. The arrangement consists of a glass tank filled with tobacco smoke from a small bulb, in the nozzle of which is placed a cigarette with the burning end inwards. The lenses are placed in the tank, and their positions can be altered at will. If sunlight passes through a grating with horizontal bars placed at one end of the tank, the paths of the rays become visible in the smoke, and the focus of the first lens L_1 forms a luminous point which can be

* Grey, *Phil. Trans. Roy. Soc.*, Vol. I, p. 172 ; Priestley, " History of Optics " (1772), Vol. I, p. 209.

moved towards and through the second lens L_2. A slot is cut in the latter in order to show simultaneously the direct and refracted bundles of rays behind the lens.   Since *all* rays emerging from one point and falling on the lens combine again at one point, it is immaterial for the formation of the image whether the whole lens or only a part of it is present.   If the portion of the lens present is covered with a plane piece of red glass, the direct beam remains *white*, whilst the refracted beam is coloured *red*.   In order to make the movement of the object point more convenient, another lens may be mounted in front of the lens L_1, so as to make the rays from L_1 as convergent or divergent as is required.

With this apparatus, which resembles a *working model*, all the laws relating to lenses can be demonstrated very beautifully.   Naturally, the lens L_2 may be replaced by a slotted dispersive lens or concave mirror.

The refractive indices for differently coloured rays are different, so that the images of a given object point formed by rays of different colours fall at different places ; this phenomenon is the so-called chromatic aberration of lenses.   The above apparatus can be used to demonstrate this aberration.   If a complete lens is substituted for L_2, and the right- and left-hand halves are covered with plane red and blue glasses respectively, the white cone of light from the focus of L_1 divides into red and blue cones, the apex of the former being farther removed from L_2 than that of the latter.   It may also be observed that the cone of light from L_1 has a red border between the lens and the focus and a blue border beyond the focus ; this also demonstrates chromatic aberration.

The motion of object and image, in the same direction in the case of lenses, and in opposite directions in the case of mirrors, can also be clearly shown.

All the phenomena of condensing lenses can also be understood by assuming that the lenses consist of an infinite system of small prisms with different refracting angles, the refracting edges being turned away from the axis, and the sizes of the angles increasing with the distance from the axis.   In the case of dispersive lenses, on the other hand, the refractive edges of the prisms are turned towards the axis.

38. A closer investigation of lens aberrations (departures from the law of homocentricity), which are of special technical interest, will not be undertaken here, but methods of demonstrating these aberrations will be described.   Some of these aberrations are *regular*, such as *spherical* aberration and *chromatic* aberration, whilst others are *irregular*, such as those which are due to accidental errors in *grinding* and to want of *homogeneity* in the glass.

Nearly all the aberrations can be shown with a simple lens whose surfaces form considerable portions of spheres.   The moulded lens of 65 cm. focal length and 24 cm. aperture from a Tschirnhausen apparatus is particularly suitable for these experiments.   With such a lens the spherical aberration—the greater convergence of the edge rays and the meridian curve, *convex* to the axis, of the bounding surface of the light from the lens—can be clearly seen in a smoky atmosphere.   It is desirable to allow the sunlight diverging from a point on the axis to fall on the whole aperture of the lens.

Prechtl * demonstrated this aberration by placing on the lens a diaphragm with two holes near the axis, and two near the periphery (Fig. 54). The rays of light passing through the holes a, a' combine at a point nearer to the lens than the point at which the rays through b, b' combine, as can easily be proved by allowing the four beams to fall on a piece of paper.

In a given lens spherical aberration and chromatic aberration are both present simultaneously, but the former can be isolated by placing in the path of the light falling on a lens LL (Fig. 55) a deep

FIG. 54.

red glass GG. If a diaphragm aa with a small hole in it is placed at the focus of the edge rays, the image on a screen SS consists of a small red ring with a red central spot. If, however, the screen is moved towards b, the position where the central rays combine, the ring decreases in size until it coincides with the central spot.

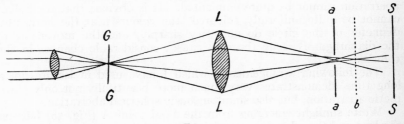

FIG. 55.

Prechtl's method of showing spherical aberration may be somewhat modified in order to demonstrate chromatic aberration. Sunlight is allowed to pass through a convex lens, and near the focus through four closely-fitting sectors (Fig. 56) of red (r) and blue (b) glass, which are cemented with Canada balsam between tolerably plane pieces of glass. It then falls on a diaphragm B, which covers the lens under investigation, so that the holes r, r appear red and the holes b, b blue. When the blue beams combine on a screen, the red beams are separated, but, on moving the screen farther from the lens, the red beams combine and the blue ones separate.

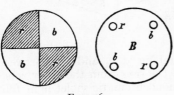

FIG. 56.

Chromatic aberration can be seen, as already mentioned, from the fact that a section of the beam from the whole aperture of the lens has a red boundary between the lens and the real image, and a blue boundary beyond the image. It can be shown more clearly by means of an

* Prechtl, " Praktische Dioptrik," Vienna (1828).

arrangement which was apparently first adopted by Toepler.* The light from an axial point A (Fig. 57) falls on a lens and forms a large circle of illumination on the screen SS. If a diaphragm B is moved from below until it covers the focus of the *green* rays, the rays from green to violet fall on the upper half of the circle, whilst those from green to red fall on the lower half; each semicircle of illumination thus exhibits a *bright, distinctive* colour. In this experiment spherical

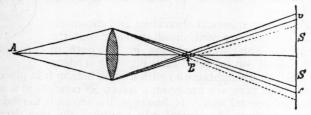

FIG. 57.

aberration cannot be quite eliminated. It is obvious that the halves cannot be quite uniformly coloured, the colours near the horizontal diameter of the circle do not vary sharply, and the movement of the diaphragm B along the axis causes considerable changes in the colours.

The following arrangement,† which I have used in lectures for a long time, demonstrates very much more beautifully not only chromatic aberration, but also simultaneously spherical aberration.

White sunlight emerging from the axial point A (Fig. 58) falls on the lens and the edge rays for violet and red light combine at v and r

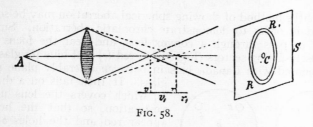

FIG. 58.

respectively, while the central rays combine at v_1 and r_1. Between these points lie the combining points of the rays from the other zones of the lens. If in the first place only monochromatic violet light falls on the lens and a diaphragm with a small hole is gradually moved away from the lens, the hole being kept on the axis, only the central rays pass through the hole and form on the screen S a bright spot C. As soon, however, as the point v is reached, a violet ring R is also formed on the screen, and on moving the diaphragm farther this ring

* Toepler, "Beobachtungen nach einer neuen optischen Methode," Bonn (1864).
† E. Mach, *Poskesche Z. f. phys. u. chem. Unterricht*, Vol. 2 (1888).

contracts until it finally coincides with C, so that only the central spot remains.

When white light is employed the central spot is white, and adjacent to the contracting violet ring are somewhat larger blue, green, yellow, and red rings. This ring-shaped spectrum contracts as the diaphragm is moved away from the lens until it coincides with C, so that there finally remains a white central spot with a red border.

If the hole, with its central point on the axis, is made fairly large, not only do these rays pass through which combine at the central point, but also the rays from all combining points which correspond to cone surfaces of *smaller* aperture than those cones which can be constructed with the rim of the hole as base and these points as apexes. The ring-shaped spectrum thus becomes *broader* and *less pure* and, with a sufficient increase in the size of the hole, changes into a *white* ring with violet border and red centre; on moving the diaphragm away from the lens this ring also contracts, and ultimately coincides with the central spot.

39. In addition to the above-mentioned aberrations which are *necessarily* present on account of the spherical form of surface and the dispersion of the lens substance, lenses possess *accidental* errors of construction and irregularities in the glass, and therefore in the refractive index. Huygens * investigated the glasses which he wished to use for lenses. He had these roughly plane polished, and examined them with oblique illumination in front of a bright background with a dark border, so that any irregularity became evident by the deflection it caused. Huygens employed an original method of testing finished lenses. With respect to the light which is *reflected* from the second surface, a lens acts as a concave mirror; if $\mu = 3/2$, and both surfaces have the same radius of curvature r, the whole system acts as a concave mirror of focal length $r/4$, or radius of curvature $r/2$. Huygens † mounted the lens vertically in a dark room and moved it to such a distance that the whole back surface became illuminated by the flame of a candle held in the hand. This happens when the image of the flame formed by the equivalent concave mirror falls on the eye. The flame and the eye are then close together on opposite sides of the centre of curvature of the equivalent mirror. Errors, due to polishing and lack of homogeneity, which cause sufficient deflection are visible as irregularities in the illumination of the lens. If the radius of curvature was 40 feet or more, Huygens employed a small telescope for observation.

Foucault ‡ applied an improvement of the same principle to the testing of the errors of telescope mirrors. The improvement consisted in placing a small source of light L (Fig. 59) near the centre of curvature and mounting a diaphragm B so that the image of the source fell on its edge, the eye being placed behind B. Since the light is screened

* Huygens, " De formandis vitris."
† Huygens, " Opuscula postuma. De formandis poliendisque vitris ad telescopia " (1703), p. 274.
‡ Foucault, " Recueil des travaux scientifiques " (1878); " Memoire sur la construction des telescopes," pp. 236, etc.

off, and the eye is consequently more sensitive, the smallest quantities of light deflected to the side of the diaphragm by *small* irregularities are visible to the eye.

A. Toepler * applied the same principle to lenses. In this case the light source and its image are of course on opposite sides of the lens (Fig. 60). The image is screened off and the eye is placed behind the diaphragm. Toepler made use of a telescope for observation, so that he combined the advantages of Huygens' and Foucault's arrangements. Toepler's method is very sensitive with small light sources, large focal lengths which allow of considerable deflections, and judicious (not complete) screening off. If an irregularity *m* (Fig. 60) in the polishing or in the optical density causes a stronger deflection downwards, the position *m* immediately appears brighter. If, on the other hand, the deflection is upwards, light which otherwise would have reached the eye falls on the diaphragm, and the position appears darker. With Toepler's method a lens which is *completely* free from spherical and chromatic aberrations would appear uniformly illuminated, the intensity of the illumination depending on the amount of screening.

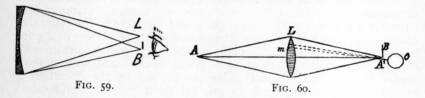

FIG. 59.   FIG. 60.

Since it is necessary to use a somewhat extended light source, each point of the lens receives rays from different points of the source, and these rays intersect in the plane of the lens. If, therefore, the eye or telescope is focussed on the lens surface so that the surface and the retina are in conjugate planes, an *image* of the lens is seen, and the performance of the lens can be judged from the illumination differences in the image. Even if a sufficiently bright light source of negligible extension could be used, the light diffracted by unequally bright portions of the lens would still form an *image* on the retina.†

40. Toepler's method is so sensitive that even small irregularities in the air in the neighbourhood of the lens, caused by heat, gases, or sound waves, can be made visible if a suitable arrangement is adopted.

The phenomena can be projected on a screen. Let LL (Fig. 61) be a lens, A a small source, and A′ its image. If it is desired to project a real image L′L′ of double the size of LL on a screen at a given position, M is the position for the *projecting* lens. The line LK parallel to the axis and the line KL′ then give the focus P of this lens. Through the other focus P_1, draw P_1N parallel to LTA′, and NS parallel to the

---

* Toepler, " Beobachtungen nach einer neuen optischen Methode " (1864).

† I have drawn attention to this because I have received the impression, from French and German reviews of the observations on projectiles, sound waves, etc., published by myself and my co-workers, that the Toepler " Schlieren " method has not always been properly understood.

axis. Then the intersection of TS with the axis gives the new position of the image of A, that is, the position of the diaphragm B.

The hot mantle of air round a candle flame can be shown very beautifully by this method. Also, if a counterpoised vessel on a balance is placed in front of L, it sinks when carbon dioxide is poured into it, and the gas, although otherwise invisible, can be seen quite clearly in the image L'L'. Such an experiment shows that for the sense-perception of an object or an occurrence sometimes only the quantitative conditions are lacking, and that these can be produced artificially.

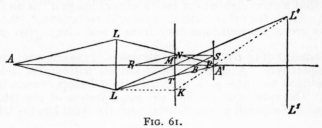

FIG. 61.

The method is also useful in showing the difference between an image-forming lens and the image of a lens. If an extended light source is used at A, and a candle-flame is placed in front of LL, the image A' changes only in intensity, if portions of the lens LL are covered, whereas the image of the covered portions is formed at L'L'. On the other hand, if the lens M is partly covered, only the intensity of the image at L'L' alters, the actual screening not being sharply imaged at L'L'. The reason is that LL and L'L' are conjugate planes, but not M and L'L'.

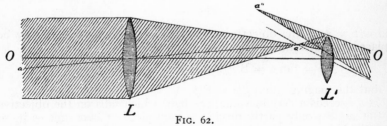

FIG. 62.

41. As has been mentioned, Lagrange and Möbius defined the telescope as a system whose focal lengths are both infinite, so that parallel incident rays emerge from the system parallel. Although applications of theory to optical instruments cannot be treated very fully here, the telescope may serve as an *example* to draw attention to the various questions which arise in the construction of such instruments.

As the simplest case, let us consider the two-lens astronomical telescope which is focussed for a long-sighted eye that can combine on the retina parallel incident rays. In this case the above definition holds.

Let a bundle of parallel rays from a very distant point *a* (Fig. 62) fall on the objective L in a direction making a small angle with the axis OO. These rays combine with the undeviated ray through the centre of the lens in the focal plane of L at the point a', the image of a. If the eyepiece L′ is arranged so that its first focus coincides with the second focus of L, the rays from a' emerge from L′ as a parallel bundle, which is parallel to the principal ray $a'r$, whether this ray is actually present or not. The figure is, of course, diagrammatic, the actual relative dimensions being exaggerated for the sake of clearness. If L′ is made to approach L, the rays emerging from the system are divergent, so that a short-sighted eye sees a virtual image a'' at an infinite distance. If, on the other hand, L′ is moved away from L, the emergent rays are convergent, and they form a real image after passing through L′.

Let O and O′ (Fig. 63) be the middle points of the objective and eyepiece respectively. A distant object, which *without* the telescope would subtend an angle a, is seen *with* the telescope subtending an angle β. The ratio β/a is called the *magnification* of the telescope. Since now B′F is small in comparison with the focal lengths OF = P

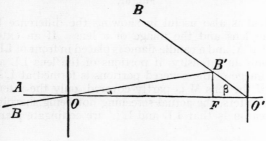

FIG. 63.

and O′F = p of the objective and eyepiece, the angles a, β may be replaced by their tangents ; thus

$$a = \tan a = \text{B′F}/\text{P} \quad \text{and} \quad \beta = \tan \beta = \text{B′F}/p,$$

so that the magnification $\beta/a = \text{P}/p$.

If a exceeds a certain value, the light which falls on the objective at the angle a only partly reaches the eyepiece or even misses it, so that the object can only be seen faintly through the telescope or not at all. The limiting value of a (or its tangent, since only small angles are under consideration) determines the field of view. If we *arbitrarily* take as the limit of the field of view the angle at which the ray through the *middle of the objective* intersects the *edge* of the eyepiece, that is, an angle for which the intensity of the images is less than half that on the axis, we have

$$\tan a = \frac{\text{R}}{\text{P} + p} = \frac{\text{R}}{\text{L}},$$

where R is the radius of the ocular lens aperture and L the length of the telescope tube. If the magnification is to be considerable, the focal length of the ocular must be small in comparison with that of the objective, but then a practical limit to the eyepiece aperture is set by the smallness of the radius of curvature, spherical aberration, etc. Huygens discussed these relations exhaustively.

42. The bundle of light, parallel to the axis, which falls on the objective aperture OO (Fig. 64) emerges from the eyepiece aperture *mm* parallel to the axis, but its diameter is reduced in the ratio p/P, and its cross-section in the ratio $(p/P)^2$, so that the beam is condensed in the ratio $(P/p)^2$. Since, now, each element of the image is increased in area $(P/p)^2$ times, the image remains, apart from losses due to reflection (Lagrange, 1803), *just as bright* as without the telescope. This holds so long as the cross-section of the emergent beam is *greater* than the aperture of the pupil of the eye. With very great magnifications the cross-section of the emergent beams is *smaller* than the pupil aperture, so that the brightness of the image *decreases* with increase in the *magnification*. Only with objects having *no apparent* extension, such as the fixed stars, does all the light which the objective *aperture* receives fall on one *point of the retina ;* in such cases much more light is received than is possible with the pupil of the unaided eye. On this account stars can be seen with the help of a telescope which otherwise

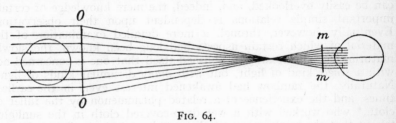

FIG. 64.

would be invisible. If the heavens are observed in the daytime the stars are not visible owing to the diffuse sunlight in comparison with which the light from the stars disappears. With considerable magnification, however, the *surface illumination* is, to put it shortly, diminished, whilst the *point illumination* is increased, so that the stars become visible.

In 1803 Lagrange pointed out that the ratio of the diameters of the incident and emergent parallel beams serves to determine the magnification of the telescope ; this is at once obvious from the above. If a telescope is mounted so that sunlight falls on it parallel to the axis, then the magnification is given by D/d, where D is the diameter of the *effective* aperture of the objective and d is the diameter of the beam emerging from the eyepiece ; this latter can be measured by allowing the beam to fall on a piece of cardboard. The light which is incident on the objective may be partly screened by internal stops. In order to find the *effective* aperture of the objective, the actual aperture may be gradually reduced until it just begins to affect the emergent beam. The method given by Lagrange for determining the magnification is, moreover, quite independent of the construction of the telescope. He therefore compared this method with the application of the principle of virtual displacements in mechanics.

CHAPTER VI

THE COMPOSITION OF LIGHT

Newton's Theory of Colour and Dispersion

The foregoing insight into the theory of optics was obtainable without distinguishing between different kinds of light, since all light was considered homogeneous and identically constituted. Actually, the differences between the kinds of light manifest themselves so insignificantly under certain circumstances that they can be easily overlooked, and, indeed, the mere knowledge of certain important simple relations is dependent upon their observation. Eventually, however, through a more detailed examination of the material of which certain aspects had long been known, the slowly maturing view necessarily established itself that one is concerned not with a *single* kind of light, but with *many* dissimilar kinds of light. Naturally, the rainbow had awakened interest even in the earliest times, and the experience of a related phenomenon by the fuller of cloth,* who worked with a wet drop-covered cloth in the sunlight, taught that the rainbow was conditioned by rain in sunlight. During the first decade of the fourteenth century, a German Dominican monk, Theodoricus de Saxonia,† gave an explanation of the rainbow similar to, only less complete than, that given later by Descartes. Marcus Antonius de Dominis ‡ based his explanation on experiments with glass spheres, both solid and filled with water. Descartes.§ who also noticed the rainbow in fountains, deduced that illuminated water drops are essential to its composition, and, recognizing that the size of the drop was immaterial,‖ experimented with glass spheres filled with water. Thus he explained the outer rainbow by two refractions and two reflections, the inner one by two refractions and one reflection. He found that only those rays could reach the eye with the necessary intensity which subtend angles of 51° 57′ and 41° 30′ res-

---

* Cf. Aristotle, " Meteorologie," Book III, Chap. 2.; and Plutarch, " Lehrmeinungen der Philosophen," Book III, Chap. 1.
† Author of a manuscript discovered by Venturi, to be found in the libraries of Bâle and Leipzig, entitled " De radialibus impressionibus."
‡ Perished in 1624 in a prison of the Roman Inquisition.
§ " Plus la dioptrique, les meteores et la geometrie, que şont des essais de cette methode," A. Leyde (1637). " Discours de la methode," p. 250, etc. The size of the drops is only immaterial for approximate considerations ; the contrary is the case if, following Airy and Mascart, one considers the question as a diffraction problem.
‖ Cf. Priestley, " Geschichte der Optik," Fig. 43

pectively with the continuation of the line joining the sun to the observer.* Descartes could not explain why the rainbow is coloured nor why the order of the colours is opposite in the two bows. However, the explanation of the rainbow is one of the most important of Descartes' contributions to physics.

The colour phenomena associated with prisms, whose resemblance with the rainbow is certainly striking, also excited curiosity for a long time. Father Tigautius, in his mission report from China, and Kircher (1601-1680), in his " China illustrata," mentioned prisms as articles of luxury beloved by the Orientals. De Dominis † supposed that the ray passing through the smallest thickness of glass in a prism is red, whilst the light of longer path becomes violet, which naturally does not agree with the phenomena with plane-parallel plates. Marcus Marci ‡ (1595-1667) regarded the colours as dependent on the degree of refraction, and also observed that further refractions did not alter the colours any more. He regarded the colours, however, as feeble or dim light. Rosenberger is very probably correct when he assumes that Marci was hindered by the ignorance of the exact law of refraction from anticipating Newton's discovery. Indeed, colour cannot be distinguished as a special kind of light characterized by its refractive index if the idea of refractive index is lacking. Franciscus Maria Grimaldi § (1619-1663) drew attention to the spreading out of the spectrum. He pointed out that colour is not connected with a particular angle, and that it is not changed by further refraction when once formed. Robert Boyle ‖ (1627-1691) collected the numerous ideas which had appeared from time to time with regard to the nature of colour. Colour was to the Peripatetics a property of bodies which was disclosed by light, to the Platonics a kind of flaming emanation ; others held colour to be a mixture of light and darkness, and chemical and dynamical theories were also in vogue. Boyle could not reconcile himself with any of these theories. The formation of colour out of black and white, for example, was unintelligible to him ; refraction must play an important part. His idea was that colour is a modification of light.

This was the condition of affairs when Newton (1642-1727) took up these questions. According to his own account, he began his studies in the year 1666. He endeavoured to construct lenses of aspherical form, but found the chromatic aberration much greater and more troublesome than the spherical aberration. He believed that his experiments with combined prisms of various substances (water, glass, etc.) proved that chromatic aberration could not altogether be removed. His interest in the improvement of the astronomical telescope, which had caused him to carry out these experiments, led him then to the

* Only rays at minimum deviation are parallel to the neighbouring rays and reinforce the latter sufficiently.
† " De radiis visus et lucis in vitris perspectivis et iride." Venetiis (1611), Chap. 3, p. 9.
‡ Thaumantias, " Liber de arcii cœlesti deque colorum apparentium natura." Authore Joanne Marco Marci. Pragae (1648).
§ " Physico-mathesis de lumine, coloribus et iride." Bononiae (1665).
‖ " Experimenta et considerationes de coloribus," which appeared first in English in 1663. See also Brewster and Wilde.

construction of a reflecting telescope in the year 1668. In 1671 Newton sent a better specimen to the Royal Society, which published a description in its " Transactions " in 1672. Newton's experience with prisms had, however, excited his interest in the colour problem, and from his researches in this direction came far more important results. Newton appears first to have forsaken the old ideas about the year 1668. His dissertation, " A New Theory about Light and Colours," was presented to the Royal Society on 6th February, 1672. We find from this that it was in the main a much more searching analysis that had led him to make his great discovery. It struck him as most remarkable that the length of the spectrum projected on the wall of a room was about five times that of the illumination on the wall caused by the unrefracted rays, which passed at the side of the prism. Experiment showed that the interception of different rays by slabs of glass had no effect. The idea of a scattering by irregularities in the glass must also be excluded, since the combination of two oppositely orientated prisms gave the same image as without a prism at all. The rays from the edge of the sun's disk subtend an angle of $31'$; but this small difference in the incidence was insufficient to explain the spreading out of the spectrum ; it was $2° 49'$ too long. The assumption of a curved path of the light rays was found likewise untenable. Finally, it occurred to Newton to submit the different parts of the spectrum to refraction in a second prism, and then it was observed that they underwent unequal amounts of refraction. Sunlight thus contains components of different refrangibility. Newton then expounded the theory at which he had arrived. There are rays of different refrangibility, which are at the same time distinguishable by colour. To each definite refrangibility belongs a definite colour. The refrangibility and colour of a given kind of light cannot be changed by reflection, refraction, absorption, or transmission through thin coloured plates. Change of colour can apparently only take place when one is dealing with mixed colours. A distinction must be drawn between simple colours, inseparable by refraction, and such mixed colours, which may make the same impression on the eye. White sunlight is a composition of all possible colours. The colour of bodies is due to different coloured components of the incident light being radiated again in different amounts. Since then the nature of colour does not lie in the bodies, but in the light itself, light must be a substance.

Although the negative elements of Newton's line of thought were already present, nobody before him had submitted them to such a minute intellectual reasoning and experimental proof as he had done, and he was thus led to a positive perception of the laws governing the phenomena ; this represents an important expansion of knowledge. On the whole, the same drama repeats itself as with the development of dioptrics. An unlooked-for and remarkable phenomenon presents itself, excites curiosity, technical interest increases the latter, and with the comprehension of this one phenomenon a multitude of facts are disclosed, explained, and elucidated. Newton himself was conscious of the value and magnitude of his discovery. This is evident from his letter * of 18th January, 1672, to Oldenburg. It is also conceivable that the small interest which his achievement awakened embittered him. He explained facts, while Hooke † wanted to wrangle over hypotheses. His conflict with misconception and the inexact repetition of his experiments by Pardies, Linus,‡ and others, must have depressed him. Thus it is quite conceivable that there probably grew up a certain amount of insincerity and restraint in the exposition of Newton's researches. In no other place did he expound his method of investigation so clearly and openly as he did in his optical publication. The study of his later writings is thereby made more difficult, and the profit which an insight into his methods could give is partly lost. The prejudice of Newton's opponents against such a radically new point of view is, however, only too comprehensible.

Besides Newton's communications in the " Transactions," there are two accounts in greater detail at our disposal—" Opticks," the Latin translation of which was undertaken by Clarke, § and the " Lectiones opticae," ‖ from Newton's lectures during the years 1669 to 1671. " Opticks " contains the complete Newtonian theory. The " Lectiones " have, however, more the character of class lectures ; many exercises in elementary dioptrics are dealt with. Of the Newtonian discoveries proper, only the colour and dispersion theory, apart from the colours of thin films and diffraction, is mentioned. In addition, some fine experiments are described which are not to be found in the " Opticks." We will next look more closely into the contents of the " Opticks," which even nowadays furnishes enjoyable lectures.

Right at the commencement of the book Newton states that he does not intend to explain the properties of light by hypotheses, but rather to establish the existence of these simply exhibited properties by reasoning and experiment. The whole of Newton's mode of investigation, the character of which was probably made quite clear to him by his conflict with Hooke, is quite distinct, and forms an appropriate pattern for future research. There next follow some simple definitions.

After a further short introduction dealing with dioptrics, Newton gives an account of some experiments with pigment colours. A

* " I desire that in your next letter you would inform me for what time the Society continue their weekly meetings ; because, if they continue them for any time, I am purposing them to be considered of and examined on account of philosophical discovery, which induced me to the making of the said telescope, and which I doubt not but will prove much more grateful than the communication of the instrument, being in my judgment the *oddest if not the most considerable detection* which hath hitherto been made in the operations of nature."

† Cf. " Micrographia, or some Physiological Descriptions of Minute Bodies made by magnifying glasses, with Observations and Inquiries thereupon," London (1664). " The Posthumous Works of Dr. Robert Hooke," London (1705). " Lectures on Light," Lect. VII, p. 138.

" Memoires of I. Newton," by D. Brewster, London (1885). Vol. I, Chap. VI, pp. 127, etc. ; Chap. VII, pp. 151, etc.

‡ Brewster, *loc. cit.*, Vol. I, Chap. IV, pp. 78, etc. See also Rosenberger, *Geschichte der Physik* (1882), Part II, pp. 198, 238, etc.

§ " Opticks : or, a Treatise of the Reflexions, Inflexions, and Colours of Light," 1704, in English ; translated by Samuel Clarke into Latin in 1706.

‖ " Lectiones opticae," 1728 in English ; 1729 in Latin. London.

straight half-red and half-blue strip of paper, when viewed against a
dark background through a prism (Fig. 65), appears with the blue part
more deviated.   If the same strip is wrapped round with fine threads,
it can be observed that the sharp real image formed by the lens (Fig. 66)
is more remote from the lens for the red part than for the blue.   In
this ingenious and instructive manner, on the basis of already generally

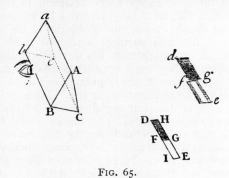

FIG. 65.

recognized laws, Newton obtained the view that red light is refracted
less than blue.   The rays which traverse a prism at minimum deviation*
subtend equal angles with the incident and emergent faces of the
prism, and small variations in the angle of incidence do not cause appreciable variation in the deviation by reason of the property of the
minimum.   For this reason similar rays of sunlight, which subtend an

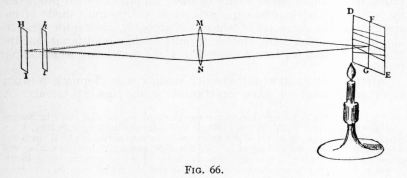

FIG. 66.

angle of 31′ with each other at incidence, emerge from the prism inclined
at the same angle.   The length of the spectrum is thus explicable only
by unequal refraction of the different colours.   That the spreading out
cannot be due to a diffusion, as Grimaldi held, can be proved at once
by experiment.   Behind a prism with its edge horizontal, which produces a vertical spectrum, another prism is placed with its refracting

* Newton, " Optice," lat. red, S. Clarke, Londini (1719), p. 27.

edge vertical (Fig. 67). Instead of a spreading out in two dimensions, the spectrum is now oblique; moreover, the blue, which is more refrangible in the first prism, is refracted more in the second prism

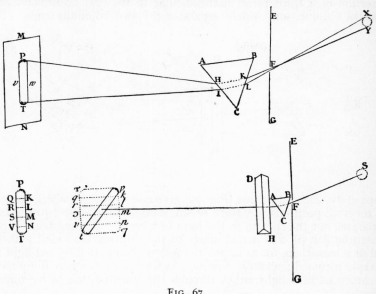

FIG. 67.

also. In Fig. 68 sunlight emergent from a fully illuminated prism passes through a small aperture in a screen on to a second screen having another small aperture, and the light passing through the latter traverses a second prism. If the first prism is now slowly turned, it

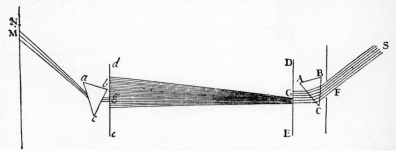

FIG. 68.

can be seen how the different colours fall successively on the second prism in a *fixed* direction determined by the two apertures, and how the red is least and the violet most refracted by the latter. This is the so-called *experimentum crucis*, one of Newton's principal experiments.

Newton demonstrates this crucial experiment in different and, to a certain extent, very surprising forms. Two prisms (Fig. 69) with parallel similarly oriented edges are placed near to one another so that the violet end of one spectrum adjoins the red end of the other ; the insertion of a third prism perpendicular to the first two makes both spectra oblique, and widely separates the two adjoining ends. Two

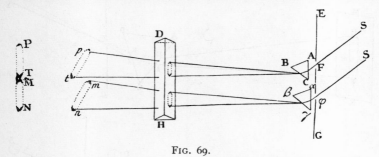

FIG. 69.

oppositely oriented prisms (Fig. 70) give rise to spectra which coincide in reversed positions. A third prism, crossed with respect to the first, separates out the spectra in the form of a cross. If a spectrum is projected on a book and a real image of the printing is formed with the aid of a lens, then, for example, the letters illuminated by red light are sharply focussed ; as soon, however, as the *same* letters are illuminated by green or blue light either through the sun's motion or by turning

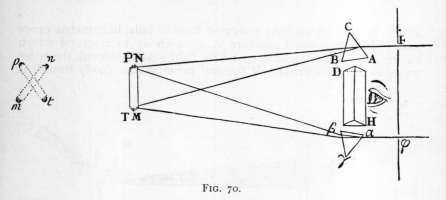

FIG. 70.

the prism, the screen on which the image is formed must be moved nearer the lens in order to obtain a distinct image.

A piece of paper illuminated by two different spectral colours by means of two prisms appears to the eye as illuminated by a mixed colour ; through a prism, however, two pieces of paper can be seen illuminated, each by one of the colours of the mixture, and the farther away one goes with the prism, the greater is the separation.

The more refrangible colours are more strongly reflected, that is, they reach the limit of total reflection at a smaller angle of incidence. Let a ray (Fig. 71) be reflected and refracted at the hypothenuse face of a right-angled prism. The refracted rays spread themselves out into a spec-

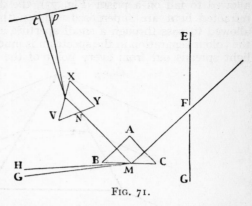

trum, while the reflected rays remain undispersed by reason of the symmetrical action of the prism face. If the reflecting prism is turned in the sense of increasing angle of incidence, the violet light in the spectrum disappears first, having apparently slid into the surface, and the reflected light assumes a violet tinge. The reflected rays can also be spectrally separated, and the disap-

FIG. 71.

pearance of the violet in the refracted light observed in conjunction with a reinforcement in the reflected light. This experiment is also given in a modified form. Instead of a totally reflecting prism, a combination of two right-angled prisms is introduced (Fig. 72). The

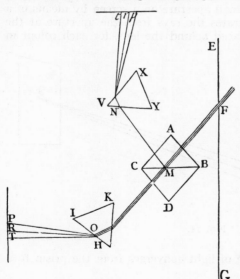

ray refracted at the hypothenuse face, although passing obliquely through the thin air gap between the two, assumes the original direction after entering the second prism, and leaves it unresolved. With an increasing angle of incidence, brought about by a corresponding rotation of the pair of prisms, the refracted ray becomes coloured yellow, then red, and finally vanishes completely. If the reflected and refracted rays each pass through a prism, the two complementary spectra can once more be observed. The colours which are cut off in succession from the spectrum of the refracted light appear in and

FIG. 72.

reinforce the spectrum of the reflected light. This is another example of the ingenious and instructive process by which Newton builds up his theory on the longest known and undisputed theory of reflection, and further elucidates the latter. Light is thus seen to be composed of dissimilar constituents which can be separated, not only by refraction, but also by reflection.

Newton then turns to methods of separating the different colours, i.e. to the production of a pure spectrum. If a wide beam of light is allowed to fall on a prism (Fig. 73), the different coloured beams of refracted light are superposed. If, on the other hand, sunlight is allowed to pass through a small aperture and then fall on the prism, the colour separation in the spectrum is much better, but even now the light spreads out from every point of the aperture in cones of apex

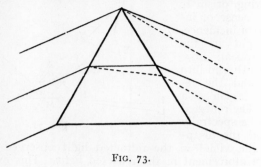

FIG. 73.

angle 31'. A complete separation is not possible in this way. Newton then forms an image of the small aperture on a screen by means of a lens (Fig. 74), which concentrates the rays from the aperture at the image. If a prism is now placed behind the lens, for each colour in

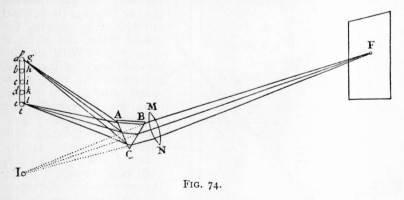

FIG. 74.

the spectrum a separate cone of light converges from the prism to a different point of the screen.

Newton noticed that, instead of the small circular aperture which was usually employed, a slit parallel to the refracting edge of the prism was more advantageous, since it afforded a broader spectrum.* Incidentally, he mentions that triangular slits can be employed (Fig. 75) for which at one edge of the spectrum the colour separation will be

* Newton, " Optice," p. 64.

very small, while at the other it will be complete. To obtain the best results the room should, as Newton indicates, be well darkened, while the prism used should have perfectly flat and polished faces, and be made from homogeneous glass. Any streaks or bubbles can be screened off by black paper.

Homogeneous light is refracted without any trace of " diffusion " or scattering. Thus if one piece of paper is illuminated by sunlight, and another by light which is homogeneous, the former appears extended in a spectrum when seen through a prism, while the latter is seen as it would appear to the naked eye. The most delicate limbs of a fly are seen plainly through a prism, even if they are indistinct and

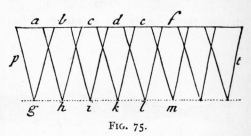

FIG. 75.

unrecognizable by daylight or in light of a mixed colour, and the same is true of a page of print.

These experiments enabled Newton to show that the sine law, which had been enunciated for light as a whole, held for each colour individually. Newton continues with a discussion of dioptric and catoptric telescopes, and mentions his experiments on achromatism. Colours are not modifications of light which are *created* by refraction,

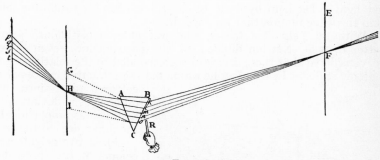

FIG. 76.

or produced by a mixture of light and darkness, but are *already contained* in white sunlight. If sunlight strikes the whole incidence face of a prism (Fig. 76) a white beam of light, coloured only at its edges, emerges, but a spectrum emerges from the small aperture in a screen placed in the white part of the beam. The colours were thus already present in the white light and, moreover, as rays having different directions. If the dispersed light proceeding from a prism (Fig. 77) is refracted by a lens which forms an image of the *prism* on a screen, the image appears *white*, since it is the convergence point of rays of all colours. The colours can even be seen in the white beam of light which leaves the prism if a piece of paper is held in the beam and its inclination varied (Fig. 78). First one colour and then another illuminates the paper most.

That the colour and refrangibility of a given kind of light are *not changed* by further refraction follows from the experiments of Newton described above, but reflection, diffusion, and the like, also do not change them. Brightly coloured objects, such as vermilion, gold,

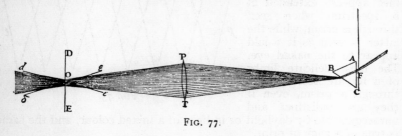

FIG. 77.

flowers, vegetables, soap bubbles, peacocks' feathers, etc., when placed in a spectrum in a dark room, appear only of the colour which is incident upon them. Thus if sunlight were monochromatic, all bodies would appear, with varying brightness, of the one colour. The homogeneous light which either directly or by the illumination of an object excites the sense of red, Newton called " red-making," or more simply red, light. The light by itself, however, is no more red than the sound is in the wave motion that produces it.

With the help of a friend, who was able to distinguish colours better than he, Newton divided off the spectrum into seven colours. He considered that these divisions corresponded to the relations of the diatonic scale.* In this way he estimated the refractive indices of the coloured rays, since small differences in deviation can be taken as proportional to the differences of the sines.

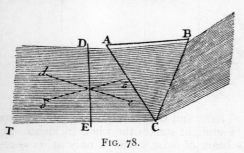

FIG. 78.

From two neighbouring colours of the spectrum a colour can be formed by mixture which is the same as the intermediate spectral colour. There are, however, colours which are missing in the spectrum, for example, purple, which is formed by mixing spectral red and spectral violet. The most interesting mixture, however, is white. This is investigated in detail. If a spectrum is formed on a screen in a dark

* Newton, " Optice," pp. 118, 120, etc.

room and a sheet of paper is placed near to it so that it is illuminated by the diffusion of light of *all* colours, the paper appears white. If, however, the paper is brought closer to one particular colour, this becomes the predominating colour of the paper. Let the spectrum formed by the prism P (Fig. 79) be received by the lens L, which forms a *white* image P′ of the prism. In front of and behind this image the intersections of the rays composing the beam produce spectra having

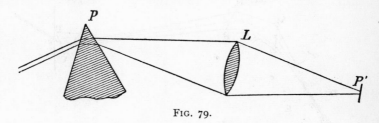

FIG. 79.

the order of the colours different on the two sides. Thus the rays have crossed one another *without any mutual reaction*. This result seems to have played an important part in Newton's later experiments. If one or other colour is separated out and removed either in front of or behind the lens, the arrangement and character of the remaining colours is unaltered, but the white image of the prism becomes coloured the moment that any appreciable part of the spectrum is cut off by a screen. When a tooth-shaped screen (Fig. 80) is passed across the spectrum

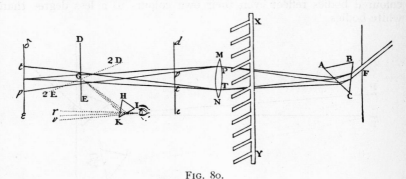

FIG. 80.

the colour of the image changes in a continuous manner, provided that the teeth are not too numerous or too narrow. In the latter case there is no noticeable change in colour, the image remaining white. If the image is viewed through a prism placed in front of the eye, a spectrum having dark bands, corresponding to the missing colours, is seen.* If the "comb" is moved to and fro with sufficient rapidity the image of

* Newton, "Optice," p. 147, etc.

the prism appears white. The dispersed rays from a prism may be rendered parallel again by means of a second oppositely oriented prism (Fig. 81), and combined by means of a third so as to form white light. A spectrum projected by a prism on a screen appears, when viewed through a second prism placed near to the first and similarly oriented (Fig. 82) as a *white* spot, which becomes coloured at once if

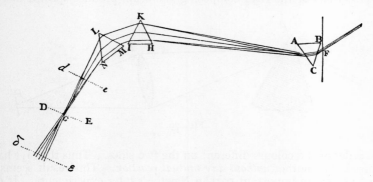

FIG. 81.

one part of the spectrum is screened off. Newton then remarks that soap lather, when inspected closely, exhibits all colours, but if viewed from a distance appears white. Coloured powders may also be mixed so as to form white, but the latter is always a dull white or grey, since coloured bodies reflect even their own colours to a less degree than white bodies.

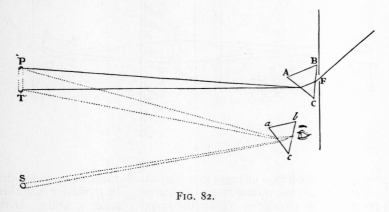

FIG. 82.

Newton also gives a rule, which his experience showed to serve fairly satisfactorily, to determine the hue and saturation of a mixture of given colours. The spectrum is considered as being constructed round a circle (Fig. 83), and the different colours are given lengths

PLATE III

Js. Newton

"hypotheses non fingo"

1691

proportional to the diatonic scale, which, according to Newton's idea, corresponded to the actual conditions. If one ascribes to each ray a mass, the resultant of each *single* colour is represented by the centre of gravity of its sector, and the resultant of a mixture of *all* colours, namely, white, by the centre of gravity of the whole circle, that is, the centre.

For a mixture of the colours in proportions other than those in which they are contained in the spectrum, Newton assumes the same rule to be applicable. The single colours of the mixture have to be given a mass proportional to their intensity, which is applied at the centre of gravity of their appropriate sectors, and the centre of gravity of the whole is found. The distance of the latter from the centre of the circle represents the degree of saturation, while the radius on which the centre of gravity lies gives us the hue of the resultant mixed colour. Newton remarks that he did not succeed in forming white from *two* colours which lay diametrically opposite to one another; whether it were possible with *three* colours, he did not know, but it certainly

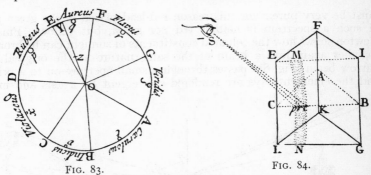

FIG. 83.

FIG. 84.

could be formed with four or five. He finally remarks that, in the case of the mixture of coloured powders, it was not the quantity of powder, but the intensity of their radiations, which was the determining factor. All the colours occurring in nature are either spectral colours or mixtures of them. Newton now found no difficulty in explaining all the phenomena seen by looking through a prism at an extended bright object on a dark background or vice versa; by dividing up the extended object into elements and superposing the spectra of each, he explained in advance all the phenomena which a century later Goethe arrayed as decisive arguments against Newton's theory. Newton's analysis of the following phenomenon is worthy of note. Suppose the bright sky is viewed through a reflecting prism (Fig. 84). On looking at the hypothenuse surface a bright field of view can be seen separated from a darker region by a bluish bow-shaped region convex towards the former. In the latter, however, the hypothenuse face is also transparent so that objects lying beneath the prism, if they are bright enough, can be seen bounded by prismatic colours. The explanation lies in the smaller angle of total reflection for the more refrangible end of the spectrum. Newton also perfected Descartes' theory of the rainbow with respect to the colours. The colour of natural objects * he explains by assuming a stronger reflection of those rays which correspond to the colour of the object. Vermilion is bright red in the red light of the spectrum, whereas it is almost black in the green. Objects usually reflect, in addition, rays other than those of their characteristic colours. Thus the spectrum used for this purpose

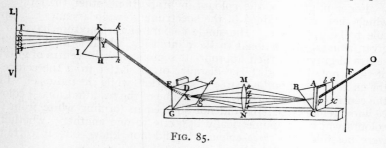

FIG. 85.

must be very pure ; for this reason red-lead placed in the green part of such a spectrum is neither red nor green, but yellow. Finally, Newton shows how the coloured constituents of sunlight can be brought together again into a beam of the same nature as the original. A narrow beam (Fig. 85) passes through a small aperture on to a prism, and the emergent rays are rendered convergent by a lens and made

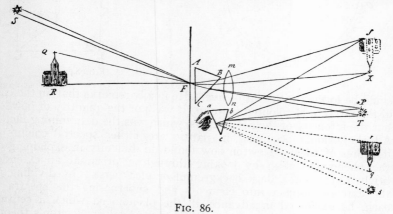

FIG. 86.

parallel again by a second prism so that the rays of different colours coincide once more.

A modification of the experiment, in the " Lectiones opticae," may be mentioned. A lens (Fig. 86) forms an image of a landscape on a screen in a dark room. The interposition of a prism behind the lens effaces the image, but on looking through a similarly oriented prism placed near the other, the image of the landscape can be plainly seen,

* Newton, " Optice," pp. 151, 161, 171, etc.

since spectrally separated rays from the screen to the second prism, being parallel to the rays falling on the screen, are superposed once more on passing through the prism. In the " Lectiones " the action of plane parallel plates is also investigated, the reason for the absence of a spectrum being that the rays, although dispersed on passing the first face, are rendered parallel again on leaving the second, so that there is no further separation. The separation itself is inappreciable for plates of small thickness and small dispersion. Totally reflecting prisms thus produce no coloration if both the refracting faces are inclined symmetrically towards the reflecting face, since the divergence of the rays is reduced to zero again for the emergent light.

It is permissible at this stage to mention some instructive modifications of Newton's experiments. Newton emphasizes the fact that many experiments succeed only when a very pure spectrum is employed, but his caution was not always sufficiently observed by those who repeated his experiments, and many experiments, Newton found, only succeeded well when long distances were at the experimenter's disposal. The experiment of Fig. 74 is only really successful if a pure spectrum

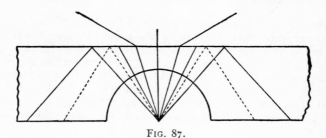

Fig. 87.

is projected, with the prism at minimum deviation, on to a screen having a small aperture or slit. If, so as to avoid disturbing the images or the minimum deviation, the different parts of the spectrum are caused to pass over the aperture by means of a mirror, or totally reflecting prism, the second prism shows the variation of deviation with colour at once, without the use of further resolution. The " comb " experiment necessitates the production of a pure spectrum on the lens, used as a screen, if the remaining colours are to be seen separate and distinct through the second prism ; otherwise the edges of different coloured portions are obliterated on account of the impurity of the spectrum.

One modification serves to depict some of the effects which would be seen if one looked at a water-air surface from below the surface of the water. This can be realized more comfortably by means of a thick polished plane parallel plate (Fig. 87) having a hemispherical hollow at the centre of which the eye is to be placed, while the other surface is covered with a piece of ground glass. If the room is light on the same side as the hollow and dark on the other, an illuminated circular portion caused by simple reflection from the matt surface of the ground glass is seen surrounded by a blue border separating it from a much more brightly illuminated portion produced by total reflection. A

bright illumination on the side of the ground glass produces a bright
circular field of view in the middle, separated from a dark outside
region by a red border. In the latter case the red border has a slightly
greater radius than the blue border in the former, since violet is the
first colour to be totally reflected with increasing angle of incidence,
while red is the last, and is consequently still transmitted. If a combination of two totally reflecting prisms (Fig. 88) is illuminated by an
approximately parallel beam of sunlight, and images of the pair of

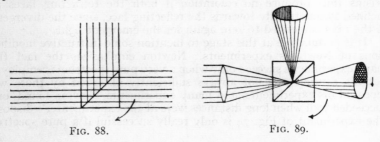

Fig. 88.   Fig. 89.

prisms are formed on screens by means of the reflected and transmitted
light respectively, then on turning the prisms in the direction of the
arrow, in the first case the image of the hypothenuse surface suddenly
changes from a uniform blue to a brighter white, while in the second
the change is from yellow to red and then black. The prisms must have
very good plane surfaces for this experiment to work well.* If the
incident light is made convergent by a lens (Fig. 89), then each ray of
the incident cone of light corresponds to a particular angle of incidence,

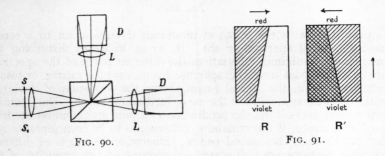

Fig. 90.   Fig. 91.

and if the reflected and transmitted beams are intercepted by screens,
two areas of different brightness, separated by the blue bow-shaped
border first noticed by Newton, are seen on the first screen, while on
the second there is a completely dark area corresponding to total
reflection, separated from a bright one by a red border. The borders
are, of course, displaced by turning the prisms. As a further experiment a screen having a horizontal slit may be placed before the lens
in the incident beam (Fig. 90). The light converges to the hypothenuse

interface of the prism combination with vertical refracting edge, and is received by the lenses L, L and prisms D, D, having their refracting edges horizontal. The lenses form images of the slit SS, and throw sharp spectra with vertical dispersion on to two screens. If the two spectra, R formed by reflection, and R′ by refraction, are imagined placed side by side (Fig. 91), the latter is seen to terminate at an oblique edge, while the former has a brighter right-hand portion separated by an oblique line from a darker left-hand portion. The superposition of the spectrum R on R′, after rotating it about a vertical axis (lying in the plane of the paper) on account of inversion by reflection, would create a uniformly bright spectrum. In the spectra the horizontal abscissæ in the directions of the arrows represent increasing angle of incidence, the vertical ordinates in the direction of the arrow decreasing refractive index. If sunlight has been dispersed by a prism (Fig. 92) into differently inclined coloured rays, the spectrum can be confined to rays of any given colour by means of total reflection on allowing them to pass through two pairs of prisms R_1 and R_2, since by turning R_1 and R_2 in the direction of the arrows, the spectrum is cut off from the violet and red ends respectively. As the sun's rays are not perfectly parallel, however, the colours will not be extinguished abruptly.*

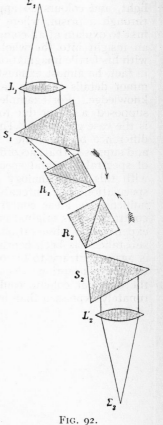

FIG. 92.

For the demonstration of the dependence of the colour of objects on the incident light, the following has proved successful. Several cylinders, brightly painted red, yellow, green, and blue, are concealed in a dark room. Common salt on a piece of platinum foil is introduced into a Bunsen flame, thus producing a highly homogeneous yellow illumination, whereupon the cylinders are revealed in varying shades of yellow, the yellow one most brightly, the red one more faintly, and the blue one almost black. If daylight is suddenly let into the room, the variety of the colouring, of which there was previously no trace, creates quite a surprise.†

The magnitude of Newton's contribution to optics can only be correctly estimated by trying to enter into the ideas then and previously

* Cf. E. and L. Mach, " Versuche über Totalreflexion und deren Anwendung," *Sitzungsber. d. Wiener Akad.*, Vol. 113, Part IIa, 1904.
† A lecture experiment of long standing. Cf. also E. Mach, " Leitfaden der Physik," p. 133.

current. It was then very natural that the most naïve conception of colour, which is such an intrinsic quality of bodies, should be one in which colour was a property of the body itself. Why should they have thought that the most transient colours, those of the rainbow, were qualified to solve the riddle of colour ? The chemical view is not surprising, and the idea concerning the mixture of light and darkness was quite convenient, for coloured light is generally less bright than white light, and colours do appear at the edge of a beam of light passed through a prism, where it borders on the shade. Newton was the first to explain at all completely the prismatic colours, and thus obtain an insight into the whole subject of the theory of colour, in which, with his fertile imagination, he was able to reveal a host of new truths ; in fact, he almost exhausted this branch of the subject. It is only in minor details that he can be corrected with our wider present-day knowledge. For example, the colour of natural objects is not, as he supposed, a colour due to reflection, but to absorption ; at least this is the case generally. The fact that Newton overlooked the essential difference between the mixture of pigmentary and spectral colours, and supposed that, according to experiments with pigments, a mixture of spectral blue and spectral yellow should give green, is consistent with this. His analogy between colour and the diatonic scale is a speculation quite untenable at the present time, and had a detrimental influence on ideas concerning the construction of mixtures ; it was contrary to his original purpose, namely, to arrive at explanations by experimental observation. His hypothesis that light was a material substance has been continually in opposition to prevalent ideas, and is again contrary to his original purpose, since it was a purely hypothetical conception. Nevertheless, the stability and invariability of the different colours could scarcely have been better and more fortunately expressed than by comparison with a material substance.

CHAPTER VII

THE FURTHER DEVELOPMENT OF THE THEORY OF COLOUR AND DISPERSION

THE various modifications and refinements which Newton's theory of colour and dispersion has experienced in the course of time will now receive consideration. Let us take first the theory of colour, of which even temporary retrogressions have to be recorded. Newton was cognizant of the distinction between the physical and physiological properties of light, for he could not fail to observe that to an infinite number of indefinitely small possible variations in refractive index there corresponded only a finite number of colour sensations, but he has left us little from which to draw conclusions as to what is to be considered the relation between the two properties. The parallelism between colour and the pitch of sound, which to Descartes seemed probable in connexion with his dynamical theory, rests on a very slender foundation. The tone ratios, which are the essence of music, have no physiological equivalent, for there are no thirds, fourths, or fifths in the domain of optics. Red is red, without there being any connexion with green, or any other colour, and any conception of the colours of the spectrum as a musical scale is purely arbitrary and quite worthless. A physiological continuum of colour-tints does indeed correspond to the physical continuum of the spectrum, but the former is considered as composed of a finite number of elements.

The paradox contained in Newton's assertions probably disturbed Brewster,* and led him to formulate his theory of colour, which was based on some rather importune experiments. Doubtless he had in mind the experience of the artist, who is able to obtain with tolerable ease any desired tint by mixing red, yellow, and blue pigments. Brewster considered he was able to show that spectral colours can be varied, contrary to Newton's conclusions, by absorption in coloured glasses. He found, for example, that the yellow of the spectrum is broadened by viewing it through blue glass. He accordingly drew a distinction between the analysis of light by refraction and by absorption, for by the latter resolution is obtained when it cannot be further increased by refraction. According to Brewster's idea there are only three kinds of physically different light—red, blue, and yellow—which three extend themselves with varying intensity over the *whole* spectrum (Fig. 93), thus producing varying proportions of mixture. He considered that orange is a mixture of red and yellow, green of yellow

---

* Cf. David Brewster, " A Treatise on Optics," London (1837), p. 74.

and blue, and violet of blue and red.   In parts of the spectrum the
fundamental colours greatly excel the mixed proportion in intensity,
so that the latter is not observed.   This means to say that, according
to Brewster, colour is not intimately connected with refractive index.
It is difficult to understand why an investigator of such high standing
as Brewster should have held this view to be correct, especially as he
was in full knowledge of Wollaston's and Fraunhofer's discoveries of
the dark lines in the solar spectrum, and the different distribution of
intensity of the colour in stellar spectra, coloured flames, and electric
sparks, and so on.   As Helmholtz * has shown, Brewster's absorption
experiments are based on an illusion, for the spectra which he used
were impure and contained white light, since sufficient care was not
taken to eliminate scattered light.   In this case the supposed spectral
colours are mixed colours, which may quite easily be altered by absorption.   Brewster's idea that spectral green is a mixture of yellow

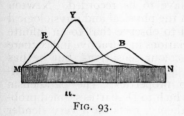

FIG. 93.

and blue was also shown to be incorrect
by Helmholtz.   Yellow and blue pigments produce green for the reason
that the particles of yellow absorb the
more refrangible end of the spectrum,
while the blue particles absorb the less
refrangible portion, so that in the
mixture the green middle portion is
left.   On the other hand, by mixing
the same two spectral colours, in-
stead of a subtraction there is a summation, which gives white.
Brewster's theory certainly contains more paradoxes than the Newtonian theory.

Prior to Brewster, Thomas Young † had been concerned with the
same questions.   He criticized Newton's analogy between colour and
the pitch of sound as imaginary ; his views are closely connected with
Wollaston's observation.‡   The latter looked directly through a prism
at a slit, and could see only four essentially fundamental colours—red,
green, blue, and violet—which, on denoting the total length of the
visible spectrum by 100, assumed the lengths 16, 23, 36, and 25 respectively.   Some dark lines were also observable.   The narrow band of
yellow to be seen between the red and green was considered by Wollaston and Young to be caused by the overlapping and mixing of the two
latter colours.   Young assumed that there were only three colour
sensations, namely, red, green, and violet ; a mixture of red and green
gave yellow, one of green and violet the sensation of blue, while a
mixture of violet and red produced crimson or purple ; finally, the
combination of red, green, and violet gave rise to a sensation of white.
A triangle, having one corner red, another blue, and the third violet,
from which the colours spread out towards the centre with decreasing

* H. v. Helmholtz, " Physiologische Optik," Hamburg (1896), p. 304.
† Thomas Young, " Miscellaneous Works," London (1855), Vol. I. p. 170, " Pro-
duction of Colours " (from *Phil. Trans. Roy. Soc.*, 1802).   See also " Lectures on
Natural Philosophy," Lect. XXXVII.
‡ Cf. T. Young, *loc. cit.*, Vol. I, pp. 176, 177 ; Wollaston, *Phil. Trans. Roy. Soc.*,
1802.

intensity and overlap, was devised by Young to represent every possible colour combination. The centre of gravity of such a triangle would appear white. Young was cognizant of the different distribution of the colours and their discontinuity in the spectra of coloured flames and electric sparks, and knew that the yellow of a flame impregnated with common salt could *not* be spectrally resolved, but, in spite of this, he obtained no definite explanation of the connexion between the physical and physiological properties of light. Although he had the unmistakable intention of disentangling the two, he succeeded in confusing them still further.

Thus slowly and laboriously the view was developed that a sharp distinction must be drawn between the physical and physiological properties of light, namely, that *to an infinite number of kinds of light having continuously variable physical properties there corresponds only a small number of colour sensations.* Thus light which is physically identical has an identical physiological action, but the reverse statement, that light which has the same physiological effect must have an identical constitution, is not true, because the physiological action is determined by independent conditions which have their origin in the human organism. Brewster was quite incorrect when he assumed that all light which appears, for example, yellow, was physically iden-

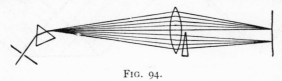

FIG. 94.

tical, although it had different refractive indices and different periodicity. Young also allowed himself to be guided by incorrect physical conceptions in his selection of the fundamental colour sensations ; he chose red, green, and violet because every kind of colour can be mixed by compounding the two outermost and the middle colour of the spectrum. For physical reasons he considered yellow and blue to be mixed sensations, although he knew that the yellow of the salt-impregnated flame was not in any way necessarily a mixed colour, since it was not spectrally resolved. Helmholtz * and Maxwell † have rescued the theory of Young from oblivion ; the former borrowed it practically without alteration, and assumed with Young three kinds of nerve fibres which were sensitive to red, green, and violet respectively, but added that each nerve could be sensitive also to the three processes together, and that other fundamental colour sensations could be selected. Actually, Helmholtz replaced the violet later by blue.

Helmholtz effected some important developments in the theory of colour. If a part of the spectrum falling on a lens, as in Newton's experiment, is deflected by means of an achromatic prism (Fig. 94),

---

* Helmholtz, " Physiologische Optik," p. 345.
† J. C. Maxwell, " On the Theory of Compound Colours with Reference to Mixtures of Blue and Yellow Light," *Brit. Assoc. Report,* Edinburgh (1856) ; also Helmholtz, " Physiologische Optik," p. 383.

two coloured images are formed which if superposed would give rise to white light. Two such colours are called complementary. It is not necessary, however, as Newton had previously recognized, for white to contain all the colours of sunlight. Helmholtz * reduced the complementary colours to simple spectral colours. He produced a spectrum from an appropriate V-shaped slit (Fig. 95), which caused each spectral colour to be superposed on every other one in turn, and by varying the obliquity the relative intensity of the colours could be altered. In this manner red and greenish-blue, orange and cyanic-blue, yellow and indigo-blue, greenish-yellow and violet, were observed to be respective complementary colours. Certain differences of opinion with Helmholtz caused Grassmann † to investigate more closely the validity of Newton's construction for mixtures, and he found it permissible to extend the analogy of a centre of gravity construction. A mixed colour lies between its components, each mixture is equivalent to white plus a single colour, to the continued admixture of a single colour corresponds a continuous variation of the colour of the mixture, and, lastly, colours of identical appearance give rise to identical mixed colours. The analogy with the properties of the centre of gravity of a system of point masses is obvious. In spite of its merits the Helmholtz

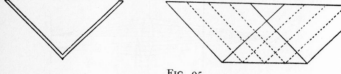

FIG. 95.

theory of colour suffers from many inconsistencies, some of which will presently be mentioned.

Many years ago, when I had the opportunity of taking a passing glance at Young's theory, I was sensible of the fact that neither the number nor the type of primary-colour sensations assumed by Young would admit of an unbiassed analysis.‡ Only those sensations can be designated fundamental for which the mind is able to distinguish no further constituents. These are red, yellow, green, blue, white, and black. In orange there can be physiologically distinguished red and yellow, while in violet the mind is sensible of blue and red. It is impossible to say from what constituents white is composed ; it is formed from constituents physically, but physiologically it is simple. In a like manner, the possibility of forming yellow by mixing a certain spectral red and spectral green does not determine yellow as a mixed sensation. Black is the sensation of complete absence of light. Thus the physical properties of light must be ascertained by physical experiments, and the physiological properties by psychological experiments.

* Helmholtz, " Physiologische Optik," p. 352.
† Grassmann, " Zur Theorie der Farbenmischung," *Pogg. Ann.*, Vol. 89 (1853).
‡ Mach, " Über die Wirkung der räumlichen Verteilung des Lichtreizes auf die Netzhaut," *Sitzungsber. d. Wiener Akad.*, Vol. 52 (Oct., 1865).

To avoid unnecessary reservations there must be assumed as many different (chemical) nerve processes in the optic centre of the brain as there are optical sensations or qualities separable purely by psychological analysis, and no more.* Hering †, following the hypotheses of Johannes Müller,‡ and sensible of the above criterion, also adopted red, yellow, green, blue, white, and black as fundamental colour sensations. Hering, however, went further, and with Plateau § stipulated that not only the disturbance of the organs of vision from equilibrium by a stimulus, but also the return to equilibrium, is a sense perception, and thus not only the katabolic process but also the metabolic process (or, as Hering calls them, the dissimilation process and the assimilation process) is a sensory-process. Hering arranged the fundamental sensations in three pairs, in which the first member represented an assimilatory, and the second a dissimilatory process. Thus, for example, in the pair black-white, black represents the assimilatory and white the dissimilatory process ; two other such pairs are red-green and yellow-blue. The sensation of white is excited by the whole spectrum together, and black results as a reaction from the former. Fig. 96 illustrates

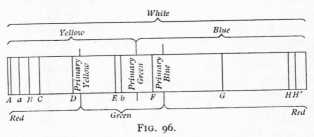

FIG. 96.

the rôle played by the different parts of the spectrum in the excitation of the above-named colour sensations. The sensation of white is excited by all rays, red from A to a position between D and E near to D, and from a position near F to H, yellow from A to a position between E and F, and blue from there to H. Green is excited by that part of the spectrum which does not correspond to red, so that red and green, and similarly green and blue, hold contending positions. This "antagonism" gives rise to the complementary colours. It is impossible for the sensations of red and green or yellow and blue to be produced together at any one spot on the retina. If the excitation of the respective constituents of the pair is equally powerful, the two colours of each pair annul one another, and the sensation produced by the two pairs is that of white. This theory not only corresponds with the

* Mach, *Reicherts and Dubois' Archiv* (1865), pp. 633, etc.
† Ewald Hering, " Zur Lehre vom Lichtsinne ; " six communications to the *kais. Akad. d. Wissenschaft*, Wien (1878) ; " Über Newtons Gesetz der Farbenmischung," " Lotos," Prague (1886).
‡ Müller, " Zur vergleichenden Physiologie des Gesichtssinnes der Menschen und Tiere," Leipzig (1826) ; " Handbuch der Physiologie," Vol. 2 (1840).
§ Plateau, *Bulletin de l'Acad. Roy. des Sciences de Bruxelles* (1835), No. 2, p. 52 ; No. 3, p. 89.

most rational principles of research, but also conforms most accurately to all the known facts.

The development of the physiological theory of colour was materially accelerated by the discovery of colour-blindness. Dalton * himself observed that he could distinguish fewer colours than other people, and was the first to investigate the matter scientifically.† As is now known, there is a red-green, a yellow-blue, and also an extremely rare total, colour-blindness. Persons affected with the first observe only a yellow and blue spectrum, the second class see a spectrum which is red at both extremities and green in the centre, while to the third class the spectrum appears entirely white.

The colour theories of Goethe ‡ and Schopenhauer § will now be briefly mentioned, although they have had little influence on the history of physics. Goethe considered colour principally in so far as it is a quality in the eye and is the outcome of an action and reaction in the latter. His observations on subjective colours are quite valuable, but he allowed his insight thus obtained to influence his opinions in the domain of physics to too great an extent. He considered the complicated phenomena with turbid media as fundamental, and in a quite useless manner tried to explain the prismatic colours by means of them. Schopenhauer was similar to Goethe ; he considered that, when the retina receives a colour sensation, only a part of its complete activity is utilized. Thus red and green were the two qualitatively equal halves of the retinal activity, while orange and its complementary blue represented two-thirds and one-third, yellow and complementary violet three-quarters and one-quarter respectively, of the full activity. This was assumed in the most naïve fashion, without confirmation, and without questioning the exact sense of such a conception. Although he had a more complete knowledge of exact science than Goethe, Schopenhauer confined his judgment in a similar manner to the results of physical experiments. It was necessary to enter so far into questions of physiology as is of interest to physicists.

Newton's theory was approved by Pardies, Hooke, and Huygens from theoretical points of view as soon as it appeared. The objections raised by Linus and Rizzetti were based on incorrect repetition of the rather refined experiments of Newton. The much later objections of Goethe only demonstrate his complete inability to follow a quantitative physical experiment and, what is worse, his inability to criticize his own understanding of the facts. Newton's niceties and cautions appeared to him as dishonourable or inept procedures. Nevertheless, Goethe was not prevented from making important observations and discoveries in this domain as in other domains of natural science. Those who wish to estimate the impression which Goethe's theories made on contemporary physicists should read the voluminous but

---

* John Dalton, " Extraordinary Facts relating to the Vision of Colours," *Memoirs of the Literary and Philosophical Society*, Vol. 5, Part 1, Manchester (1794).
† A. Seebeck, " Über den bei manchen Personen vorkommenden Mangel an Farbensinn," *Pogg. Ann.*, Vol. 42 (1837) ; Vol. 48 (1846).
‡ J. W. Goethe, " Beiträge zur Optik," Weimar (1791 and 1792).
§ A. Schopenhauer, " Über das Sehen und die Farben," Leipzig (1816).

most astonishing and authoritative critiques of a prominent physicist like Malus.*

Newton's theory of dispersion also has in course of time undergone many changes. Amongst the cleverest and most intelligent of Newton's contemporary opponents was Lucas.† His experiments were rigorous and valuable, and Newton came to a better understanding with him than with his other contemporaries. If only certain differences between his and Newton's results, which were doubtlessly due to the different kinds of glass in the prisms, had been more closely discussed, the theory of dispersion would have at once made an appreciable advance. Newton considered that refraction and dispersion went in parallel, that is to say, that a substance which under certain circumstances gave rise to twice the deviation also caused double the dispersion. Such a state of affairs would make achromatic lenses and prisms impossible. Euler ‡ was of the opinion that the eye was achromatic, and consequently considered that lenses filled with liquid could be utilized for achromatic instruments. Dollond § was not able to achieve this; although he later manufactured achromatic prisms and lenses from two kinds of glass. Klingenstjerna ‖ had already deduced the possibility of such a combination from a critical discussion of Newton's experiments on achromatism.

The most important advance in the theory of dispersion since the time of Newton was brought about by the discovery of the fixed lines in the solar spectrum. Wollaston had not appreciated his discovery, and had also incorrectly interpreted it. Its worth was first generally appreciated when Fraunhofer ¶ observed them for a second time, and published his observations in the *Journal of the Munich Academy of Science*. Fraunhofer informs us that an interest in the improvement of achromatic telescopes urged him to investigate more closely the refraction and dispersion of different kinds of glass. First, he measured the lengths of spectra projected from prisms on a screen, but found this method too inaccurate. Then he experimentally varied the angles of two combined prisms until the combination was achromatic, and from the ratio of the angles he could deduce the desired criteria. With small-angled prisms even this process was inaccurate ; on the other hand, if large-angled prisms were used, these could be tested for achromatism by mere inspection with the naked eye. When a sharp dark edge on a bright background is viewed through such a combination by means of a telescope, although in certain cases it has a maximum

---

* Malus, *Ann. de Chem.* (1811). Also see *Gilberts Ann.*, Vol. 40, p. 103.

† D. Brewster, "Memoires of I. Newton," Vol. 1, pp. 83, etc. Wilde, *loc. cit.*, Vol. 2, pp. 139, etc.

‡ L. Euler, " Sur la perfection des verres objectifs des lunettes," *Mem. de l'acad. de Berlin*, 1747 (1753 and 1754) ; L. Euleri, *Dioptrica Petrop. et Lips.* (1771).

§ John Dollond (1706-1761), " Letters relating to a Theorem of Leonhard Euler for correcting the Aberrations in the Object," *Tilloch's Phil. Mag.*, 2 (Nov., 1798), p. 177. *Phil. Trans.*, Vol. 50, p. 733.

‖ Samuel Klingenstjerna (1698-1765), " Tentamen de definiendis et corrigendis aberrationibus luminis in lentibus refracti, etc." Petrop. (1762).

¶ Joseph Fraunhofer, " Bestimmung des Brechungs-und Farbenzerstreuungsvermögens verschiedener Glasarten," *Denkschrift d. kgl. Akad. d. Wiss in München*, Vol. 5 (1817), (" fur 1814 u. 1815 "). See also Brewster, " Optics," p. 85.

distinctness, it never appears quite colourless, on account of the different dispersive powers of red and violet, and of the other colours, in the two kinds of glass.   The dispersive powers of single colours in the spectrum are difficult to determine, on account of the gradual colour transition in the spectrum and the lack of sharp boundaries ; for, although coloured glass and coloured flames show bands in the spectrum, no sharp colour boundary is evident.   Only in the spectrum of a " fire " and a tallow candle is there a sharp reddish-yellow line, always situated at the same position, and this line Fraunhofer denoted by R. For these reasons he had occasion to construct a device of his own for observations with homogeneous light. Thus a lamp placed in front of a prism gave rise to a spectrum (Fig. 97), of which a narrow beam of a particular colour fell on a distant prism. Thus only this narrow region of colour could be seen on looking through a theodolite telescope placed behind the prism. Several such lamps gave rise to separate and distinct narrow spectral regions, and above these lamps another was placed which produced the sharp line R, by means of which the lamps could be replaced in the same positions after removal. In this way the dispersion in different kinds of glass and liquids could be studied for the different colours. With liquids an appreciable temperature variation of the effect was apparent which makes them unsuitable for achromatism requirements. Fraunhofer intended to devise a similar apparatus for sunlight, but this proved unnecessary.   It was

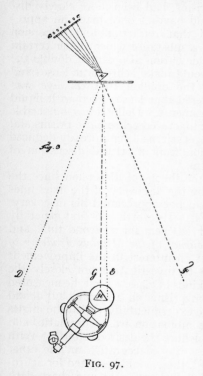

FIG. 97.

when he was looking for the sharp R line in the solar spectrum that he discovered the fixed lines.

Sunlight from a distant narrow slit was caused to fall on a prism, set at minimum deviation, and the spectrum was viewed through the telescope of a theodolite.   There appeared in the spectrum a large number of dark lines, which vanished on turning the prism so that the angle of incidence became greater, but reappeared on shortening the telescope by pushing in the eyepiece ; while if the angle of incidence was decreased the telescope had to be correspondingly lengthened. He found that the lines always appeared in the same position in the spectrum, and did not constitute colour boundaries, for there was no appreciable difference in the colour on either side of each line.   The lines also were not caused by diffraction from the narrow slit, and were evidently an intrinsic property of the solar spectrum. The single bright R line from the lamp appeared in the same place in the spectrum as the dark line which Fraunhofer denoted by the letter D. On account of their sharpness, these dark lines were eminently suited to the purpose of defining the adjoining colours, and rendered possible an exact determination of refractive index and dispersion, and for this purpose the common elementary formulæ were deduced. Since, as mentioned above, the amount of dispersion is not the same for all colours, colour aberration cannot be altogether eliminated, and has as a first approximation to be reduced to zero for the brightest rays of the spectrum. Thus Fraunhofer compared the different parts of the spectrum photometrically, by means of a special ocular device, with the radiation from a lamp. The absence of a diffraction effect could be proved by substituting for the slit a circular aperture in the window shutter, which would change the appearance of any diffraction formation. The aperture gives rise to a linear spectrum, in which in the first instance no lines would be detected, but, on placing behind the telescope objective a cylindrical lens with its axis parallel to the direction of dispersion of

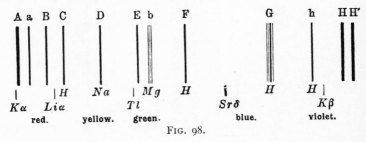

FIG. 98.

the spectrum, the same lines reappeared. In such a manner Fraunhofer produced a spectrum of Venus and found it identical with that of the sun ; the spectra of fixed stars, however, when produced in a similar manner, differed from the solar spectrum. Spark spectra were also examined. When a prism giving a greater dispersion was used, the line R (= D) appeared double.

A few illustrations of Fraunhofer's discoveries may be permissible.

Fraunhofer denoted the principal lines of the spectrum by letters of the alphabet, and at the same time determined their minimum deviations in a prism filled with water, so that they could again be recognized with certainty at any future time. A good inspection of the diagram (Fig. 98) of the spectrum from a flint glass prism will, however, suffice for its recognition. The grouping of the lines alone serves as a distinguishing feature. In any case, the D line can be found by illuminating one-half of the slit, in the manner described later, with a spirit flame impregnated with common salt. This gives a spectrum which consists only of a bright yellow line, which corresponds exactly in position with that of the D line. The dark line A has a position corresponding exactly with that of a bright line in the spectrum of a potassium flame. The spectrum of glowing hydrogen contained in a Geissler tube contains three bright lines, which are usually denoted by H_α, H_β, and H_γ respectively. H_α is identical in position with C, H_β with F, while H_γ lies between G and H. The A line lies in the extreme red and is usually only visible on screening off the other parts of the spectrum. The strong double line H is easily recognized, and lies very close to the

	B	C	D	E	F	G	H
Flint glass (Fraunhofer)	1·701050	1·702642	1·707264	1·713134	1·718673	1·728423	1·738154
Crown glass (Dollond)	1·607933	1·608933	1·611428	1·614660	1·617457	1·622696	1·640373
Water at 15° R.	1·330935	1·331712	1·333577	1·335851	1·337818	1·341293	1·344177
Turpentine at 8·5° R.	1·4704	1·4715	1·4744	1·4783	1·4817	1·4881	1·4938
Oil of cassia at 10° C.	1·5963	1·6007	1·6104	1·6249	1·6389	1·6698	1·7039
Carbon disulphide at 24·2° C.	1·6114	1·6147	1·6240	1·6368	1·6487	1·6728	1·6956

violet end of the spectrum. Prisms constructed of the strong yellow flint glass of Merz usually considerably absorb the more refrangible component of H, so that only a half of the double line is seen distinctly.

The Fraunhofer lines form an excellent means for the exact definition of diffe nt kinds of light. It is much more precise to speak of the refractive index of the D line, or of the light emitted by glowing sodium vapour, that is to say, of the component of sunlight which is absent at the same place in the spectrum, than merely of yellow light, which comprises several kinds of light of different refrangibility. The discovery was therefore very important in connexion with the theory of. dispersion.

A determination of the refractive index of the Fraunhofer lines in different substances very soon brought the conviction that refraction and dispersion bear no simple relation to one another. The table on p. 112 gives the refractive indices for several media.

Denoting the refractive index of B by μ_B, that of E by μ_E, and that of H by μ_H, μ_E represents the mean refractive index, while $\mu_H - \mu_B$ is a measure of the dispersion. We thus see that the mean refractive index and the dispersion do not run in parallel. The mean refractive indices of two substances do not in any case bear the same relation to one another as their dispersions ; for example, for crown glass and oil of cassia, the mean refractive index is *almost equal*, whereas the disper-

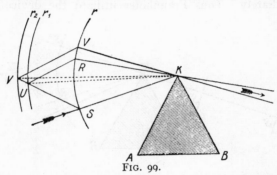

FIG. 99.

sion of oil of cassia is about three times that of crown glass. Oil of cassia refracts the red rays *less* and the violet *more* than crown glass. The distribution of the colours in the spectrum with different substances, also, is not geometrically similar ; flint glasses, for example, draw out the violet part of the spectrum proportionally more than the other parts. Let the different kinds of light corresponding to the lines A, B, C, . . . H be represented by a succession of points marked off as abscissæ along an axis. If lengths proportionate to the refractive indices are marked off as ordinates from each of these points, then their extremities form a curve, which is called a " dispersion curve." It follows from the above that such dispersion curves have different shapes for different substances.

The refraction and dispersion through a prism of a beam of white light incident on one face can easily be followed by means of a two-fold application of Snell's construction (Fig. 99). An arc of a circle of arbitrary radius r is described with the intersection of the prism faces as centre, in a plane perpendicular to them. Two other arcs of radii, r_1 and r_2, such that $r_1/r = \mu_r$, $r_2/r = \mu_v$, the refractive indices for red and violet respectively, are also drawn. If SK represents an incident

ray, and SUV is perpendicular to the first face and UR, VV perpendicular to the second face of the prism, then UK, KV represent the two rays
in the glass, and RK, VK the rays which emerge into the air.   Suppose
a prism with sharp edges (Fig. 100) is placed on a horizontal sheet of
paper, and the intersections of the edges with the paper are marked.
Let a beam of sunlight be made to pass through a small slit so that it
is incident on the prism and also grazes the paper.   Then, by reversing
the above construction, the refractive indices may be determined.   In
this case KA, KB, SK, RK, and VK are given.   The arc r is drawn with
arbitrary radius, and the intersection of the perpendiculars VV, UR,
S″V give the radii r_1 and r_2, and thus the refractive indices.   The same
result can also be attained in broad daylight by looking past the edge
of the prism at the slit and at the red and violet ends of the spectrum,
and fixing the line of vision by inserting pins in the paper.   The
inaccuracy of such a method is obvious, since, for example, the eye
cannot accommodate on the edge, slit, and pin at one time, and the
application of a telescope to increase the accuracy of vision suggests
itself immediately.   Thus Fraunhofer utilized the device of a very

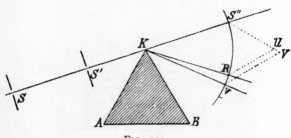

FIG. 100.

distant slit in conjunction with a telescope.   In the modern spectro-
meter the slit is placed in the focus of a telescope objective, which is
equivalent to replacing the former by an infinitely distant object, thus
obtaining an increase in intensity of illumination, together with
greater compactness.
   In Fig. 101 the two limiting rays 101 and 303, showing grazing
incidence and grazing emergence respectively, are constructed ;   in
both cases the deviation is a maximum.   For the ray 202, symmetrical
with respect to OH, the deviation is a minimum.
   The formula due to Fraunhofer * is useful for determining refractive
indices.   At minimum deviation the incident and emergent rays are
symmetrical with respect to the dividing plane of the prism (Fig. 102).
Half of the deviation occurs at the entrance into, and the other half
on emergence from, the prism.   If a is the angle of incidence, β that
of refraction, and D the deviation, then $\sin a / \sin \beta = \mu$, and from the
figure

   * J. v. Fraunhofer's " Gesammelte Schriften," München (1888).   Also " Denkschrift," p. 15, *loc. cit.*

$$\frac{\sin \dfrac{A + D}{2}}{\sin \dfrac{A}{2}} = \mu.$$

Whereas Newton formed a real image of the spectrum on a screen, Wollaston's method utilized the dioptric apparatus of the eye in place of Newton's lens and the retina in place of the screen. In Fraunhofer's apparatus, on the other hand, and in modern spectrometers, additional auxiliary dioptric apparatus is used in conjunction with the eye, but the essentials are the same as in Newton's method.

It is remarkable that Newton, with all his careful experimenting, had not noticed the fixed spectral lines ; this would have been easily conceivable if he had experimented only with circular apertures, but he not only recommended, but actually used, a small rectilinear slit.

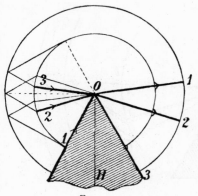

FIG. 101.

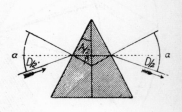

FIG. 102.

The only conclusion which can be drawn is that he and his followers did not work with all the requisite conditions accurately fulfilled at the same time, namely, a sufficiently narrow slit, minimum deviation, and insertion of the screen at the correct distance of the image. The fixed lines are observable without any refined apparatus when, for example, a beam of light is concentrated between two distant narrow slits and allowed to fall on a prism. Thus Newton's followers could not have varied his experiments a great deal, or the lines would have been noticed.

The discovery of the fixed lines was due, we have seen, to interest in scientific problems, and the accurate determination of dispersion which it made possible facilitated the construction of prisms having either deviation or dispersion reduced to zero.

Achromatic prisms and lenses were made possible by the fact that the relation between the mean deviation and the dispersion was not a simple one. The requirements for such achromatic prisms can be determined by means of Reusch's construction. Suppose we have the prism A (Fig. 103), whose refractive and dispersive data are given by the three circular arcs denoted by A. B is the prism, which when placed alongside A in the inverse direction is to form an achromatic combination, and the arcs B represent the dispersion data which are to be determined by the construction. The prism B is assumed to be shifted parallel to itself so that the refracting edges of both prisms coincide at K. The white incident rays give rise, according to the familiar construction, to the two rays KS (red) and KT (violet) emergent from A. For the further construction for the prism B, the lines SU, TV are first drawn perpendicular to the incidence side of B. For the combination to be achromatic, the two perpendiculars through U and V to the emergence side of B must both coincide in the same point of the innermost circle ; thus both lines must coincide, and UV

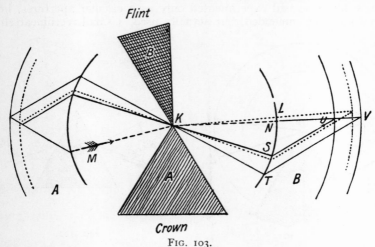

Fig. 103.

must be part of the common perpendicular, which fixes the position of the emergence face of B. KN is then the achromatized emergent ray.

It must be borne in mind that a superposition of *red* and *violet* rays does not mean that *every* ray leaves the prism combination in the same direction ; if the colour distribution in the spectra produced by A and B is very different, complete achromatization will be impossible. If the position of the yellow in the spectrum is denoted by the dotted line (Fig. 103), and is nearer the red for prism A and nearer the violet for prism B, the construction shows at once that the emergent yellow ray is inclined to KN. A prism achromatized for red and violet will thus give an image bordered not by red and violet, but by fringes of other colours. Fig. 105 represents an achromatic crown-flint glass combination.

Prisms can also be combined so as to give zero deviation for a particular colour, but without having the dispersion reduced to zero. These are the so-called direct-vision prisms. The dispersion requirements can again be determined by the same construction. In Fig. 104

the arcs of circles at A and B correspond to the prisms A and B which
are to be thus combined.   The white incident ray MK gives rise to
the rays KS (red) and KT (violet) emergent from the prism A.   SV,
TU are the construction lines perpendicular to the incidence side of B.
If the red ray is to remain *undeviated* on emergence, KN must form the
extension of MK, and VN must be perpendicular to the emergence

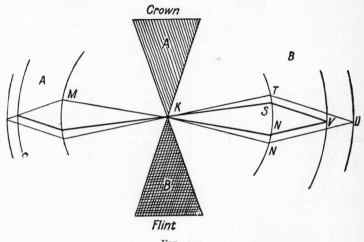

Fig. 104.

face of B, the position of which is thus determined.   Direct-vision
prisms are usually of the form shown in Fig. 106, in which the more
darkly shaded portions represent flint, and the lighter portions crown
glass.

    The discovery of the fixed spectral lines was not only of practical
importance, but also had important theoretical consequences.   The
fact that in the light from the sun there is not a continuous variation

Fig. 105.

Fig. 106.

of refrangibility, but that certain constituents are missing, was sure
to be of philosophical interest, as soon as attention had been drawn to
the phenomenon.   The stellar spectra presented similar yet distinct
characteristics, while the spectra of terrestrial light sources exhibited
to a certain extent the same peculiarities in distribution.   There was
the coincidence of the bright yellow line in the spectrum of a candle
flame and the dark line in the solar spectrum.   This was a problem
which required solution, and an ardent study of spectra commenced.

Brewster * discovered the homogeneous yellow light of the flame fed with common salt, and the dark lines in the absorption spectrum of nitrous acid. Ångström investigated the spectrum of the electric spark and concluded that it consisted of the combined spectra of the electrodes and of the gas in which the spark occurred. Plücker and Hittorf † carefully investigated the spectra of glowing gases in electric discharge tubes. The recognition of a substance by its characteristic spectrum was no longer a matter of difficulty.

Kirchhoff ‡ investigated more closely the coincidence of the sodium flame line R with the D line which Fraunhofer had already observed.

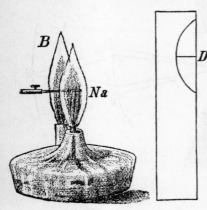

In doing this he found that, when a sodium flame was placed in the path of the sunlight in front of the slit of the spectroscope, the D line of the sun's spectrum appeared darker and broader than without the flame. This caused him to conclude that the sodium flame might absorb the same rays as it emits. Several experiments suffice to show that this is really the case. Roscoe heated some sodium in a sealed glass tube containing hydrogen until it vaporized, and observed that the tube appeared dark when placed between a sodium flame and the eye, but was quite transparent in front of a candle flame.

FIG. 107.

The feeble illumination of a spirit lamp flame is changed to bright yellow when common salt is sprinkled on the flame. Whereas a candle flame is seen extended in a spectrum when viewed through a prism, this sodium flame appears quite unchanged in colour, form, and sharpness. If a slit is placed in front of the latter, parallel to the refracting edge of the prism, the image seen through the prism is confined to the same width as the slit ; thus the sodium flame emits yellow light only, this having the same refractive index as the Fraunhofer D line in the solar spectrum. If a platinum wire is placed horizontally in the faintly luminous Bunsen flame (Fig. 107) so that it glows a bright white, on looking at it through a prism with refracting edge horizontal, a bright continuous spectrum with vertical dispersion is seen. On placing a spirit lamp flame containing sodium in front of the Bunsen flame, a dark D line is seen in that part of the spectrum for which the sodium flame covers the Bunsen flame. Sodium vapour thus absorbs

---

* D. Brewster, " Optics," pp. 78, 137, etc.

† J. Plücker, " Über die Konstitution der elektrischen Spektra verschiedener Gase und Dämpfe." *Pogg. Ann.*, Vol. 107 (1859). With J. W. Hittorf, *Phil. Trans. Roy. Soc.* (1865).

‡ R. Kirchhoff and R. Bunsen, " Über die Fraunhoferschen Linien," *Berlin. Akad.* (Oct., 1859).

the same light as it emits (Kirchhoff). Similar experiments can be performed with lithium chloride, rubidium chloride, etc., only the spectra concerned are more complex, consisting of several different coloured bright lines.

The relation between emitted and absorbed light had already been conjectured by Euler, though on the basis of incorrect views, as a general one common to all bodies. Foucault * made observations on the emitted and absorbed light of electric arcs. Ångström and Stokes † very nearly discovered the general law.

Kirchhoff, ‡ however, was fortunate enough to suspect that the relation followed from a more general *heat law*. Between a system of bodies, which is everywhere at the same temperature, there exists a state of what is called kinematical thermal equilibrium, in which each body radiates out to the others exactly the same amount of heat as it receives from them during the same interval of time. The quantity of light (or heat) which is radiated (from unit area) in unit time may be called the emissive power of the substances, while the corresponding quantity of light (or heat) which is absorbed by the substance may be termed the absorption coefficient. Consider an absolutely " black " body S, that is, one which absorbs the whole of the light (or heat) incident upon it ; this has the absorption coefficient $a = 1$ and the emissive power e, say. Let K be another body in thermal equilibrium with the body S, and having an absorption coefficient A and emissive power E. Equilibrium is only possible on one condition, namely, that if at a given temperature K has an absorption coefficient equal to only one-half of that of S, it can only have one-half the emissive power of S, otherwise equilibrium would soon be destroyed. K and S can be considered, for example, as the only bodies present, being bounded by two parallel infinite planes. The condition for thermal equilibrium between S and K is then that

$$\frac{A}{a} = \frac{E}{e} \text{ or } \frac{E}{A} = \frac{e}{a} = e$$

for each temperature. The ratio E/A thus depends only on e, that is, on the temperature. Such a conception as the above is not complete, however, for heat radiation consists of many kinds of rays which in general are not perfectly interchangeable, and these different kinds of rays are radiated in quite different proportions by different bodies. It is thus clear that a thermal equilibrium of one particular kind of ray may be disturbed by the action of rays of another kind. Thermal equilibrium is thus only possible in general if $\frac{E}{A} = e$ for each kind of ray in particular. Consequently, for each kind of ray E/A depends

* Léon Foucault, " Note sur la lumière de l'arc Voltaique." *Société Philomatique* (20 janvier, 1849).

† G. G. Stokes, " On the Theory of Certain Bands seen in the Spectrum," *Phil. Trans. Roy. Soc.* (1848), p. 227. " On the Simultaneous Emission and Absorption of Rays, etc.," *Phil. Mag.*, Vol. 19 (1860).

‡ Kirchhoff, " Über den Zusammenhang zwischen Emission und Absorption von Licht und Wärme," *Monatsber. d. Berlin Akad.* (Dec., 1859).

only on the emissive power of a perfectly " black " body for the same rays at the same temperature. If now a series of bodies K, K , K" . . . with respective emissive powers E, E', E" . . . and absorption coefficients A, A', A" . . . for one kind of ray, is compared with S, which has the emissive power e for the same ray at a given temperature,

$$\frac{E}{A} = \frac{E'}{A'} = \frac{E''}{A''} = \ldots = e.$$

It follows from this that those bodies which radiate a particular kind of ray more strongly also absorb the same rays to a greater extent.

This explains the reversal of the spectrum. As already mentioned, a sufficiently intense continuous spectrum, when viewed through a sodium flame whose spectrum is the single bright D line, shows in contrast a dark D line. If I is the intensity at the D line of the continuous spectrum, m the absorption coefficient of the flame, and I' its intensity, the region of the D line in the former will have the intensity I — mI + I' when seen through the flame. This may be either greater or less than I according as I' — mI is positive or negative. With a sufficiently bright source viewed through a sodium flame of sufficiently low temperature, this reversal of the D line cannot fail to be seen.

Draper found that the most dissimilar kinds of bodies, when heated in a piece of gun-barrel, all become red or white-hot at the same time, that is, at the same temperature. With increasing temperature the red rays appear first, then the orange, yellow, green, blue, and finally violet, the disappearance with cooling being in the reverse order. This can be effectively demonstrated with a stretched platinum wire heated electrically. The current is slowly increased while the wire is viewed through a prism with its edge parallel to it. The greater the temperature, the farther the extension of the spectrum towards the violet.

With the help of Kirchhoff's law and the above experiment with the platinum wire, Draper's law can be deduced. Suppose a substance K begins to emit D radiation at a temperature $t = T$; then, if the substance is opaque to D radiation at all temperatures, A > O. Thus for a temperature $t > T$, $\frac{E}{A} = e > O$ for D radiation. This means to say that the body S commences to emit D radiation at the same temperature as K and, since $\frac{E}{A} = \frac{E'}{A'} = \frac{E''}{A''} = \ldots e$, all of the bodies K, K', K" . . . , which are opaque to D radiation, that is, for which A, A', A" . . . *differ from zero*, commence to emit D radiation at the same temperature.

With the aid of his law, Kirchhoff gave the explanation of the Fraunhofer lines in the solar spectrum. If the sun is considered as a glowing solid or liquid body surrounded by an atmosphere of gas, the continuous spectrum of the solid central portion contains the dark lines at the same place as bright lines would appear in the spectrum of the glowing gaseous atmosphere. These bright lines are actually observed

in the protuberances of the solar atmosphere.   An investigation of the
coincidence of the Fraunhofer lines with the spectral lines from the
terrestrial light sources serves for a chemical analysis of the sun's
atmosphere.

Since Newton's ideas of dispersion long remained confined within
their original bounds without any natural expansion, many prejudiced
notions arose.   One of these was the proportionality between refractive
index and dispersion, which has already been dealt with above.
Another concerned the order of the colours and the refractive indices ;
it was generally supposed that the prismatic deviation must increase
in the order : red, orange, yellow, green, blue, violet, and that no
other arrangement could exist.   This idea appeared to be so well
founded that even mathematical theories were developed on the basis
of an assumed constitution of matter, to show that no other was
possible.   The first of these theories was due to Cauchy.*   He
assumed that the separation of the smallest divisions of matter was
not vanishingly small compared with the wave-length of light.   The
light which comprised in its wave-length a smaller number of particles
was more strongly refracted.   Cauchy developed a formula by means of
his theory, expressing the increase of refractive index as a function of
decreasing wave-lengths, which was in good agreement with ob sevation.

Consequently, when Leroux † first noticed a greater deviation in
the red than in the violet with a prism filled with iodine, the observation was hailed as an illusion, and no further notice was taken of it,
so that it was forgotten.   Much the same thing befell the observations
of Quincke,‡ who concluded from interference experiments with pieces
of thin metallic foil that there was an unusual order of refractive
indices.   The observations of Christiansen § and Kundt ‖ in this
direction fundamentally reformed the theory of dispersion.

As is well known, the sine of the limiting angle of incidence for
total reflection is the reciprocal of the refractive index ; thus we have
the method which Wollaston was the first to apply for determining
the refractive index of opaque substances.   When Christiansen
applied this method to fuchsine (aniline red) he discovered a quite
abnormal behaviour, for whereas most substances exhibit a fairly
sharp boundary of total reflection (Newton's blue fringe), no distinct
limit was apparent at all for reflection from crown glass at the surface
of a fuchsine solution.   Further, it was obvious, when the totally
reflecting face of a crown glass prism was covered with fuchsine solution, that for *perpendicular* incidence the reflected light was *green*

---

* A. L. Cauchy, " Sur la théorie mathémat. de la lumière." *Compt. Rend.*, Vol. 2
(1836) ; " Sur les vibrations de l'èther, etc.," *Compt. Rend.*, Vol. 7 (1838).

† Leroux, *Compt. Rend.*. Vol. 51 (1861).

‡ G. Quincke, "Optische Eigenschaften der Metalle," *Wied. Ann.*, Vol. 119
(1863) : " Brechungsexponente der Metalle," Vol. 119 (1863).

§ C. Christiansen, " Brechungsverhältnis des Fuchsins," *Pogg. and Wied. Ann.*,
Vols. 141 and 143 (1870 and 1871) ; " Farbenzenstreuung des Fuchsins," Vol. 146
(1872).

‖ A. Kundt, "Anomale Dispersion," *Pogg. and Wied. Ann.* (1871 and 1872) ;
" Beziehung zwischen Dispersion und Absorption des Lichtes " (1874) ; " Anomai
Dispersion im gluhenden Na-Dampf " (1880).

instead of white, and on increasing the angle of incidence the reflected light very gradually changed to *blue, violet, purple, rose*, and, with very *dilute solutions only*, finally to *white*. By spectrally examining the reflected light Christiansen found that already at perpendicular incidence *green light was totally reflected*. An increase of the angle of incidence caused total reflection to set in for the *blue, violet, red, orange, and finally yellow*, in succession. To study this abnormal behaviour directly, Christiansen filled a hollow prism of very small angle with fuchsine solution, and passed a beam of light through it close to its refracting edge (on account of the strong absorption by fuchsine). He thus found for the refractive indices for the Fraunhofer lines :—

		18·8 per cent Fuchsine solution in alcohol.	Alcohol.
B	. .	1·450	1·3628
C	. .	1·502	—
D	. .	1·561	1·3654
E	. .	—	1·3675
F	. .	1·312	1·3696
G	. .	1·258	1·3733
H	. .	1·312	1·3761

This shows that the usual order of refractive indices is completely destroyed, and in comparison with alcohol fuchsine has a very considerable dispersion.

The method of total reflection which Christiansen tried does not permit of an accurate determination of the refractive index, and the hollow prism method is not reliable on account of the strong absorption. Thus it occurred to Christiansen to apply the Newton prism combination, introducing a thin layer of fuchsine solution between the two prisms (Fig. 108), and to examine the spectrum of the transmitted (and therefore not yet totally reflected) light. I am convinced personally that this process, which would be quite reliable for substances with low absorptions, will not give good results with highly absorbing substances, for the rays which are nearly totally reflected are almost parallel to the surface and will have a considerable path in the fuchsine, even if its perpendicular thickness is small, and thus be absorbed. This may be the reason why the method was never actually applied by Christiansen.

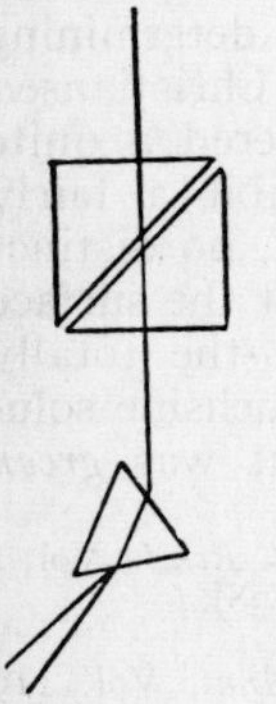

Fig. 108.

Kundt examined a large number of substances for anomalous dispersion and found that it was a property of all substances which possess a high *absorption* and marked *surface colours* and in the crystalline form are dichroic. Kundt first used a hollow prism of very small angle (about 10°) which he filled with the substances under test. If such a prism is filled with fuchsine and placed with its edge vertical in front of a vertical slit illuminated by sunlight, the spectrum seen through the thin part near the edge of the prism, which is placed to the right, say, has the violet part on the left side, with a dark space to the right followed by the red, orange, and yellow parts, the violet being re-fracted least and the yellow most. The Fraunhofer lines do not all appear equally sharp, since several parts of the spectrum are super-posed on account of the equality of refractive index, and some of the lines are completely invisible. To account for this, Kundt assumed certain refractive indices to be *indeterminate*. Such an assumption is unnecessary if it be remembered that the fuchsine prism acts as a diffracting slit, which has different widths for different colours. The most strongly absorbed colours are only transmitted close to the narrow edge ; thus for these the equivalent width of the slit is least, and con-sequently (as diffraction phenomena indicate) the optical images have the least definition. The less absorbed colours can traverse a greater thickness of the prism, and for these the images are sharper.

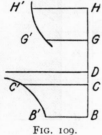
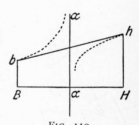

FIG. 109.   FIG. 110.

Kundt also devised a more elegant method in which Newton's crossed prisms were employed. Consider a normal prism, illuminated with sunlight, oriented with its refracting edge horizontal and pointing downwards, so that it forms a spectrum with violet uppermost and red below. A second prism with its edge vertical and to the left, placed between the eye and the former, would displace the spectrum from the first obliquely, the violet left above and the red right below. The same prism, if filled with a solution of cyanine, which gives an anomalous dispersion, would give the form of spectrum shown in Fig. 109. The first prism with normal dispersion produces a spectrum BCDGH, while the second, in combination with the first, displaces the spectrum into the two curved branches B'C' and G'H'. The curve thus formed indicates directly the manner in which the usual order of refractive indices is disturbed. Fuchsine and other substances having anomalous dispersion show similar effects, which, however, are more complicated if the substances absorb in several regions of the spectrum. Kundt recognized a connexion between absorption and anomalous dispersion, which may be indicated in the following way. Let the spectrum with the Fraunhofer lines be arranged along BH (Fig. 110), while the corre-sponding refractive indices are denoted by the respective ordinates. The normal dispersion curve obtained by joining the extremities of

the ordinates may be denoted approximately by the line *bh*. If now
the substance with anomalous dispersion has the property of strongly
absorbing the light at the region *a* of the spectrum, the effect is to
shift and separate the dispersion curve into the two branches denoted
by the dotted lines.   Thus, on approaching the absorption region from
the red end of the spectrum, the refractive indices increase above the
normal values, while on approaching it from the violet end, they
decrease below the normal values.   Normal dispersion may be considered as a special case of the anomalous, in which for the normally
dispersive substance the absorption region lies beyond the violet end
of the visible spectrum.

Whilst the total reflection method gives quite reliable proof of
the existence of anomalous dispersion, it does not give results of great
accuracy, and the use of anomalous dispersive prisms has attendant
complications such as reduction in intensity of illumination, so that

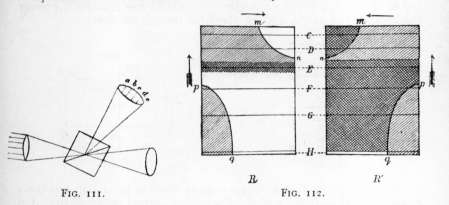

FIG. 111.   FIG. 112.

for a long time full confidence was not placed in the results.   For these
reasons I endeavoured with G. v. Osnobischin to vary the method of
total reflection in such a manner that the results could be made as clear
and unambiguous as by Kundt's method.   Our method was further
improved later.*

The method was to introduce a fuchsine solution of considerable
concentration, about 5 per cent., between flint glass reflecting prisms
(Fig. 111).   The large dispersion was obvious immediately, for, instead
of the narrow blue fringe, the whole cross-section of the reflected cone
of light was filled with broad coloured bands.   The more concentrated
the solution, the broader were the coloured bands.   A repetition of
the reflection produced colours of great brilliancy.   Coloured bands
likewise appeared in the refracted cone of light ; these, however, were
not completely complementary to the former on account of the
absorption.   Using a fuchsine solution between the hypotenuse faces

of flint glass prisms, arranged similarly to those in Fig. 90, Chapter VI, the reflected spectrum R and the refracted spectrum R' appear somewhat as indicated in Fig. 112.   The limiting curves of total reflection form two quite separate branches mn and pq, similar to those obtained by Kundt by crossing a normally and an anomalously dispersive prism. The boundary mn in R is sharp with only one reflection ; on the other hand, the boundary pq can only be distinguished by close inspection. All the boundaries are sharp in the spectrum R', however, but their positions are influenced by the misleading effect of the absorption due to the layer of fuchsine, which the rays at angles approaching that of total reflection traverse obliquely and thus with appreciable absorption. It is thus advisable to confine attention to the spectrum R.   The next improvement consisted in increasing the definition of the limit pq by repeated reflection at parallel surfaces.   Several reflecting prisms were thus utilized (Fig. 113), on the hypotenuse faces of which cells were cemented to hold the fuchsine solution.   Two such reflections alone sufficed to make the pq boundary distinct in the spectrum R.   In the earlier experiments the rays spreading out from different parts of a slit were focussed by a lens on the totally reflecting surface.   This

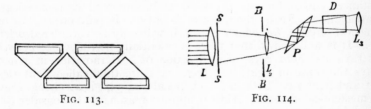

FIG. 113.   FIG. 114.

does not exclude the possibility of rays arriving at different angles at the surface from the same point of the slit, which detracts from the sharpness of the limit of total reflection.   The following arrangement overcomes this source of error.   The sunlight is received by the lens L_1 (Fig. 114), which is covered by the slit SS.   Before the light arrives at the reflecting surface, it traverses the lens L_2, which is its focal length distant from the slit SS.   This causes only parallel rays to fall on the reflecting surface, but these have different angles of incidence for different parts of the slit.   After traversing the reflecting prism P and the direct-vision prism D, the rays fall on the lens L_3 of long focal length, which forms an image of the slit as an infinitely distant object at its focal distance, at which a sharp spectrum appears.   The lens L_2 is covered by a diaphragm BB which makes it impossible for direct rays from the slit to fall on the reflecting surface, as these would superpose an image of the slit on the spectrum.   If the above precautions are observed, the principle of the crossing of an anomalously dispersive totally reflecting prism and a normally refracting one, to describe them in brief, can be used to reproduce very elegant spectra objectively.   In the above case the greater the concentration, the longer are the spectra thus produced.   A practicable experiment such as this, free from obvious objections, was desirable in order to unravel the important phenomena of anomalous dispersion, which is so closely allied to the *chemical* nature of colour dispersion.   We shall not discuss here the molecular theories of anomalous dispersion of Sellmeier,* Helmholtz,† and others.

The closer study of the spectra of different sources of radiation by Ångström, Plücker, Kirchhoff, Bunsen, and others, has afforded the present-day knowledge that luminous solid and liquid bodies, with a few exceptions (didymium compounds), give continuous spectra while gases and vapours give discontinuous spectra.   In the former, all the colours are uniformly present, whereas the latter are characterized chemically by the presence or absence of certain kinds of radiation. The spectrum of a gas or vapour consists as a rule of several bright lines (line spectrum) ; there may also be present, however, broader bands having characteristic shading, which remind one of grooved pillars (band spectra).   In the case of many gases and vapours, the occurrence of a line spectrum or a band spectrum apparently depends on the density and the temperature (Plücker, Hittorf, Wüllner).   The experiments in this direction are, however, not yet complete.

The question as to why solid substances, or liquids in droplet form, give a continuous spectrum when in a glowing state, and gaseous substances a discontinuous spectrum, can be answered with some degree of satisfaction.   Really the question is not one in pure optics, but one of general physics, for which reason it will only be considered briefly here.   It is well known that there is essentially no difference between heat rays and light rays.   One fraction of heat radiation in general excites the sense of light, and these rays are thus called light rays. Heat and light rays both cause chemical changes, heat changes, and also mechanical changes.   Thus it appears reasonable to consider each origin of radiation as a chemical disturbance from equilibrium, or as a (periodic) *chemical vibration* which when powerful enough is able to destroy completely the chemical combination.   Vapours or gases, on the other hand, must be allotted a simpler (chemical) constitution than that of solid or liquid bodies, in which the cohesive properties of the parts (which can, however, also be considered as relations of a chemical nature) are involved.   It thus follows that the number of possible kinds of disturbance from equilibrium and their corresponding vibration periods is extremely great for solids and liquids, whereas these may be reduced to a small number in the case of gases.   I have endeavoured elsewhere to give a theoretical discussion of these relations, and I will only add that it is a rational procedure to substitute, in place of the *special relations between the (hypothetical) atoms*, the *chemical relations between the chemical components*.

If incident white light be transmitted by a substance, the several constituents are in general not transmitted with equal facility.   Experiment shows, moreover, that a fraction of the light is retained and produces the heating and chemical changes, etc., of the substance. This fraction is said to be *absorbed*. .An unequal absorption of several of the coloured constituents may cause the transmitted light to be coloured; thus the spectrum, through cobalt glass, of white light incident upon it contains several strong absorption bands, and the transmitted light appears blue. The ordinary colours of different substances (pigment colours) are absorption colours, light which is reflected superficially being usually white. If a mirror is formed from a coloured substance, for example, from red sealing wax, it will produce (at grazing incidence) a colourless image. The usual origin of a pigment colour is the re-emergence from the surface, through irregularities in refractive index, of light which has penetrated a short distance into the substance. Such light is coloured by absorption, and mingles on emergence with the externally scattered white light. Only comparatively few substances colour the light merely by superficial reflection, and these exhibit the so-called surface colours. To this class belong many of the metals, the aniline colours in the solid form, etc.

The spectral absorption bands of many substances are often as characteristic of their chemical nature as the line spectra of vapours. Whereas many absorption bands are broad and diffuse, some may be extremely sharp, for example, in the case of didymium salts. Characteristic bands may be present in the case of solid, liquid, or gaseous substances. Of the last class, the numerous and to a certain extent narrow bands of nitrogen peroxide (Brewster), and of iodine and bromine vapours, are especially remarkable. Newton was not quite correct when he supposed that colours of natural objects were reflection or surface colours, for they are absorption colours. Such a result also follows from Helmholtz's experiments with pigment mixtures. The development of this point of view was materially strengthened by Brewster's numerous experiments on the absorption of solid, liquid, and gaseous substances.

The invariability of refractive index and colour of one kind of light, which was assumed by Newton, involves apparent exceptions in many instances; these have received a certain amount of attention in the past, but have only of late years been studied exhaustively. Kircher * described the behaviour of an infusion of Lignum nephriticum, which is quite transparent by transmitted light, but a bright green by scattered light. Boyle † also investigated the same phenomenon. Newton ‡ mentioned that thin gold leaf was yellow by incident light and blue or green by transmitted light, and that therefore yellow light was strongly reflected by gold, and blue transmitted; he believed that the phenomenon with Lignum nephriticum could be similarly classified. Closer investigation of this latter phenomenon has shown, however, that it is due to light of one colour ceasing to exist when it is taken up and absorbed by the substance, light of another kind being in general re-emitted. The phenomenon was termed by Brewster

* A. Kircher, " Ars magna lucis et umbrae—De ligno quodam admirabili aquam in omne genus colorum tingente."

† Robert Boyle (1627-1691), " Experimenta et considerationes de coloribus," London (1663). " On the Light of Fish," *Phil. Trans. Roy. Soc.*, 1672.

‡ J. Newton, " Lectiones Opticae," Par. II, Lect. I, Prop. V; also " Optice," pp. 177, 287, etc.

" internal," and by Herschel " epibolic," dispersion. Stokes * was the first to discover its true nature when using fluorspar, and called it " fluorescence." Fluorspar or a solution of quinine sulphate shows a superficial coloured shimmer, which by sunlight extends well below the surface and is of a different colour from that of the incident light.

Brewster condensed sunlight into a cone by means of a lens, and allowed it to fall on to a solution of sulphate of quinine. The whole cone exhibited a blue shimmer, which was less pronounced the greater the distance of penetration of the light. The light thus loses its power of exciting fluorescence after passage through the quinine solution, a fact which was emphasized by Stokes. On the other hand, Stokes noticed that the bluish cone is observable through a thick layer of the solution without appreciable decrease of intensity. He also noticed that a similar fluorescence is observable in many yellow glasses when the same light is incident upon them, but that the fluorescence shimmer thus excited can be seen without difficulty through the same glass. It thus appears that the exciting light is different from the light produced by the fluorescence, or that a change of one kind of light into another has been effected. Coloured glass can be utilized to detect weak fluorescence by taking the substance to be tested into a dark room, into which light can only enter through blue glass, and viewing it through a piece of yellow glass. The blue glass gives preference to the transmission of the rays which excite fluorescence, while the yellow glass prevents the blue rays from entering the eye and only allows the less refrangible fluorescent light to pass.

The phenomena relating to fluorescence were also investigated spectrally by Stokes by means of three different methods. In the first method, sunlight was dispersed by prisms and a section of the whole spectrum was made to enter the fluorescent solution in a glass vessel by means of a condensing lens. Since all the different colours were present in the solution, it was easily observable that the red end of the spectrum was almost inactive and was only visible because of particles suspended in the liquid, and that the violet end was most active in producing fluorescence.

The second method was to project a spectrum on to a vessel filled with the quinine solution, used in place of a screen. The spectrum thus formed across the solution was much longer at its violet end than it would have been on an ordinary paper screen, and this extended portion contained many new dark lines, the most prominent of which Stokes denoted by k, l, m, n, o, p. This new part of the spectrum is termed ultra-violet, and it is this portion which is most effective in producing chemical reaction : for example, it causes the decomposition of silver salts. J. Müller and Mascart were thus able to photograph the ultra-violet portion, and the latter named a number of lines contained in it by the letters J, M, N, O, P, Q, R, S, T.

In the third method the sunlight was dispersed by a prism, but only a small part of the spectrum was projected in a cone into the solu-

---

* G. G. Stokes, " On the Change of Refrangibility of Light," *Phil. Trans. Roy. Soc.* (1852).

PLATE IV

FRANCISCVS MA
GRIMALDI BON.SIS
SOCI. IESV

Ego idem Francisus M.ª Grimaldus.

tion by means of a lens. The action of different portions was investigated separately, the results naturally being identical with those of
the other methods.

The second method can be further developed. Suppose that a
very narrow horizontal spectrum is formed on a fluorescent screen by
means of a prism with refracting edge vertical. This spectrum is
viewed through a second prism having its refracting edge horizontal
and pointed downwards, say. If there were no fluorescence, the usual
oblique spectrum would be seen as in Newton's experiment, formed
by the ordinary reflection and deviation. Since, however, numerous
fluorescence colours develop where the first spectrum strikes the screen,
the second prism arranges them one above the other by vertical dispersion. Thus, in addition to the oblique spectrum RH (Fig. 115),
there is the almost rectangular spectral illumination FF. Vertical
lines drawn through the extremities of this spectrum indicate the
spectral region of fluorescent activity. The region extends from F to
the extreme ultra-violet. Horizontal lines through the boundaries of

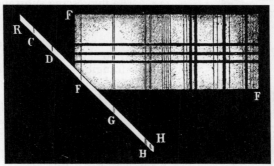

FIG. 115.

FF indicate which colours are excited by fluorescence ; these extend
from R to F.

Stokes came to the conclusion that the kinds of light which have
the principal fluorescent action also undergo marked absorption in the
fluorescing substances. It is expedient to replace glass prisms and
lenses by quartz prisms and lenses for these experiments, quartz being
far more transparent to the ultra-violet rays than glass ; indeed, so
much so that the ultra-violet rays are often visible without transformation by fluorescence owing to their increased intensity. The most
important result which Stokes obtained was that, in fluorescence, *rays
of greater refrangibility are always transformed to rays of lesser refrangibility*, and never in the reverse direction. The researches of Stokes
were taken up by V. Pierre, Hagenbach, and Lommel, who investigated
a large number of fluorescent substances.

The device represented in Fig. 116 is very useful for the demonstration of fluorescence. A rectangular framework with blue glass on
two sides (*a* and the opposite side) and yellow glass on the other two
(*b* and the opposite side) is placed round a cube of uranium glass or

other fluorescent substance, which is partly covered by paper. If sunlight enters the cover through the blue glass, the cube appears a bright yellow-green through the yellow sides. On turning the cover through a right angle so that the sunlight enters through the yellow, the cube appears through the blue as dark brown as the paper appears in both cases. Whereas the paper always sends back to the eye only the light which has been transmitted by the blue or yellow glass, the uranium glass cube transforms the blue light into yellow-green, which is transmitted by the yellow ; in the reverse case, however, the yellow light is not changed by the uranium glass to blue, the colour which is transmitted by the blue glass. This is in correspondence with Stokes' law.

Lommel endeavoured to show that Stokes' law was not perfectly general by means of observations of a change from rays of lesser to

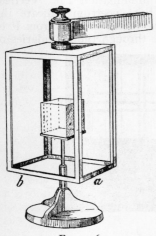

greater refrangibility in the case of eosin. In conjunction with B. Brauner, I repeated and confirmed this experiment by means of the arrangement shown in Fig. 114. The fluorescing substance was carefully introduced between both pairs of prisms. If the first pair of prisms cut off the less refrangible end of the spectrum up to a line x, and the other the more refrangible end as far as the same line, the phenomena observed by Stokes could be verified. But with the reverse order of extinction of the spectrum, in many cases Lommel's observations were verified. For the reasons which have been given on pages 122 and 125, I do not now consider this type of experiment conclusive. It will be noticed that the two pairs of prisms replace the different coloured glasses of Fig. 116, a gain in precision being thereby effected.

FIG. 116.

Many facts concerning phosphorescence have been known for quite a long time, but a systematic study of the subject only commenced in modern times. Even Aristotle was acquainted with the emission of light in the dark, without any appreciable heat development, by putrefying substances. This has proved to be due to a slow combustion, similar to the process with phosphorus, which is to be distinguished from the true optical phosphorescence, in which no gross chemical change of the active substance takes place. In 1604 the shoemaker Casciorolo discovered the phosphorescent stone of Bonn, a baryta mixed with alumina. This substance might be called a light-storer, since it is luminous in the dark after exposure for a time to sunlight. La Galla * and Kircher † described this substance, and Balduin,

* Giulio Cesare La Galla (1571-1624), . . . " De phenomenis in orbe lunae novi telescopii usu a Galilaeo nunc iterum suscitatis, physica disputatio. Item de luce et lumine altera disp," Venet (1612).

† A. Kircher, " Ars magna, etc.," pp. 18 and 19. Beccari, " de Phosphoris," Bolog. (1744).

Beccari, Canton, Marggraf, Osann, and P. Heinrich discovered others. Placidus Heinrich * carried out some comprehensive experiments on phosphorescence, and tested many mineral, animal, vegetable, and artificially manufactured substances for phosphorescence; he also investigated the phosphorescent action of heat, fracture, pressure, impact, friction, electrification, etc. As he knew that different phosphorescent substances were luminous for different lengths of time after exposure to light, Heinrich enclosed himself in a light-tight chamber, in which he could immediately inspect the substance which had been exposed to light. He thus discovered a large number of very weakly phosphorescent substances. In this manner the number of known phosphorescent substances was greatly extended.

Phosphorescence is very closely allied to fluorescence. Many substances have the property of being luminous for longer or shorter periods in the dark after exposure to electric light or sunlight for a short time. Calcspar and diamonds show this effect. Among the artificially manufacturable phosphorescent substances are the sulphur compounds obtained by the combustion of sulphur with calcium, baryta, strontium, etc. The intensity and duration of the after-glow varies greatly with these substances, and is not simply related to their chemical nature, but depends to a certain extent on the physical peculiarities of their previous treatment and formation. The colour of the after-glow is also very variable.

It occurred to E. Becquerel † to inquire whether or not phosphorescence was a property common to many substances but, owing to its transient nature, could not be observed by the common methods. He thus introduced the substances to be observed between disks rapidly rotating about a common axis, the disks being provided with equidistant apertures such that an aperture of one disk was situated between two apertures of the other. Sunlight passed through the apertures of one disk intermittently on the substance tested, while the latter was viewed through the apertures of the other, the arrangement being such as to make the substance invisible when exposed to sunlight and only visible when not illuminated. Becquerel thus discovered that many substances, till then not known to phosphoresce, began to become more and more luminous as the speed of rotation of the disk increased. The process is evidently a much-accelerated repetition of the previous ones, in which the substance is exposed to sunlight and quickly brought into the dark chamber, exposed to sunlight again, and so on, the rotating disks performing this so quickly that, for a speed of 100 revolutions per second, the substance could be observed at even 0·0006 second after exposure to illumination.

Ordinary glass and uranium glass, when placed between the disks, fluoresce *green, calcite* and *aragonite, orange-yellow*. All solid substances which fluoresce also exhibit phosphorescence. Only fluorescing *liquids* showed no phosphorescence. Becquerel therefore came to the conclusion that fluorescence may be considered as a short duration

* P. Heinrich, " Die Phosphorescenz der Korper," Nürnberg (1811).
† A. Ed. Becquerel, *Ann. de chim. et phys.*, Vols. 55 and 57.

phosphorescence and, on the other hand, phosphorescence may be looked upon as a long duration fluorescence.

Becquerel's experiment can easily be performed with a pair of disks attached to any rotation mechanism. For demonstration purposes, however, the apparatus can be modified by using a cylindrical drum fixed to a spindle (Fig. 117). One end of the drum and the circumference have apertures placed in the same meridian planes through the axis ; the other end of the drum is removed. If a phosphorescent and a non-phosphorescent substance are placed inside the drum, so that each receives illumination through the apertures in the end, the effects can be observed through the circumferential apertures. If the head is moved round slowly in the direction of rotation of the drum, all phases after the illumination can be observed, so to speak, stroboscopically. If this be done, both substances can be seen illuminated

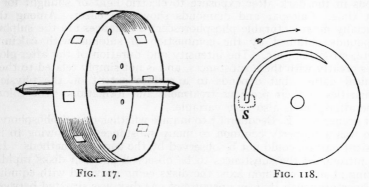

Fig. 117.   Fig. 118.

in the first instance, after which the non-phosphorescent one becomes dark, while the phosphorescent one is seen in a fading illumination.

The phosphorescence of glass can be shown in the following simple manner. The lacquered rotating disk (Fig. 118) of a Holtz electrification machine is placed so that the sun's rays are focussed on it by means of a large condensing lens. If the image is screened from the observer's eye by a small object S, on rotating the disk with gradually increasing speed a bright circular tail is observed, which extends farther round the disk the greater the speed of rotation, and finally becomes a complete circle. In this way the alternation of illumination and observation is avoided, the effect being more marked, and showing all phases after illumination simultaneously.

Becquerel also investigated the spectral distribution of phosphorescence, which proved very complicated, the light emitted being in general different from that producing the phosphorescence.

always being present. Light must therefore enter into the shadow. The fringes both within and outside the shadow were invariably parallel to the edges of the shadow of the thread, but in each case the distance apart of the fringes was said to be indeterminate [131]. Coloured fringes were observed inside the shadow. The non-homogeneous radiation evidently consists of the portions near the edges of the geometrical shadow, and progressively towards the centre of the shadow, superposition of waves from round both edges of the thread causes interference until the position of the central white is reached, at which place there is no difference of path involving colour, for here all wave-lengths experience the same condition and thus no difference of path is apparent here. He [sic] (Grimaldi) made allowance for a definite, though small depth also should out in a wave, namely, when it has become homogeneous...

CHAPTER VIII

PERIODICITY

THE periodic nature of light was first suspected from the work of Grimaldi * (1613-1663). He was the first to make careful experiments with prisms, and to render a much clearer interpretation of the observations possible by working in the dark and admitting the light through small apertures. His real work, however, was the discovery of diffraction phenomena, which he observed with accuracy, and whose essential details he recorded with such fidelity that the subject could no longer remain in obscurity. Grimaldi found that when a small opaque body was placed in the cone of sunlight which emerged from a small aperture

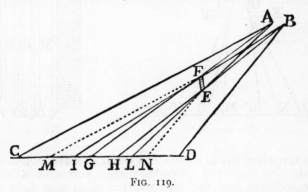

FIG. 119.

(Fig. 119), the shadow which it cast was somewhat broader than it would have been if the light were propagated rectilinearly past the edges of the opaque object. Light underwent the same deflection or " diffraction " at the edges of the second slit GH in Fig. 120 after entrance through the first slit CD. Grimaldi thus made the following statement : " Lumen propagatur seu diffunditur non solum directe, refracte ac reflexe, sed etiam quodam quarto modo diffracte." He observed three coloured fringes bordering on the shadow, each fringe being narrower than its next neighbour on the side of the shadow. With a sufficiently bright light source fringes could also be seen inside the shadow (Fig. 121), an odd number of the brighter fringes

* Franciscus Maria Grimaldi, " Physico-mathesis de lumine coloribis et iride," Bononiae, 1665.

always being present.   Light must therefore penetrate into the shadow. The fringes both within and outside the shadow were generally parallel to the edges of the latter.   If the obstacle which cast the shadow (e.g. a strip) was bent in an angle (Fig. 123), feather-shaped fringes were formed inside the shadow.   This non-uniform and periodic distribution occurring at the passage round the edges of opaque objects (Fig. 122) probably reminded Grimaldi of the similar occurrence when water flows round obstacles projecting from its surface, or of the wash of a moving ship, for he remarks : " Lumen videtur esse quid fluidum perquam celerrime et saltem aliquando etiam undulatim fusum per corpora diaphana."   Light was thus considered analogous to a liquid which could also spread out in waves, namely, when it passed round an object.   This was the most definite conception of the laws governing the phenomena which Grimaldi could evolve.   Further on in his treatise

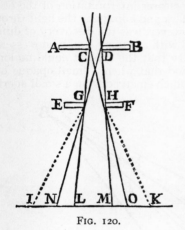

Fig. 120.

Fig. 121.

(p. 342) a spreading out in spirals as a result of wave motion is briefly considered.   On page 187 Grimaldi makes a remark which would appear to indicate that the superposition of rays of light can also produce darkness : " Lumen aliquando per sui communicationem reddit obscuriorem superficiem corporis aliunde primus illustratum." Had not this conclusion been based on an illusion, it would have formed an important anticipation of later knowledge.   Thus if an image of the sun is produced by the passage of light through a small opening, the image is darker at its edges, and on arranging two small openings close enough together (Fig. 124) for the images to be super- posed at one part, the darker edge of one image is seen continuing round through the other, although for this region different rays of light have been superposed.   As I showed a long time ago,* however, the pheno-

* Mach, " Über den Einfluss räumlich und zeitlich variierender Lichtreize auf die Gesichtswahrnehmung," *Sitzb. d. Wiener Akad*, Vol. 115, Part IIa (June, 1906) ; also, " Über die Abhängigkeit der Netzhautstellen voneinander," *Vierteljahrsschrift für Psych.* (1868).

menon is not of physical, but of physiological, origin, since the sensation of brightness does not depend on the intensity of illumination
alone, but also upon its differential coefficient with respect to the area
of the illuminated surface.

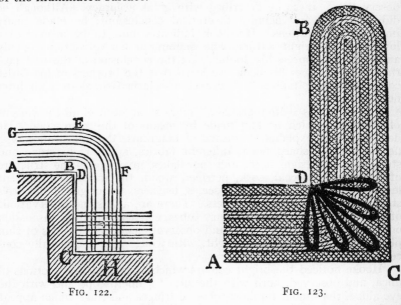

FIG. 122.   FIG. 123.

Apart from an account of experiments, Grimaldi's treatise contains many speculations as to the nature of transparent bodies, the
reflection of light in air, the porosity of substances, especially water,
the transparency of substances to magnetic action, a comparison be-

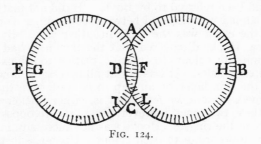

FIG. 124.

tween light and sound, and so on. Grimaldi mentions that reflection
at rough surfaces is specially favourable to the sorting out of undula-
tions and colours, so that coloration may not be due to simple reflection or a single or two-fold refraction, but may be caused by "diffraction." In conclusion, there follows a long discussion as to whether
light is a substance or is fortuitous. The speculative content of the

book gives a peculiar impression to the modern reader, and is largely the cause of the under-estimation of its value.

On the whole, it must be said that Grimaldi discovered many beautiful and important results, which were the outcome of skilled observation ; these he described with great accuracy. Although he did not draw any definite theoretical conclusions, he made many important suggestions. His book indicates him to be a man of a lovable and upright nature, who announced his convictions openly and did not suppress his doubts. At the conclusion of the first posthumous edition of his book, we learn that the brothers of his Order composed the epitaph : " P. Franciscus Maria Grimaldus vixit inter nos sine querela."

Hooke, in his " Micrographia," gives an account of all the various observations which he had made by means of the microscope. He describes, and explains by means of diagrams, the appearance of a needle-point, a sharp razor, different fabrics, splinters of stone and steel, and the designs in ice and snowflakes, investigates the structure of vegetable charcoal, cork, petrified wood, the nature of different leaves, mildew, moss, hair, fish-scales, feathers, the origin of the bee's sting, and examines many insects. There are also some observations of a physical category on capillary tubes, elasticity of air, a discussion on telescopically visible stars, and observations on the colours of thin plates and the diffraction of light, with which we are especially concerned here.

Hooke noticed the bright colours which appear in thin sections of mica, and observed, both with the aid of a microscope and with the eye alone, the similar rainbow-coloured fringes and rings which appear in the air interstices of the same mineral. The latter he could imitate by pressing together two well-cleaned pieces of plate glass. He then showed that all transparent bodies, if obtained in sufficiently thin layers or laminæ, show the same colours, for example, substances like thin-blown glass, oil of turpentine, pitch, spirit of wine, and bubbles, which last had been referred to by Boyle. It did not matter whether a transparent lamina was enclosed between two similar or different substances, for the effect was the same in either case. By splitting off layers of mica, Hooke discovered that the thickness had to lie within two broad limits for colours to appear ; neither too thick nor too thin layers exhibited colours. It was not at all necessary, however, for the thickness of the thin layer or air gap to be uniform ; the layer could be like a convex or concave lens, that is, either thicker or thinner in the middle, these two cases, however, giving rise to opposite sequences of the colours in the rings.* Hooke was not successful in determining the thickness appropriate to each colour. Opaque substances, which

* " Nor is it necessary, that these coloured Laminæ should be of an even thickness, that is, should have their edges and middle of equal thickness, as in a Looking-glass plate, which circumstance is only requisite to make the Plate appear all of the same colour ; but they may resemble a Lens, that is, have their middles thicker than their edges ; or else a double concave, that is, be thinner in the middle than at the edges ; in both which cases there will be various coloured rings or lines, with differing consecutions or orders of Colours ; the order of the first from the middle outwards being Red, Yellow, Green, Blue, etc. And the latter quite contrary." " Micrographia," p. 53.

reflected no light back from their second face, never showed colours, even when they were of the necessary thickness for transparent substances ; thus Hooke concluded that an interaction between the light reflected back from the front and back faces was the criterion for the production of colour. The phenomena were not intimately connected with the particular kind of illumination employed.

Hooke then enters into a discussion on the nature of light. Fiery (luminous) bodies, he says, are engaged in violent motion between their parts. The diamond, when rubbed in the dark, is luminous, evidently because of the motion imparted by the friction ; this light-producing motion cannot be continuous in one direction, for the parts remain together, nor can it be a rotation, for such is only compatible with the liquid state ; it must therefore be a vibratory motion, and, on account of the hardness of diamond, a very rapid one, i.e. of very short period. He supposed the velocity of propagation of the disturbances to be very great.

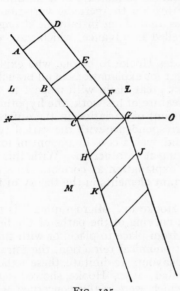

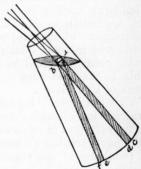

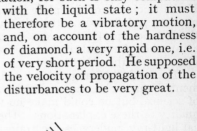

FIG. 125.   FIG. 126.

If a ray of light is refracted towards the normal on passage from a first to a second medium (Fig. 125), Hooke assumed, as Descartes had done, that the velocity in the second medium is greater than in the first, and that therefore the wave-surface is oblique to the direction of the ray (as in Fig. 125). If sunlight falls obliquely on a water surface after passage through a small aperture, the well-known coloured patch of light is formed (Fig. 126). According to Hooke, the extreme rays come from the extreme edges of the sun. For white light the wave-surface is perpendicular to the direction of propagation, while rays with oblique wave-surfaces could exhibit colour. The dark medium bordering on the part occupied by the light reduces the intensity of the wave motion ; for the blue rays (Fig. 126) the weakening affects the more advanced portion of the oblique wave, while for the red the rear portion is affected. He concluded " that blue is an expression on the retina of an oblique and confus'd pulse, of light whose weakest part precedes, and whose strongest follows. And that red is an impression on the retina of an oblique and confus'd pulse of light, whose strongest part precedes, and whose weakest follows." He postulated only two primary colours, red and blue, the others being produced by a mixture and dilution of these.

By means of such a theory, which did not require any great intellectual or experimental demands on its composer, Hooke considered himself able to explain the colours of thin laminæ. Thus the light reflected back from the front face of the thin plate was supposed to combine with the weakened component reflected from the back face, and the stronger and weaker wave-surfaces in general did not coincide. If the thickness of the plate was assumed to increase in a continuous manner, it followed on this theory, through the periodic variation of the distance apart of the wave-surfaces, that at one instant the stronger, at another the weaker, surface travelled in advance, which gave explanation of the colours.

The book " Micrographia " indicates Hooke to be one who experimented, made observations, and sought for explanations in all branches of science, but he could make no very great claim with respect to the quality of these explanations. The feature of his work, the hypothetical light-ray, undergoes a certain amount of variation in the different cases, apparently in some kind of correspondence with the varied type of phenomena under consideration, and even a certain amount of force is employed in some instances to bring it into action. With this he remains contented, and he hails his explanation as correct. In spite of this, he detected a few very important elements in the theory of the colours of thin plates.

What is termed " inflexion " by Hooke in " Micrographia " is not diffraction in Grimaldi's sense, but a curving of the paths of the light rays by variation of refractive index from place to place, or with time. In the same treatise he mentions astronomical refraction, the mirage, and twinkling of the stars, and endeavours to imitate these experimentally (p. 218). On 27th November, 1672, Hooke showed some experiments to the Royal Society which were really concerned with diffraction. Although he considered them original, these experiments were essentially an incomplete and inaccurate repetition, with a few variations, of Grimaldi's. Hooke pointed out that the diffraction appearances are the same whether they are produced by the sharp edge or by the back of a razor. He was inclined to the view that light has a tendency to spread out sideways in all directions in which it is not prevented from so doing by neighbouring light. A report dealing with these questions appears later in Hooke's " Posthumous Works " (1705), page 188.*

On 9th December, 1675, Newton presented to the Royal Society a short report on his experiments on the colours of thin laminæ, and a longer account of the same matter appears in his " Opticks " of 1705. We will confine our attention to the latter. When Newton, probably

* Cf. also Priestley, Vol. 1, p. 172.

in his experiment of Fig. 72, pressed together the hypotenuse faces of two prisms which were slightly convex, he noticed a small patch on these faces which appeared completely transparent even when light was totally reflected from the rest of the surface, but which was black for reflected light, as if the glass presented no discontinuous surface to the light. When the prisms were turned so that the air layer allowed some light to pass, coloured rings appeared round the same patch. Under the circumstances, however, the phenomenon was very complicated, since the dispersion of the prism has an auxiliary effect. In order to investigate the matter in a less complicated manner, Newton placed on a double convex telescope objective a plano-convex lens with its plane side uppermost. The thickness of the air layer thus increased from the centre outwards, and on pressing the lenses together a system of coloured rings appeared which were concentric about the point of contact of the lenses. The latter appeared black when there was actual contact. With increase of pressure the coloured rings developed in the centre and moved outwards, while with a reduction of pressure they moved back again and vanished in the centre ; this showed that a particular colour corresponded to a particular thickness of the air gap. By means of this arrangement Newton acquired a complete insight into the whole phenomenon, and at the same time the possibility of determining the thickness of the air gap from the known radius of curvature of the glass.

The phenomenon was even simpler if the lenses were illuminated by a single spectral colour. In this case numerous bright and dark rings of the same colour were visible, the rings extending as far as the edges of the glass, whereas in the former case only eight or nine rings could be seen, the colours of these becoming more and more indistinct with distance from the centre, finally not being distinguishable from white. It was thus clear that, for a continuously increasing thickness of air gap, the rings alternated in succession from light to dark. If a continuous succession of the spectral colours from red to violet was projected on to the lenses, the rings could be seen to draw together and, with a reversed succession of colours, to spread apart. " And it was very pleasant to see them gradually swell or contract accordingly as the Colour of the light was changed."

The appearance of the rings with white light thus proved to be due to a superposition of innumerable monochromatic rings of unequal radius. The parts of the lens combination which indicated dark rings by reflected light showed bright rings by transmitted light and vice versa, so that the two phenomena would together produce a uniform illumination. The effects with white light were similarly related. Similar effects were to be observed with thin layers of mica and with soap bubbles, and the latter, if sufficiently thin, were found to produce quite dull, black patches which did not reflect any light ; in these often smaller, still darker patches were visible. Both indicated a faint reflection in very intense light (e.g. sunlight). If mica was used and its surfaces, especially the back ones, moistened, the colours were less brilliant, but their hue remained the same. The colour was thus seen to depend on the thickness and substance of the laminæ alone and not on the surrounding medium. If Newton's lens combination was viewed through a prism, the different coloured rings were seen displaced by unequal amounts, which produced a new appearance. When the dispersion had an appropriate value, numerous white segments of rings having varying extent could be seen which were produced by the superposition of the blue, red, and intermediate rings. A lamina for which, on account of its thickness, no rings are visible to the naked eye will show rings when viewed through a prism.

If Newton's lens combination is viewed obliquely instead of normally, the radii of the rings increase according to a law determined by Newton. He measured the radii of the rings by means of compasses, keeping the eye vertically above the centre of the rings on the horizontal lens. The radii of the darker rings increased outwards in the ratios $\sqrt{0}$, $\sqrt{2}$, $\sqrt{4}$, $\sqrt{6}$, while the bright rings formed the series $\sqrt{1}$, $\sqrt{3}$, $\sqrt{5}$, $\sqrt{7}$. From this it could be deduced that the respective air thicknesses formed the series 0, 2, 4, 6, and 1, 3, 5, 7. For these measurements a correction was applied for obliquity of the line of vision, and for the convexity of the surface of the upper lens. Such measurements could be made both for monochromatic and polychromatic rings.

From these observations Newton deduced a new confirmation of his view of the composition of white light from different and dissimilar constituents. In addition to the difference of colour and of refractive index, a new distinguishing factor was now evident, of which we shall speak more fully in a moment.

Under the circumstances, and owing to the order in which the results had presented themselves to Newton, it was natural that he should view the phenomenon as essentially a varying reflection of the light by the second surface of the lamina upon which the light was incident. He thus attributed to the light periodic " fits " of reflection and transmission. If reflection occurred at the thickness 1, it also happened at 3, 5, 7, 9 . . . , whereas the thicknesses 2, 4, 6, 8 . . . produced transmission. As is shown by counting the rings for monochromatic illumination, and as a result to be mentioned later indicates, several thousands of such changes or periodic variations of the " fits " can follow in succession. The effect must depend on both surfaces of the lamina, as well as their distance apart, for when one of the surfaces of a section of mica is moistened, the intensity of the colours is reduced. The alternate transmission and reflection must be actually *performed* at the second face, for if it were effected at the first, it could not be dependent on the second surface. Some kind of periodic disposition must be brought into play at the first surface and be propagated to the second (" Opticks," 1721, p. 254). " What kind of action or disposition this is ; whether it consists in a circulating or a vibrating motion of the Ray, or of the Medium, or something else, I do not here inquire. Those that are averse from assenting to any new Discoveries, but such as they can explain by an Hypothesis, may for the present suppose, that as Stones by falling upon Water put the Water into an undulating Motion, and all Bodies by percussion excite vibrations in the Air ; so the Rays of Light, by impinging on any refracting or reflecting Surface, excite vibrations in the refracting or reflecting Medium or Substance, and by exciting them agitate the solid parts of the refracting or reflecting Body, and by agitating them cause the Body to grow warm or hot ; that the vibrations thus excited are propagated in the refracting or reflecting Medium or Substance, much after the manner that vibrations are propagated in the Air for causing Sound, and move faster than the Rays so as to overtake them ; and that when any Ray is in that part of the vibration which conspires with its Motion, it easily breaks through a refracting Surface, but when it is in the contrary part of the vibration which impedes its Motion, it is easily reflected ; and, by consequence, that every Ray is successively disposed to be easily reflected, or easily transmitted, by every vibration which overtakes it.   But whether this Hypothesis be true or false I do not here consider.   I content myself with the bare Discovery, that the Rays of Light are by some cause or other alternately disposed to be reflected or refracted for many vicissitudes."

When light is incident on the surface of a substance, it must be partly reflected and partly transmitted. Newton assumed that the periodic " fits " were contained in the light as soon as it left the luminous body producing it, and that they followed at regular intervals. The method of determining the period of these fits, and the distance apart in space of similar states of the light, is evident from the following considerations. The fraction of the incident light which is reflected at the first surface of a lamina may, following Newton, be neglected. If a " fit " of the transmitted fraction arrives at the second face at the same time as the next following " fit " arrives at the first, i.e. after a complete period, the former is then transmitted by the second face, and the lamina consequently remains dark. If, however, the light arrives at the second face after a half period, it is reflected from the latter back to the first, at which, since another half period has elapsed, it is transmitted, so that the lamina appears bright. The thickness of air layer which corresponds to the first bright ring of a particular colour from the centre is thus the half period for this colour in air. By the same principle Newton could determine the periods in other media. When a liquid, e.g. water, was introduced into the space between the lenses, the rings of the same order were smaller. It was apparent that the corresponding thickness for a liquid was obtained by dividing the thickness for air by the refractive index for air-liquid. Thus for the case under consideration the thickness for water was three-quarters that for air.

This will suffice in order to understand Newton's ideas upon this subject, and it will not be necessary to enter into the complicated propositions which he had to deduce for cases in which his theory led him into difficulties. One consequence is obvious : *Newton's experiments were the first to give a clear demonstration of the relevance of the periodic nature of light, whereas in Hooke's theory it plays a doubtful rôle as if it had been introduced by accident.*

Only brief mention need be made here that Newton endeavoured to explain the colour of natural objects by means of the theory of thin plates by assuming the smallest divisions of matter to be transparent and of definite dimensions. Newton's idea can be advantageously demonstrated by means of a thin sheet of mica, of uniform thickness and colour, cut into small pieces which are then haphazardly mixed together. This theory, which has been taken up in modern times by Wrede, has not shown itself justifiable in any way. For instance, the colour of a substance is not, as it would be according to Newton's theory, complementary to the absorption colour, but in the general case is the same, and the spectra of the colours of different substances in no wise confirm this theory. Out of curiosity, it may be mentioned that Newton was not without object in testing his theory, for he thought it might be possible to distinguish the smallest divisions of matter if the microscope were sufficiently improved.*

An account of Newton's theory of reflection and refraction will be found on another page.

Newton describes in " Opticks " an original discovery of his of a colour effect obtained with a glass amalgam-backed concave mirror. Sunlight was allowed to impinge on the mirror through a small aperture in a card placed at its centre of curvature. Round the opening on the side of the card towards the mirror faint coloured rings, similar to the rings with Newton's lenses by transmitted light, were visible. Measurement indicated the same ratio of the radii, and illumination with different spectral colours gave effects similar to those with the lenses. If the amalgam was removed, the rings became still fainter. It was found that the first glass surface was essential to the production of the effect, for the latter persisted when a concave metal mirror was used. Newton's explanation, which he thought probable, was as follows : The light which passes through the glass surface is in the " fit " of transmission and is reflected by the amalgam surface, consequently in a fit of reflection, thus arriving back at the glass surface by a path of equal length, i.e. in the fit of transmission. Since this holds true for all colours, the centre of the rings is white. Every mirror also *scatters* light, which makes the surface of the mirror visible. Considering thus the light which is radiated back obliquely in all directions from a particular part of the amalgam, this, owing to its oblique path, arrives back at the glass surface in alternate fits of reflection and transmission, and thus forms rings on the screen. The objection that, for an unamalgamated mirror at least, a series of thicknesses of glass must exist for which a dark centre ought to be produced, which is not found in practice, was not alluded to by Newton. From these effects with thick plates Newton concluded, as a particular consequence, that the fits could follow one another in a regular manner over even greater distances in space. The remark at once seems obvious that, as in the case of Newton's lenses, with such a long path of the light only white light could emerge from the mirror, on account of so many coincident transmissions and reflections of the different monochromatic constituents. This was the criticism first presented by Young a century later. Newton also showed experimentally that the radii of the rings are inversely proportional to the square root of the glass thickness, If the incident beam is not central, the effect is deformed.

* Newton, " Opticks " (1721), p. 236.

A white circle then passes through the opening and its image, while joined to the circle on the inside and outside are various coloured rings. The principle of the explanation remains the same. Newton, however, makes the reader clearly understand that he does not consider his explanation infallible, for " it seemed to me " is the expression which he continually employs.

There was a close correspondence between Newton's experiments on diffraction and Grimaldi's, only Newton's method was much more refined and he devised a far greater variety of experiments. He showed that diffraction is not dependent on the presence of the atmosphere, for a hair gave the same diffraction fringes when interposed between two wet glass plates. Diffraction fringes, too, accompanied air bubbles in water or glass, and scratches and streaks in glass ; thus the substance of the medium was not essential to the phenomenon. Newton carried out the measurement of the fringe breadths on a screen placed obliquely in the path of the light, thereby greatly increasing the convenience and accuracy. Diffraction with transparent screens was demonstrated with a piece of faceted plane glass, which incidentally constitutes an interference prism, and thus produces more than the usual number of fringes. Using a cone of light of somewhat larger angle, which makes the diffraction fringes disappear, the large deflection of the light from a knife-edge could be demonstrated, as Hooke had already shown. A pair of intersecting knife-edges inclined at a small angle to one another was also used as the diffracting object, and the effect produced, a pattern consisting partly of hyperbolic fringes, was projected on a screen. Monochromatic illumination was utilized here also by the application of a prism, which indicated that the diffraction effects with white light consist of a superposition of the effects with different monochromatic illuminations, violet light forming the narrowest, and red the broadest, fringes. This investigation also is explicitly stated to be of an incomplete nature. Towards the conclusion of his " Opticks " Newton includes a few interrogations concerning problems worthy of investigation which had attracted his attention, but questions to which at the time he was not able to give a satisfactory answer, such as : Do not bodies act upon light at a distance ? Do not the rays which differ in refrangibility differ also in flexibility (i.e. susceptibility to diffraction) ? and so on. Strange to say, Newton completely ignored the inner fringes observed by Grimaldi ; he even explicitly asserted that diffraction only took place in an outward direction from the edge of the shadow-forming body, and all his diagrams give effect to this opinion.

The distinguishing features of Newton's attainments will be mentioned later, but such excerpts as these will suffice to give character to Newton as an investigator. His substitution of ready explanations of experimental results in place of arbitrary hypotheses, his wealth and genuineness of conjecture, the variety, fullness, dexterity, and accuracy of his experimental tests, and his disclosure of power to estimate the value of his data, all indicate him to be a pattern for all times in the realm of experimental research. Even if he did occasionally wander from the highway, the sharp separation between the substantiated fact and the theoretical conception made the way of return easy for his successors.

Huygens, Euler, and Hartley instituted the wave hypothesis of light, but this did not appreciably influence the study of the phenomena discovered by Newton. Not until the end of the eighteenth century did a scientist appear whose labours were worthy of special note in this direction. This was Thomas Young. Young had studied acoustics * and was conversant with the periodicity of sound waves, having often experimented with the alternate diminuendo and crescendo or tremolo effects in the phenomena of beats. Analogous effects in the realm of optics must also have considerably influenced his opinions.† He reviewed the whole subject of optics, re-examined certain considerations which had made Newton refrain from adopting the hypothesis of the wave theory, though this would have been but a very short step, and indicated the tremendous significance of such a conception. Young published several discourses on optics, of which the most important to us are those presented to the Royal Society on 12th November, 1801, 1st July, 1802, and 24th November, 1803. In the first of these publications he asserts that what is of fundamental importance is not the devising of feasible hypotheses, but the allocation of the various data under one comprehensive principle.‡ He quotes from numerous portions of Newton's writings to show how consistent these were with the hypothesis of the wave theory. Then some general laws concerning the wave theory are given, and the action at concurrence of waves having nearly the same direction are specially discussed. The colours of thin plates and of lined or scratched surfaces he explained by the concurrence of such waves. A table of wave-lengths for different colours deduced from Newton's measurements with his lenses is also included. The inconsistency in Newton's theory of the colour of thick plates is pointed out, and a better explanation, by a supposition of a difference in path of the directly reflected and scattered light from the mirror, is attempted.§ Young shows some amount of indecision with regard to diffraction, for at one time he traces it back to a reflection at the edges of the diffracting body, at another to a surrounding refractive ether atmosphere condensed about the surface of the body. The second publication ‖ contains evidence for assigning different wave-lengths to different colours, and shows that the same wave-lengths are deducible from the diffraction phenomena as from the colours of thin plates. The new ideas are illustrated by

---

* T. Young, " Lectures on Natural Philosophy," London (1807), Vol. 1. " On the Propagation of Sound," p. 367. " On the Sources and Effects of Sound," p. 378. " On Harmonics," p. 389. Waves in water and air are considered, and the nature of beats is explained.

† Young makes use of the phenomena of beats to give an analogy with the interference of light ; *loc. cit.*, Vol. 1, p. 464.

‡ Young, " On the Theory of Light and Colours," *Phil. Trans. Roy. Soc.*, 12th Nov., 1801 : " Lectures on Natural Philosophy," Vol. 2, p. 613.

§ Young, " On the Nature of Light and Colours," " Lectures on Natural Philosophy," Vol. 1, p. 471, and Vol. 2. p. 457.

‖ Young, " An Account of Some Cases of the Production of Colours," *Phil. Trans. Roy. Soc.*, 1st July, 1802 ; " Lectures on Natural Philosophy," Vol. 2, p. 633.

PLATE V

Léon Foucault

1819 - 1868

means of a newly-discovered fact concerning the colours of so-called " mixed plates." * The most noteworthy publication is the third.†
The interference principle is there discussed at length ‡ and it is stated that wherever fringes are produced these must be caused by the concurrence of two different light rays. In particular, the fringes within the shadow, as noticed by Grimaldi, are shown by means of an impressive experiment to be due to the concurrence of the light deflected by both sides of the shadow-forming body.§ For by screening off the light at one side of the diffracting body, these fringes disappear, and this can be shown to be not due to a general diminution of light intensity. This experiment would, as Brewster rightly notes, have been really unnecessary, if Young had considered that wide shadow-forming objects show *no* fringes in the shadow. Nevertheless, the result is an important one. The path difference at which maximum darkness occurred, Young found from Newton's diffraction experiments to be 0·0000127 inch, and, from his experiments with thin plates, 0·0000112 inch as the average.

The colour distribution in both cases is also so similar that it gives weight to the assumption of a common origin. Light must thus have opposite qualities recurring alternately in a regular periodic manner. Young was then able to show from the properties of Newton's rings in liquids, and so on, that light has a smaller velocity of propagation in the medium in which it is refracted towards the normal.‖ With regard to diffraction he inclines to the view that a limited portion of the light wave spreads out beyond the boundary of the diffracting medium with diminishing intensity. It is remarkable that Young was able to discern the influence of diffraction on the deformation of microscope images,¶ an effect which was later often misunderstood.

* Young, " Mixed Plates," " Lectures on Natural Philosophy," Vol. 2, p. 635 ; " Colours of Mixed Plates," *ibid.*, Vol. 1, p. 470.

† Young, " Experiments and Calculations relating to Physical Optics," *Phil. Trans. Roy. Soc.* (24th Nov., 1803) ; " Lectures on Natural Philosophy," Vol. 2, pp. 639, etc.

‡ *Ibid.*, p. 645. " From the experiments and calculations which have been premised, we may be allowed to infer, that homogeneous light, at certain equal distances in the direction of its motion, is possessed of opposite qualities, capable of neutralising or destroying each other, and of extinguishing the light, where they happen to be united ; that these qualities succeed each other alternately in successive concentric superficies, at distances which are constant for the same light, passing through the same medium. But, since we know that sound diverges in concentric superficies, and that musical sounds consist of opposite qualities, capable of neutralising each other, and succeeding at certain equal intervals, which are different according to the difference of the note, we are fully authorised to conclude that there must be some strong resemblance between the nature of sound and that of light."

§ *Ibid.*, pp. 640, etc. The outer and inner fringes are mentioned, the inner as being always less intense and white at the centre. The inner ones were observed to vanish when a screen was placed at one side of the opaque body. The wave-lengths determined from the different experiments agree.

‖ *Ibid.*, p. 635.

¶ *Ibid.*, p. 646. Young urges caution in the application of the microscope and in the interpretation of its images, and also of images formed by the eye. A small opaque object may appear bright in the middle and transmitted light may be decreased in intensity by diffracted light. (Illusion that transparent and semi-transparent objects are opaque or semi-opaque.)

Ritter and Wollaston had in the meantime discovered the non-luminous chemically active rays of light, and Young proceeded to determine the wave-lengths of these by means of the Newton lens combination. He illuminated the latter with the chemically active light and projected a real image of the rings on to a paper impregnated with silver nitrate, thus obtaining an actual impression of the rings after about one hour.*

The next appreciable advance in this direction was accomplished by Fresnel, the young engineer of road-construction, whose active interest in optics commenced in a solitary village.   With an incomplete knowledge of the wave theory, and with an insufficient acquaintance with optical literature, he commenced a study of diffraction and made measurements of these phenomena,† utilizing his

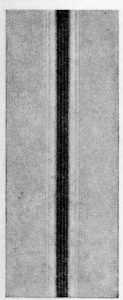

own ingenuity and getting the local locksmith to manufacture some imperfect apparatus. Genius and perseverance, and the friendly co-operation of Arago who helped him with advice and even experimented with him for a time, soon raised him to a position of mastery in this subject. The Paris Academy was soon able to confer on Fresnel the honour of numbering him amongst its fellows.

Fresnel's first steps led him to the same views as those already arrived at by Young, whose publications, however, were uninterpretable by Fresnel on account of the different language. Although Fresnel was rich in unique ideas, his forte and the chief trend of his labours lay in the correlation of principles into a consistent uniform system.

This short historical review will spare the reader much repetition, and a few details will now be considered. These indicate primarily how seldom the development of a branch of science is along logical and systematic lines.

FIG. 127.

The fringes (Fig. 127) discovered by Grimaldi can be very conveniently observed if sunlight from a heliostat is allowed to pass through a narrow vertical slit on to a wire arranged accurately parallel to it, and the shadow is intercepted on a white screen.   A piece of ground glass is suitable for less intense illuminations, this being viewed from behind, looking towards the diffracting body. If the upper half of such a screen is composed of red ground glass, and the lower of blue, the two parts being separated by a sharp horizontal line, it is at once apparent that the red fringes are much farther apart than the blue. The fringes are visible even if the illumination is only obtained from

* The Newton rings projected on to silver nitrate paper, using the Ritter and Wollaston ultra-violet illumination, are smaller than the corresponding ones for the visible violet.
† A. Fresnel, " Œuvres complètes," Paris (1868), Vol. 1, p. 6.

daylight entering through a slit in a window shutter; the fringes are formed on the surface of a lens functioning as screen, and the eye is placed at the position of the image of the slit formed by the lens, where the fringes will show up brightly on the surface of the lens. If monochromatic light enters through the slit, the fringes are naturally light (of a single colour) or dark, and contract when the illumination is made to change gradually from red to violet. This behaviour can also be observed if the above-mentioned lens, upon which the vertical fringes are projected, is covered by a screen with a horizontal slit which intercepts all except a short length of the vertical fringes. Looking at this slit through a prism with vertical dispersion (preferably a direct-vision prism), a spectrum (Fig. 128) is seen containing dark fringes which converge towards the violet end. These are the portions of the monochromatic fringes and the nearer they are to the more refrangible end of the spectrum, the closer together they appear. This description serves to indicate how all the elements of the theory of interference can be worked out directly from simple experiments of this nature.

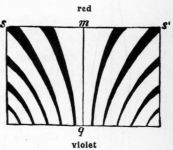

red

s   m   s'

q

violet

FIG. 128.

The facts discovered by Grimaldi were alone quite sufficient to form a conception of the mutual reaction of the light rays, but this was only disclosed by Young and Fresnel a century and a half later. In dealing with the colours of thin plates, Newton had accepted his ideas of "fits" in a far too matter-of-fact manner. The supposition of a *mutual reaction* of light rays had not seriously occurred to him and he even *explicitly refutes* such an idea when his dispersion experiments would have given him the opportunity of considering it. Had he not fatefully overlooked the inner fringes noticed by Grimaldi, they would have set him on the right track. Whereas Newton considered the light reflected from the back surface of the plate as the effective element in interference, Hooke assumed the light from both surfaces effective, but the latter's ideas give rise to a caricature of the interference principle, for they are not developed from the nature of the data obtained, but dragged in from the outside. Neither Newton nor Hooke was able to give evidence as to the correctness of their conceptions (for light reflected from the front face can only be screened off together with light coming from the back surface). In the cases investigated by Young and Fresnel, however, both rays of light are propagated symmetrically and independently of one another, and the necessity of both rays functioning in order to produce the characteristic effects can be proved, it being also obvious that both are equally efficient in action. Young also illuminated *two* small apertures in close proximity by light from a *single* opening in a window shutter and thus produced an effect analogous to one of Grimaldi's with more intense illumination. Fresnel, however, replaced the two small round apertures by two narrow vertical slits, which effected a great improvement. Young, also, did not at the outset chance to devise the crucial test for the nature of interference, but guessed the principle of it from incomplete premises and from certain similarities in the behaviour of light and sound.

Young effected the removal of the light from one side of the object by means of an opaque screen * which he brought up in front or behind the diffracting body at one side. Arago happened to replace the screen by a glass plate and to his surprise the interference effects were likewise made to disappear. Fresnel explained this result by the shortening of the light waves and retardation in the glass, i.e. by the large path difference of the two rays and the attendant loss in visibility of the interference effects. He also conceived that very thin pieces of glass or mica interposed on one side would cause a displacement of the fringes in one direction only, without making them invisible, and proved this assumption correct by direct experiment.† From these results Fresnel and Arago devised their interferential refractometer ‡ to be described below.

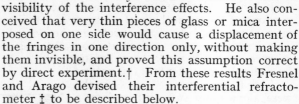

FIG. 129.

Let S (Fig. 129) represent the slit in the window shutter, AB the object producing the shadow, $\Sigma\Sigma$ the screen, and SM the plane of symmetry of the whole arrangement. If it is assumed, with Young, and Fresnel in the first instance also, that the light which penetrates the shadow has the edge of the object for its origin only, it follows immediately that the rays from A and B arrive at M by equal paths and thus reinforce one another. At P, however, the rays have the path difference BP—AP which is easily calculable from the dimensions of the arrangement. If the point P is moved continuously away from M, still remaining in the shadow, however, the path difference also increases continuously and at the same time, if homogeneous light is employed, an alternation of light and darkness is produced, which gives evidence of the periodic nature of light. If P is chosen at such a distance from M that it is at the first maximum of darkness, then BP — AP $= \lambda/2$, the length of a half period. In this way Young and Fresnel introduced a conception of the magnitude of the periods (wave-lengths) and found values which corresponded with those calculable from Newton's measurements with his lenses. For example it was found that for red light $\lambda = 0.0000005176$ metre.§

It is thus evident once and for all that two light rays proceeding from the same source and displaced or deflected inwards towards one another alternately reinforce and annul one another, so that Newton's

* Young, " Lectures on Natural Philosophy," Vol. 2, p. 640.
† A. Fresnel, " Œuvres complètes," Vol. 1, p. 75.
‡ *Ibid.*, p. 124.   § *Ibid.*, p. 18.

explanation of his rings could no longer hold. In reality, Young and Fresnel thought no more of " fits," but of the path difference of the beams of light reflected from both faces and of their interference.

If the distance between two successive " fits " for a particular colour is denoted by R, then according to Newton the lens combination shows, for reflected light at perpendicular incidence, darkness at those places for which the thickness is O, R, 3R, 5R . . . , and brightness for $\frac{R}{2}, \frac{3R}{2}, \frac{5R}{2}, \frac{7R}{2}$ . . . . According to the Fresnel-Young conception on the other hand, if L denotes the wave-length, the path difference for positions of darkness is $\frac{L}{2}, \frac{3L}{2}, \frac{5L}{2}, \frac{7L}{2}$ . . . , for brightness O, L, 2L, 3L, 4L. . . . A direct correlation of the two ideas, however, involves the difficulty that for the thickness zero, i.e. the point of contact of the lenses, there is a dark spot exactly where one would expect a zero path difference and consequently complete reinforcement. To explain this, Young took an acoustical analogy, that two reflections,

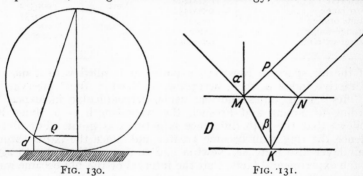

FIG. 130.   FIG. 131.

one from a rarer and the other from a denser medium, produce a phase difference of half a period between the two rays. This he found to be confirmed by experiment.* When he chose two lenses of different kinds of glass, crown and flint, and introduced oil of sassafras between them, so that both reflections took place from an optically denser medium, the phase difference was eliminated and the centre of the rings was white. Fresnel also noticed this difficulty and assumed a phase difference between the two rays, but did not provide an explanation at this stage of the investigation. Such an assumption does actually remove the difficulty ; the first dark spot corresponds to actual contact, the second is at a position where to the constant phase difference $\frac{L}{2}$ the path difference L is added, or where the light passes forward and backward over an air gap of thickness D = L/2. The successive positions of darkness correspond to the thicknesses $D = \frac{L}{2}, \frac{2L}{2}, \frac{3L}{2}$, etc. ; the positions of brightness to $D = \frac{L}{4}, \frac{3L}{4}, \frac{5L}{4},$

* Young, " Lectures on Natural Philosophy," Vol. 2, p. 636. Phase difference.

etc. For the position of the first bright ring of a particular colour we have the equation $D = L/4 = R/2$. Thus, according to Fresnel, on multiplying the air thickness calculated by Newton for the first bright ring of a particular colour by the factor 4, the wave-length is obtained.

The thicknesses of the air layer can be calculated from the radii of the rings by means of the formula $d = \rho^2/2R$, where d is the thickness, ρ the radius of the ring, and R the radius of curvature of the convex surface which rests on the plane surface (Fig. 130).

Fresnel gives the following table : —*

Limites des couleurs principales.	Valeurs extrêmes de d. mm.	Couleurs principales.	Valeurs moyennes de d. mm.
Violet extrême . .	0·000406	Violet	0·000423
Violet-indigo . . .	8·000439	Indigo	0·000449
Indigo-bleu . . .	0·000459	Bleu	0·000475
Bleu-vert . . .	0·000492	Vert	0·000512
Vert-jaune . . .	0·000532	Jaune	0·000551
Jaune-orangé . . .	0·000571	Orange	0·000583
Orangé-rouge . . .	0·000596	Rouge	0·000620
Rouge extrême . .	0·000645		

If the air space in Newton's experiment is filled with a medium of refractive index μ, then, according to Newton, the "interval" of the "fits" is μ times shorter, using perpendicular incidence, or, according to Young and Fresnel, the wave-length is μ times less. It follows that the path difference is μ times as great. For oblique incidence the ring radii become greater and, since the paths through the air layer also increase, Newton had to assume, in order to agree with the experimental facts, that the interval of the fits became much

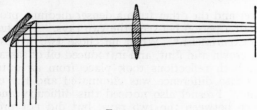

FIG. 132.

greater in proportion. Fresnel gives a much simpler explanation. If D is the thickness of the plate (Fig. 131), μ its refractive index, α the external angle between the incident ray and the normal, and β the corresponding internal angle, then the path difference is seen to be

$$\mu(MK + KN) - MP$$

$$= \frac{\mu \cdot 2D}{\cos \beta} - 2D \cdot \tan \beta \cdot \sin \alpha$$

$$= 2\mu D \cdot \cos \beta.$$

* Fresnel, " Œuvres complètes," Vol. 2, p. 24.

The classical Newtonian experiment is best demonstrated in the following form (Fig. 132). A real image of the effects produced by illuminating the Newton system by sunlight is formed by means of a lens on a screen. For this purpose a ground glass screen is very useful. If the red and blue screen is used and the line of separation is made to pass through the centre of the rings, not only many more rings can be seen than with white light, but it is observable that the radii of the red rings are respectively appreciably greater than those of the blue. Illumination with various spectral colours is best performed by means of the totally reflecting prism of p. 91. The Newton system, the projecting lens, and the screen are left undisturbed while the spectrum is displaced, and any parallax thus obviated.

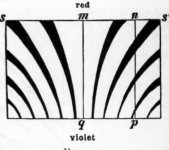

FIG. 133.

The effects which are seen in succession in the last experiment, namely that the rings contract in the violet, can be seen simultaneously in the following. The image of the Newton system illuminated by white light is projected on to a lens provided with a slotted screen so that the mid-point lies in the slit, and the effects are viewed through a small direct-vision prism (with dispersion direction perpendicular to the length of the slit SS'), the eye being placed at the focus of the latter lens. A spectrum mq (Fig. 133) is seen. This spectrum is obviously produced by the setting end to end through variable refrangibility of the portions of rings of different radii which are visible through the slit, and the figure can be considered as representing a spectral resolution of the interference effects. The light from a region n of the Newton system indicates, where spectrally resolved (np), a greater number of dark fringes the greater the distance of the region from the centre of the rings, i.e. the greater the path difference. An illumination which in-

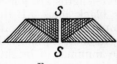

FIG. 134.

dicates when thus resolved very many equally distributed dark fringes, that is a spectrum in which each colour is present in approximately physiologically equal proportions, cannot be distinguished from *white*. For this reason no colours are visible at the edges of the Newton system, which is true in general for any interference effect at large path difference with white light. It is quite obvious from this experiment that the interference effect with white light merely consists of a superposition of the separate monochromatic effects.

If a prism of small refracting angle is placed behind the lens which is used to project Newton's rings on a screen, the effects observed by Newton, as recounted on p. 139, can be reproduced objectively. For a subjective inspection of the effects, a direct-vision prism, like that shown in Fig. 134, is to be recommended. This should be cut in halves along SS and the two parts made rotatable with respect to each other. If D be the complete dispersion of the prisms, dispersions varying from o to D can thus be produced. With this arrangement the Newton so-called " achromatized " ring segments can be seen as remote from the centre as one pleases. This prism will be utilized again in the sequel. In all these objective reproductions the effects are most distinct if the upper lens of the Newton combination is some-what wedge-shaped. Then the beams of light reflected from the front lens face and those which suffer a single, double, or treble passage through the air gap are all separated, and each can be brought separately to an image by a lens. In the first case the light reflected from the first surface produces of course no rings, but the rings are very brilliant in the second case, since the superficially reflected light is no longer superposed. In the third case two ring systems are visible, in the fourth, three, and so on.

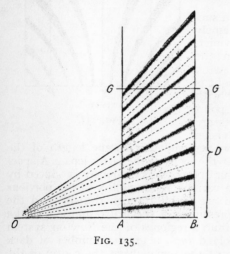

FIG. 135.

Newton gives a construction by which the colour effects in thin plates can be illustrated in a clear and simple manner. Its essentials are the following. Along a line OAB (Fig. 135), a portion AB is marked off such that OA and OB are proportional to the extreme violet and red wave-lengths respectively. The spectral colour which corresponds to each particular abscissa is then imagined to occupy the position of the perpendicular at its extremity. In the perpendicular at B lengths corresponding to 1, 2, 3, 4, 5 . . . half wave-lengths for red light are marked off and the points corresponding to numbers of half wave-lengths are joined to O by dotted lines and the others by heavy black lines. If the straight line GG parallel to AB is moved in an upward direction, its distance from AB represents the path difference, its intersection with dotted lines the maxima, and with black lines the minima, of brightness in the spectrum. As the path difference is increased, the dark fringes enter at the violet end of the spectrum and move across to the red, the number of bands continually increasing as the path difference becomes greater. It is obvious that the construction exactly corresponds to the experiment of Fig. 133. If the figure is drawn on a large scale and the shading of the heavy black lines made to fall off gradually, the dotted lines appear in a white region ; a spectrum projected between AB then indicates when purified subjectively by a second prism the colours of the Newton rings, those in the positions near AB being more saturated and those in the higher positions fainter.

In accordance with his point of view, Newton naturally makes

use of the intervals of the fits and also the thicknesses of air
layers, and introduces his untenable analogy between colour and the
pitch of sound ; for the construction the ratios of the lengths of a
stretched string are also introduced. He assumes, moreover, that in
the passage from one medium to another, all wave-lengths are changed
in the same ratio, which we now know to be inaccurate. The figure,
in order to be exact, must be specially constructed for each medium,
for in order that Fig. 135 should refer to another medium, the elements
of AB have to be respectively lengthened or shortened in order that
the lines through O shall remain straight. In reality the fringes of
Fig. 135 should not be strictly linear, but convex towards the line of
symmetry, since the prismatic deviation is not a linear function of the
wave-length. If a diffraction grating is employed in place of a prism,
the fringes will be accurately linear.

It is usually some singular and striking result, accidentally revealed, that attracts attention to a new aspect or property of nature.
In endeavouring to unravel the phenomenon, that is to find out the
conditions underlying its appearance,
knowledge is acquired of a whole host
of data of a similar character, and their
nature is at the same time independently established. Thus the fringes
discovered by Grimaldi, the colours of
soap bubbles, and the fringes and colours in mica noticed by Hooke, were
revealed by accident. The intentional
study of the conditions underlying
their production began with Hooke's
cleavage and compression experiments,
Newton's lens and plate combination,
and the Fresnel - Young diffraction
experiments. Young evolved a prac-

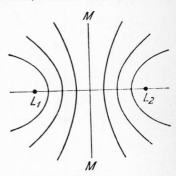

FIG. 136.

tically complete theory of the conditions for interference ; according
to his results it is essential to split up light from the *same* source into
two different beams of approximately identical direction. The path
of one or both beams can involve diffraction at the edge of an object,
reflection, or refraction. Such a view enabled, for example, a quite
original interference experiment to be invented. Thus homogeneous
light was allowed to pass through a small opening on to two neighbouring
openings or slits in a screen, and the concurrence of the diffracted
light was observed on a second screen.* When Fresnel † recognized
the interference principle from experiments involving diffraction, he
was not perfectly clear as to the nature of diffraction. It therefore
appeared to him desirable to investigate the interference principle for
a case which was free from the effects of diffraction. This led him to
devise his famous mirror experiment.

Consider two identical point sources L_1, L_2 (Fig. 136) radiating

* Young, " Lectures on Natural Philosophy," Vol. 1, p. 464.
† Fresnel, " Œuvres complètes," Vol. 1, pp. 23, 95.

light in all directions.   Points of zero path difference all lie along the plane of symmetry MM, and in general the surfaces of equal path difference consist of hyperboloids of revolution about their common axis L_1L_2.   Points exterior to L_1, L_2 in L_1L_2 produced have all the same (greatest) path difference, and thus belong to a limiting case of hyperboloid.   The intersections of the surfaces of equal path difference with a plane screen S, that is the interference fringes, may each assume every possible type of conic section according to the relative positions of S and L_1L_2 : hyperbolas, parabolas, ellipses, and, for S placed perpendicular to L_1L_2, also circles.   Except at the intersection of M with S, they are never perfectly linear, although short portions in the neighbourhood of M may appear so.

What is most interesting to us is the breadth of the interference fringes on a screen (Fig. 137) placed perpendicular to M in the neigh-

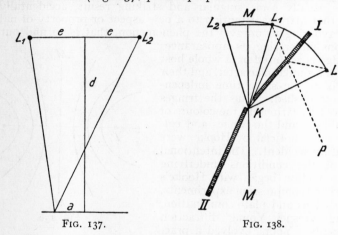

FIG. 137.   FIG. 138.

bourhood of M and at a distance d from the point of symmetry of L_1, L_2 which is very large compared with L_1L_2.   Considering a point distant a from M, the path difference is given by

$$\sqrt{d^2 + (e + a)^2} - \sqrt{d^2 + (e - a)^2} = \frac{2ae}{d}.$$

To one fringe breadth there corresponds a path difference of one wave-length ; thus $2ae/d = L$ and $a = Ld/2e$.   If L is only a ten-thousandth of a millimetre, as in the case of light, d must be considerable and e small, in order that a may not be microscopically small.

These few general remarks will render Fresnel's discussion of the mirror experiment intelligible.   A light source L (Fig. 138) is arranged in front of two plane mirrors inclined at an angle.   The plane of reference is assumed to be perpendicular to the mirrors and to pass through L.   If the ray LK is swung round behind the mirror I to L_1K so that it is inclined at the same angle behind it as in front, L_1 is the mirror image of L in I, and L_2 is similarly situated with respect to the mirror II.   L, L_1, L_2 thus lie on a circle with mid-point in K.

The light path from the source L via the mirror to an arbitrary point P is evidently equal to that from its image to the same point P. The mirror can thus be left completely out of consideration and the images L_1, L_2 considered as if actually sources of radiation. From the previous paragraphs the plane of symmetry M of L_1L_2 obviously passes through the line of intersection K of both mirrors.

Similarly to Young,* Fresnel stipulates as a primary condition for visibility of the fringes that both beams of light must have the same origin. This condition was inherently fulfilled in the experiments of Grimaldi, Hooke, and Newton which were found by accident to give interference effects. Young only briefly mentions the condition, without stating the reason for concluding it to be such. He may possibly have at one time placed a different source of illumination behind each of the two slits and found negative results, or the conclusion might also have been reached merely by a consideration of the results of his acoustical experiments. Thus two tuning-forks of the same arbitrary pitch may be made to give interference, in which case we are merely concerned with quite regular trains of waves, these being, broadly speaking, analogous in constitution to that of light. It is not to be expected that the phases of each of the coloured components of a beam of light are related to one another in exactly the same way in every beam of light, which fact is of itself sufficient to make the interference effect imperceptible. Fresnel, although he gives a lengthy discussion of his conception of the condition for interference, does not mention what led him to his conclusions.† A luminous point source may send out a regular train of waves consisting of many millions of waves. Since, however, in the case of a flame one luminous particle is continually being replaced by another, quite appreciable irregularities must appear in the wave-trains, which will bear no simple relation to one another for two different light sources. The best acoustical illustration of this is given by a swarm of bees, whose individuals are constantly changing, but in such a manner that the beats of the wings of those leaving the swarm are not in phase with those of the bees entering it. The trains of sound waves from two such swarms could not be brought to give audible interference, but those from the same swarm are capable of interfering since the same change of phase occurs *simultaneously* in each wave-train proceeding from the swarm. Another illustration of the flame is the volcano, which gives out successions of rapidly damped sounds. The

---

* Young, " Lectures on Natural Philosophy," Vol. 1, p. 464. " In order that the effects of two portions of light may be thus combined, it is necessary that they be derived from the same origin, and that they arrive at the same point by different paths, in directions not much deviating from each other."

† Fresnel, " Œuvres complètes," Vol. 1, p. 94. " Nœuds dilaté nœuds condensés car sil n'y a aucune dependance entre les centres de vibration, l'instant du depart d'un système d'ondes ne sera pas lié a l'instant du depart d'ondes voisines, puisque la cause quelconque que les engendre n'opère pas des changements simultanés dans les deux points lumineux ; dès lors les lignes d'accord et de discordance varieront de place continuellement et l'œil n'aura plus que la sensation d'une lumière uniforme ; c'est ce qui a sans doute empêché pendant si longtemps de reconnaître l'influence que les rayons lumineux exercent les unes sur les autres."

property of the flame holds also in the case of luminous solid bodies, for small temperature variations of the glowing particles which constitute the body involve small irregular variations in the amplitude of vibration, in the manner of beats, and are thus incompatible with absolute homogeneity and constancy of phase. So much for analogies. If the light from two different monochromatic sources of identical colour are brought together, say symmetrically, for interference, they would be in the same phase at the first instant, for example, and thus produce maximum brightness in the plane of symmetry, but a moment later darkness could be produced on account of a change of phase in the light from one source. For this reason the interference system would oscillate quickly to and fro, and consequently be invisible to the eye. What has been mentioned with regard to two different light sources naturally holds true for different points of the same

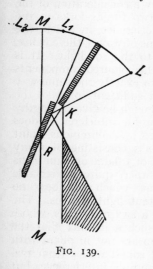

FIG. 139.

source and for light from a particular point of it which is emitted at essentially different instants. Such, if not illustrated by means of the same examples, is essentially the point of view of Fresnel. He had no particular name for the behaviour of light proceeding from two distinct sources; later two such beams were termed *incoherent*. As this term is a convenient and appropriate one, it will be used in the sequel.

Light from the same source must thus be made to fall on both mirrors for the interference to be visible, and this holds similarly for any interference experiment.

The second condition for experimental success is that the two images L_1, L_2 must be sufficiently close together since otherwise the fringes will be too narrow to be visible. The mirrors must, therefore, be inclined to one another at an angle not sensibly different from 180°. The formula $a = Ld/2e$, used in conjunction with the table on page 150, affords the desired information as to the permissible ratios of e to d.

The third condition stipulates a *small* path difference. This is especially important in the case of white light, for which the interference effects become invisible for path differences greater than about 10 wave-lengths, and the same is true approximately for coloured light if the latter is not almost homogeneous. In order that this condition may be fulfilled, one mirror must not be in advance of the other at their line of contact by more than about 1/100 mm. This is evident from Fig. 139. The mirrors are contiguous at K, but the geometrical line of intersection is at R, through which point the plane of symmetry of L_1, L_2, that is, the plane of zero path difference, passes. The two superposed beams of reflected light, however, leave the point K, and for points at which the path of difference is sufficiently small to give visible interference there is no concurrent light at all.

The fourth condition is that the light source must be of limited extent. It is obvious that two adjacent points of the same source give out light which is incoherent, and the pair of images of each of these points forms a separate system of interference fringes which is independent of the other. Since, however, the corresponding colours do not in general coincide, this causes an obliteration of the effects. If in Fig. 138 L describes a short distance to the right, L_1 and L_2 move correspondingly to the left, and the plane of symmetry M swings to the right about the edge K and carries the whole system of fringes with it. If it be imagined that during such a displacement L_1 and L_2 leave a luminous track behind them, this corresponds to a broadening or enlargement of the light source, and the obliterating effect on the interference fringes is illustrated. For L a slit which receives light from another distant slit may be used. In this case the first slit may be much broader without obliterating the fringes, since now the adjacent points of this slit produce coherent light which gives visible interference.

Bearing in mind the number of conditions which have to be fulfilled if Fresnel's experiment is to be successful, it can hardly be said that it prospered by mere accident, but rather through an accurate quantitative knowledge of the essential conditions, which was largely due to the preliminary labours of Newton, and to his exact measurement in particular.

The technique of Fresnel's experiment was in the first place very simple, sunlight being admitted through a pinhole in tin foil on a window shutter. Following Arago's advice, Fresnel afterwards used as light source the focal image formed by a small microscope lens placed in the window shutter, which produced a cone of greater angle and replaced the heliostat. A drop of honey in a hole in a metal plate was also utilized. He intercepted the fringes on a piece of ground glass and observed them through a magnifying glass, but having once accidentally looked round the edge of the ground glass, he found that this was really unnecessary,* for the fringes were so bright and distinct without the ground glass that he could use a star as the light source and measure the fringes it formed. Fresnel overcame the effects of double images by blackening the back face of the plane glass used as mirrors ; nowadays, however, obsidian glass is more conveniently used. On the other hand Arago chose to use platinum mirrors, which produced very bright images.† These were fixed by blobs of wax to a block of wood and by pressure could be arranged so as to be inclined at an angle a little less than 180°. By running the finger down the adjacent edges it could be seen whether or not one mirror was in advance of the other.‡ The fringes were then sought for in the brighter portion of the field produced by superposition of the beams from both mirrors and observed through the magnifying lens. These always ran perpendicular to the line joining the two mirror-images and could thus be easily distinguished from diffraction fringes which were parallel

---

* Fresnel, " Œuvres complètes," Vol. 1, p. 62.
† *Ibid.*, pp. 150, 183.   ‡ *Ibid.* p. 289.

to the edges of the mirrors. Monochromatic illumination by means of a prism was also employed by Fresnel, but he also adopted a suggestion of Arago and utilized deep red glass from church windows which transmitted nearly monochromatic light. In these cases the effects were very simple, the fringes consisting merely of bright and dark bands, and a comparison between the field containing the interference fringes and the side field formed by light from *one* mirror alone, served to show that the dark fringes were not merely dark in contrast to the bright ones, but were also darker than the side field. The field containing the fringes appeared of uniform brightness immediately one mirror was covered, which shows that by superposing more light an actual destruction of luminosity may be effected.

The most important experiments can be carried out merely with small point sources, and some of the most instructive ones admit of point sources and no others. Fig. 140 represents two Fresnel mirrors, the middle portion being supposed more distant from the reader than

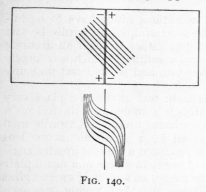

FIG. 140.

the outside ends, and the signs + and − indicate that the part in question is respectively in front of or behind the corresponding portion of the other mirror. On looking at two mirrors so arranged, the image of the source in the right-hand mirror is higher than that in the left-hand one. Through a magnifying lens interference fringes are seen in the superposed fields of light at the part where the mirrors most nearly touch, crossing the junction of the mirrors obliquely in a direction perpendicular to the line joining the two images. With the mirrors as shown in Fig. 140, the fringes are curved at their ends where they leave the superposed fields, and bend round asymptotically to the line of contact of the mirrors ; they are only straight in the case when they run parallel to the line of contact, that is, when the mirrors are in exact contact over the whole of their edges. This is evident from the following considerations. The two mirrors may be conceived as openings through which the light emerges, and from the two mirror-images of different height two long threads of equal length may be assumed to be pulled out through the openings. If now the ends of these threads are taken and made to describe paths of equal path difference, the end of one thread being held against a point of the other and both pulled taut, the initial motion will be perpendicular to the line joining the images, but as they are moved upwards, for example, the right-hand thread will catch on the line of separation of the mirrors and consequently be bent, so that the direction of motion will swing round to that of the line of separation. Similarly, if the threads are moved downwards, the left-hand one will be bent and a similar result be produced. The physical equivalent of this is that the ray from one of the images can arrive in the field of view only by being diffracted, or be brought to interfere only by passing over an indirect path. Fresnel's experiment is susceptible of modification in that the mirrors may be turned so that the central line of contact is nearer the observer than the outsides. In this case, instead of a brighter superposition field, there is a dark portion in shadow, into which the light can only arrive by diffraction, and exactly similar oblique and curved fringes are visible as in the above case, these differing only from the so-called Grimaldi fringes in their greater complexity.

A point source of light does not give effects intense enough for projection purposes. Arago thus suggested using light emerging from a cylindrical lens as light source, but also mentioned that the latter must be exactly parallel to the line of intersection of the mirrors. The reason for this is obvious. Referring to Fig. 141, the light which comes from different points a, b of the line formed by the cylindrical lens is incoherent, and the two lines formed by the mirrors are ab and a_1b_1 in which a_1 is not opposite a and b_1 not opposite b, etc. The light from corresponding points, for example aa_1 and bb_1, is coherent and forms a special set of fringes of its own. M and M' represent the central fringes of the extreme sets of such fringes, and it can be seen that the latter will obliterate each other. This can be illustrated by the following device. The slit SS is arranged oblique to the line of intersection of the mirrors, and over it is laid a blackened glass plate provided with two diagonal transparent slots ps and ng. If the plate is moved across the slit, two sets of interference fringes are seen which move relatively to one another. They

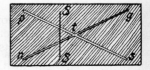

FIG. 141.

coincide only when t is opposite the slit, or when SS is parallel to the line of intersection of the mirrors.

The most perfect results are always obtained if sunlight is allowed to impinge directly on the mirrors after passage through a sufficiently narrow slit arranged exactly parallel to the intersection of the mirrors, and the fringes allowed to fall on a screen placed a long distance away. With these fringes all those experiments which have been either described or mentioned on pages 139, 146 and 151 with reference to Newton's system and the Grimaldi fringes may be repeated.

To reproduce the effects subjectively it is sufficient to admit daylight through a very narrow slit arranged exactly parallel to the mirror intersection and allow it to fall on the mirrors, the fringes being sought for with a magnifying lens. This method is to be recommended when it is afterwards intended to admit sunlight to form a projection of the fringes without shifting the mirrors.

Since it requires a little practice to find the Fresnel interference fringes, it may be useful to append a few directions as to the method of procedure.

Fresnel * himself invented a mechanical device to provide a convenient adjustment for the mirrors, of which there are numerous minor modifications in use at the present day. The usual arrangement is to provide one of the mirrors with three screws, *a*, *b*, *c* (Fig. 142), of which *a* serves to vary the angle of inclination of the mirrors, *b* and *c* to adjust the edges of the mirrors to coincidence. The mirrors are adjusted until they lie in the same plane and the adjustable one is inclined until the two images are slightly separated, the coincidence of the edges being checked by running a finger along them. The apparatus is now placed in front of the slit and the line of intersection adjusted to appear parallel to it. On narrowing the slit sufficiently, faint indications of fringes are usually seen with the aid of a magnifying lens, and these have now to be brought to the maximum visibility. They usually appear in the field which borders on the superposition field and are consequently very narrow on account of the auxiliary effect of diffraction. If the fringes appear at the left-hand side, this is an indication that the edge of the right-hand mirror is in advance of the other, and the screw *b* is used to adjust the edge and bring the fringes into the centre. Since, however, this introduces a slight obliquity of the edges of the mirrors, this tends to make the fringes invisible ; thus in practice both screws *b* and *c* are given alternate turns of small amounts in the same direction. When the fringes have been made central, a rotation of the screw *a* will give any desired breadth to the fringes. Occasionally, even when all the above directions are faithfully observed, no trace of any fringes appears. In this case the following method is always successful. A small screen having a short slit is placed in front of the magnifying lens so that the slit is perpendicular to the direction of the expected fringes and in the superposition field of the mirrors, which is plainly visible through the lens. On looking at the slit through a direct-vision prism, a spectrum is seen crossed by dark bands somewhat as in Fig. 143. If the bands are oriented in the manner indicated, obliquely downwards from left to right, the line of symmetry of the figure, that is, the zero path difference, is away to the right, outside the superposition field. To bring the interference fringes into the centre of the field, a few turns are given to the screws *b* and *c* which shift the fringes towards the violet. The criterion for this is that the fringes shall be vertical in the spectrum (perpendicular to the slit).

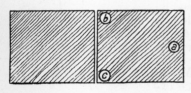

FIG. 142.

* Fresnel, " Œuvres complètes," Vol. 1, p. 186.

PLATE VI

AUGUSTIN FRESNEL.

If the experiments described above are performed with sunlight, it will be seen that a very narrow slit in the window shutter produces a quite broad diffraction image, since the sun functions as a very small light source. The mirrors also act as openings through which the light enters, and each edge of the mirrors also forms the external Grimaldi diffraction bands. The interference fringes i (Fig. 144) occur, if the mirrors are correctly adjusted, between the Grimaldi fringes g which are in turn inside the diffraction fringes b of the slit. Nothing is seen

red

violet

FIG. 143.

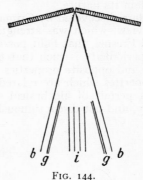

b g i g b

FIG. 144.

of the latter if daylight or an extended light source such as a bright sky is used. In this case, however, a special explanation is necessary to account for the production of visible interference fringes, for the light which arrives at the mirror I (Fig. 145) is from a whole region A of the sky, while that at the mirror II comes from a quite different region B. The visible fringes are only explicable if it is assumed that the slit is so very narrow that the light from *both* regions is spread out to so great an extent by diffraction that the effective portions of the mirrors receive approximately equal quantities of coherent light.

The narrowing of the slit functions in a similar manner when the sun is used as a light source. If the former subtends an angle of less than half a degree at the line of intersection of the mirrors, light arrives at each mirror from different points of the sun, which disadvantage is removed by the effect of diffraction on narrowing the slit.

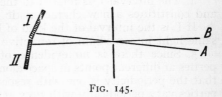

FIG. 145.

Acknowledging the necessity for the unity of the light source, that is, the coherence condition, it may be asked, how is it that these obtain in those cases where they are not obviously fulfilled ? Young's experiment with two slits does not require a special explanation. In the case of Newton's system, the explanation can be readily seen with the help of Fig. 146. When the eye accommodates itself on one point of the glass, it receives a cone of light from the glass to which correspond two incident cones which are coincident except for a negligibly small portion, at least so long as the thickness of the retarding layer is quite small. These cones consequently originate in the same group of luminous points.

If we review the logical development of our knowledge of the periodicity of light which has been the subject of this chapter, the results may be summarized as follows :—

1. The discovery of diffraction was due to Grimaldi, but his successors—Hooke, Newton, Young, and Fresnel at first—did not completely explain its nature.

2. The data discovered by Grimaldi, Hooke, and Newton gradually led to the view, which was strengthened by the labours of Newton, Young, and Fresnel, that light possesses a periodic nature.

3. The periodicity is such that the same properties recur at equal distances L and opposite properties at the intermediate distances L/2, that is, properties which are related like positive and negative quantities which permit of algebraical summation. The properties vary continuously, and not discontinuously, along the ray.

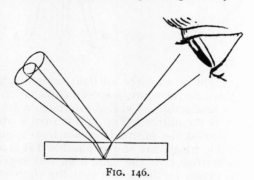

FIG. 146.

4. The interval L is related to the colour like the refractive index, and constitutes a new characteristic of the particular kind of light.

If L is the interval of the kind of light in air, then it is L/μ for the same light in a medium of refractive index μ with respect to air.

5. Since there is no evidence of permanent distinguishing properties at different points in space along a light ray, it must be assumed that the periodicity is one with respect to time, that is, that the properties vary periodically with time at the same point, and periodically in space at any one instant. The periodic time can be obtained from the spatial distance apart of the periodic properties and the velocity of propagation of light. Colour is independent of the medium and is determined by the periodic time. If the periodic time is assumed invariable in refraction, reflection, etc., the velocity of propagation in a medium of refractive index μ with respect to air is μ times smaller than in air.

6. It must be assumed that this periodicity in space and time is regular over long regions of the light ray, but experiences disturbances many million times a second.

It must be definitely remembered that this account contains nothing which is hypothetical, but the results are obtained directly, as Newton intended his results should be, from properties appearing in the course of experimental observation. Nevertheless it must also not be denied that the use of instructive hypotheses, suggested through similarity or analogy with other known phenomena, have contributed much to the discovery and establishment of these properties, which were to a certain extent conjectured in this way before they had been fully demonstrated.

CHAPTER IX

THE FURTHER DEVELOPMENT OF THE THEORY OF INTERFERENCE

WHEN the conditions necessary for interference had once been partially established by Young, and more fully determined by Fresnel, it was not difficult for their successors to devise a large number of new forms of experiment or to recognize and explain the various types of interference phenomena as they casually appeared. Interest also began to be taken in these experiments from a practical and technical standpoint. Arago * replaced the opaque screen used by Young by a glass plate D (Fig. 147) and, like Young, caused the inner Grimaldi fringes to vanish. Fresnel guessed the real cause of this disappearance at once and conceived that a sufficiently thin plate of glass or mica would merely shift the fringes laterally. For in a glass plate of refractive index μ (with respect to air), according to Newton the interval between two successive similar states (the wave-length) is reduced by a factor μ, and consequently over the light path to the right of the point of symmetry M there are more wavelengths than over the left-hand path. In order that the light shall arrive in identical phase at the point corresponding to the middle fringe, that is to zero path difference, the right-hand path must be shortened and the left-hand lengthened, or M must be shifted to a point such as P. If the glass thickness be d, the right-hand path to M is lengthened by $(\mu - 1)\,d/\lambda = q$ with respect to the other ; thus if a point q fringe breadths to the right of M is considered as representing zero path difference, the phenomena are identical with the former. It will be well to consider this fringe shift in some detail. By means of the above equation either of the four quantities μ, d, λ, q may be determined provided the three others are known. Fresnel and Arago realized the importance of this principle and took the trouble to use it to determine the differences in refractive index of hot and cold air and of dry and moist air. For this purpose the then known forms of interference experiments presented many difficulties.†

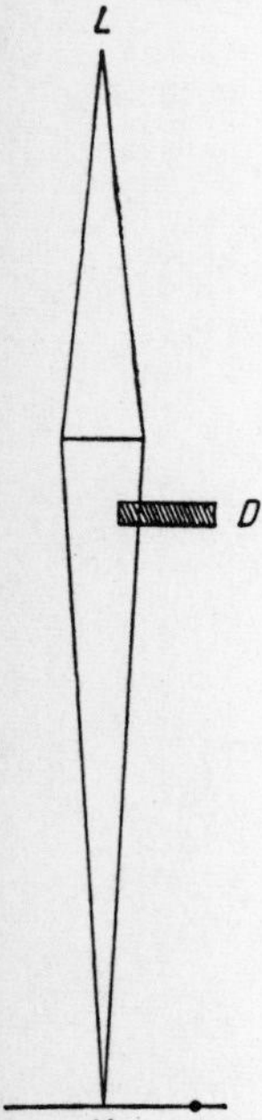

FIG. 147.

* *Ann. de Chim. et de phys.*, Ser. 2, Vol. I, pp. 199, 332 ; also, " Œuvres complètes d'Arago," Vol. I, p. 75.

† Arago, " Œuvres complètes," Vol. 10, pp. 298, 312 (Mem. scientif., I). " Memoire sur la methode des interférences appliquée a la recherche des indices de Réfraction ; " also Vol. 10, p. 718. Fresnel, " Œuvres complètes," Vols. 1, 2. Billet, " Traité d'optique physique," Paris (1858), Vol. 1, p. 160.

The arrangement of the apparatus is shown in Fig. 148. Light from the source L arrives at the telescope objective O through a slit in a screen S placed at its focus. The diaphragm S', however, allows only two *narrow parallel* beams of light σ, σ' to pass, which, after passage through two tubes closed at the ends by plane glass plates, fall on the objective O' of a second telescope. If the eyepiece of this telescope is adjusted so that the region where the two beams cross is in focus for an observer, a system of interference fringes can be seen. If one tube is now filled with dry air and the other with moist air, the fringe system experiences a lateral shift, and from its magnitude the difference of refractive index may be calculated. The conditions to be fulfilled are that both beams must consist of coherent light, and also be so far separated that they can pass one through each tube. This may only be realized by utilizing a narrow slit at S, in which case light spreads out over a part of O through diffraction, but with a sacrifice in intensity. Such an arrangement is particularly inefficient when the substances to be investigated are hot and cold air, in which case the tubes must necessarily be more widely separated. When considerable accuracy in the refractive index determination is required, a sufficiently large fringe shift must be employed, which involves the use of long tubes, but the employment of a large fringe shift again introduces fresh difficulties, in that the fringes are only distinct for small path differences. The eighth or ninth fringe is already scarcely visible on account of its feeble coloration, and a further shift makes the fringes disappear altogether from the field of view. To utilize large fringe shifts the principle of compensation was therefore introduced, that is, by interposing an object which produced a calculable fringe shift, the shift to be evaluated was exactly annulled and in this way determined.

The arrangement convenient for this purpose is shown in Fig. 149, and consists of four glass plates of equal thickness, symmetrical about a plane normal to the rays σ, σ' and through which the ray σ passes at a different angle from the ray σ'. From the angles, thickness, and refractive index, the path difference may be calculated. With such an arrangement the separation of σ and σ' and the fringe breadth remain constant. A detailed account, including diagrams, of the older form of apparatus and the compensation device is to be found in Arago's " Œuvres." Jamin later devised a much simpler and more convenient form of compensator. Supposing the rays σ, σ' to lie in a horizontal plane, two plane parallel glass plates of equal thickness

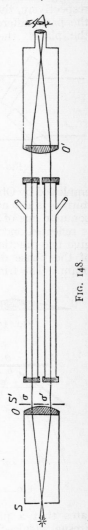

Fig. 148.

inclined at a small angle to one another may be imagined arranged in vertical planes so that the ray σ passes through one plate, and σ' through the other. If both plates are equally inclined to σ and σ' respectively, then the path difference is zero, and in any other position the path difference may be easily determined from the thickness of the plates, the refractive index, and the relative inclination. In

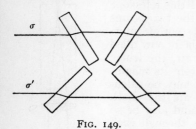

FIG. 149.

practice the plates are mounted on a goniometer, so that they may be rotated about a common axis parallel to their line of intersection.

Fresnel devised several other interference experiments. The *biprism* (Fig. 150) which produces the two optical images of the light source by refraction instead of by reflection, and is much easier to manipulate than the mirrors, was independently employed by Ohm * and by Fresnel.† Fresnel's experiment with three mirrors is also noteworthy.‡ Σ, S, S′ (Fig. 151) are three mirrors whose common line of intersection cuts the plane of the paper in O, and light is reflected once from the mirror Σ and twice from S and S′ so as to give two practically parallel beams which show interference on account of the phase difference imposed by an additional reflection in one beam. The fringe system has a dark fringe at the centre which indi-

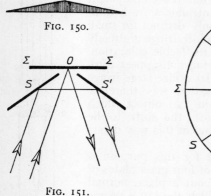

FIG. 150.

FIG. 151.

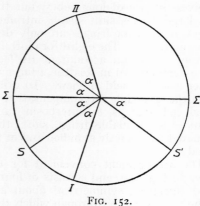

FIG. 152.

cates that a phase difference of $\frac{1}{2}$ is impressed at *each* reflection. Fresnel devised this experiment to evaluate the phase difference occurring in the case of the Newton's ring system. If a circle is drawn

* Ohm, " Beschreibung einer einfachen und leicht zu behandelnden Vorrichtung zur Anstellung der Lichtinterferenzversuche." *Pogg. Ann.*, 49 (1840), 98-109.
† Fresnel, " Œuvres complètes," Vol. 1, p. 330. *Mem. de l'Acad.*, Vol. 5, p. 419.
‡ Fresnel, " Œuvres complètes," Vol. 1, p. 703. " Memoire sur la reflexion " (1819).

in the plane of reference perpendicular to the three mirrors, using their common intersection as centre, as in Fig. 152, and the light source is imagined to lie along the radius I, the images formed by single reflection in Σ or two reflections in S and S' both lie along II. On turning the radius I counter-clockwise through a small angle β, the radius II must be turned clockwise through an angle β to give the first image, and be turned by the same amount counter-clockwise to give the second. The distance apart of these two images determines the fringe breadth.

Lloyd * obtained the same result in a simpler way by using a single mirror, by which the light coming direct from the source can be made to interfere with that from the mirror. This naturally gives theoretically only one half, and in practice much less, of the interference picture, since the plane of the mirror is the plane of symmetry, behind which no reflected light can arrive. ·If, however, a thin plate G (Fig. 153) of mica or glass is interposed in the path of the direct rays, the whole fringe system is shifted to the right and comes *completely* into view, indicating also a central *dark* fringe, that is to say, that the least possible path difference is a half wave-length. This phase difference between the direct and reflected light is intrinsic and exists, independently of the interposition of G, equally for rays of *all* colours.

Billet,† taking advantage of the principle of homocentricity, by which a portion of a lens functions in the same manner as the whole and forms an image in the same place, divided a lens in two. On placing

FIG. 153.

the parts so that the optical centres O, O' (Fig. 154) or the principal points of both halves no longer coincide, two *separate* images L_1, L_2, of a light source L are produced. The corresponding beams are superposed either in front of or behind the images in U, according as the principal points have been moved across, or pulled away from, one another. The application of a divided lens is occasionally a distinct advantage.

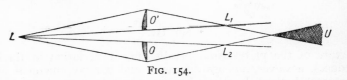

FIG. 154.

Two plane parallel glass plates inclined at an angle may also serve to separate the light source into two images. Fizeau ‡ utilized the

* Humphry Lloyd, " On a New Case of Interference of the Rays of Light," *Trans. Irish Acad.*, 17 (1837), 171.
† Billet, " Traité d'optique physique," Vol. 1, p. 67.   ‡ Cf. p. 178.

method to separate the beams σ, σ' (Fig. 155) to a greater distance and then bring them back to the same distance apart again; this materially simplified the experiment of Fresnel and Arago considered above. Brewster * noticed colours on looking at a light source through two slightly inclined glass plates of equal thickness and recognized and explained them as due to interference. The explanation is obvious from Fig. 156, which is Brewster's own figure. A slight modification

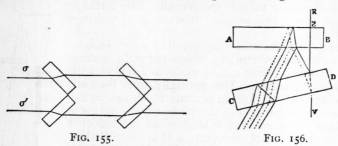

FIG. 155.   FIG. 156.

enabled Jamin † to devise the interference refractometer, an instrument especially suitable for demonstrating the Fresnel-Arago experiment. This consists of two glass plates of equal thickness arranged opposite to one another and parallel, so that the incident ray S (Fig. 157) is split up by reflection and refraction into two rays *abcd* and *aefd* which experience similar reflections and refractions, only in reverse orders, and finally coincide again along *d*S', the two constituents being in identical phase and equal in intensity. The slightest

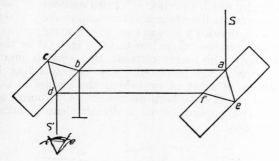

FIG. 157.

departure of the plates from parallelism, or variation in thickness, introduces, however, a phase difference and the ray emergent at *d* is consequently coloured. Rays having other directions have different path differences and hence show a different coloration. The paths of the rays are the same as if the effects were produced by *two identical*

* D. Brewster, " Treatise on Optics," London (1831), p. 111 ; also, *Ann. de Chim. et de phys.*, Ser. 3, Vol. 52, pp. 163, 171.
† Jamin, *Ann. de chim. et de phys.*, Ser. 3, Vol. 52, pp. 163, 171 ; Vol. 59, p. 282. *Compt. Rend.*, Vol. 42, p. 482 ; Vol. 43, p. 1191 ; Vol. 45, p. 892.

pairs of Newton lens systems used in combination and having very large plane parallel air gaps, the first pair producing a large separation of the rays and a large path difference, the second pair combining them again and reducing the path difference approximately to zero. On account of the large separation of the rays produced by the large thickness of glass, the interferometer is very sensitive. The mere approach of the hand towards *one* of the interfering beams, which warms the air it traverses, shifts the fringes at once and gives them a

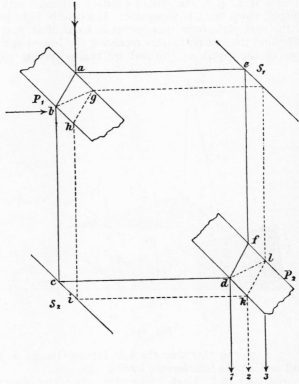

FIG. 158.

quivering motion. It is precisely the large separation of the rays that renders the arrangement capable of solving the Fresnel-Arago problem. Jamin also determined the difference in refractive index between cold and warm water and between water at a higher and lower pressure. In common with the Newton lens system, the arrangement permits the use of an extended light source and has the property that the introduced substance producing the path difference and the fringes themselves can both be seen distinctly simultaneously, an asset of which we shall speak in a moment.

Zehnder * and Ludwig Mach † both modified Jamin's apparatus at about the same time. The former devised an arrangement of four parallel plane-parallel plates of equal thickness ; this was also Mach's original arrangement, but he considerably improved it by replacing two of the plates by ordinary mirrors. The latter's object was to obtain a large field of view and at the same time as great a separation of the rays as he pleased, independent of the glass thickness. The paths of the light in Mach's apparatus are shown in Fig. 158. The rays which are directly reflected from the first plate and those which traverse it 2, 4, 6, etc., times produce different sets of interference fringes, which must be separated. If a cone of light is imagined to fall on the first plate from some point in front of it, and a lens to be placed behind the last plate, this receiving the beams 1, 2, 3 . . . , real images of the point are formed by beams having the reverse

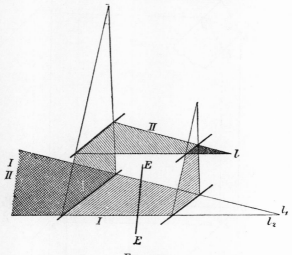

FIG. 159.

order . . . 3, 2, 1. In this way the less intense beams 2, 3 may be screened off and a pure interference system obtained.

It occurred later to L. Mach ‡ to replace the plane glass plates by very thin air "plates" contained between prisms, and in this form the apparatus was reduced practically to two reflecting and two reflecting and refracting surfaces. The diagrammatic form of Fig. 159 is particularly useful for learning the essentials of these types of apparatus, including Jamin's. The two interfering beams I and II which originate in l are indicated over the regions where they are real by the shading

* Zehnder, *Z. f. Instrk.*, 11 (1891), 275.
† L. Mach, *Sitzb. d. Wiener Akad.*, Vol. 101, Part IIa (Jan., 1892) ; Vol. 102 (Oct., 1893) ; Vol. 107 (1898) ; also, *Z. f. Instrk.* (March, 1892), (Aug., 1894).
‡ L. Mach, " Über ein Interferenzrefraktometer," *Sitzb. d. Wiener Akad.*, Vol. 101 (Jan., 1892) ; Vol. 107 (July, 1898).

and ▨ respectively. When the plates are exactly parallel and their distance apart adjusted correctly, the two real images l_1 and l_2 of l coincide. If one of the plates is now slightly rotated, l_1 and l_2 separate as in Fig. 160, and the interference fringes become visible, these evidently being produced in exactly the same manner as with the Fresnel mirrors and other arrangements, namely by light coming from both of the images l_1 and l_2. Since, however, the two beams have a large *real* separation, and only *virtually* coincide, substances may be introduced into one beam at EE (Fig. 159) without disturbing the

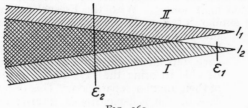

FIG. 160.

other; also the eye can accommodate *simultaneously* on the real object EE and the virtual fringes. The latter holds true even if the retardation varies from place to place over EE, a curvature and distortion of the fringes being thus produced. Such is not the case with Fresnel's and allied experiments. A substance interposed at E_1 (Fig. 160) in the beam I alone shifts the *whole* fringe system, the latter being obliterated, however, if E has not the same retardation at all points. There is obviously no effect if the substance is interposed at E_2 in the superposition field.

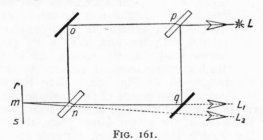

FIG. 161.

There is one apparent contradiction in the arrangement of Fig. 159. Considering Fig. 161, a small light source L has two virtual images L_1, L_2 whose interference fringes we will assume to be intercepted by *rms*. If L moves upwards in the plane of the paper, L_1 and L_2 follow a similar path and the fringes consequently shift as well. No fringe would thus apparently be visible with an extended light source, but an actual test made by looking at such a source through the arrangement shows that this is not so. The contradiction is only apparent, however, and the result may be explained as follows. If the ray L_p from L arrives at m over two different paths with a definite path difference, rays from *m* arrive back at L over the same path and with the same path difference, and an eye at L sees the same interference colour as at *m*. This holds also for the rays coming from L in other directions and meeting at *r* or *s*, and hence the eye at L sees at *rms* the same fringes as would be produced by a *luminous* pupil situated at *rms*, provided, of course, that the area covered by the pupil at L is not too great. The light of the single fringes thus comes from different points of the luminous surface when the fringes are viewed subjectively by the eye. When, instead of an eye placed at L, an optical instrument of large aperture is used, the fringes are obliterated as they would be with an extended light source. With the Fresnel mirror experiment and the other similar interference arrangements the rays from the

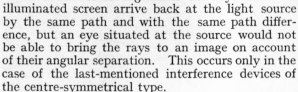

illuminated screen arrive back at the light source by the same path and with the same path difference, but an eye situated at the source would not be able to bring the rays to an image on account of their angular separation. This occurs only in the case of the last-mentioned interference devices of the centre-symmetrical type.

There is another method of securing an extended source for plane parallel plate arrangements. The source is placed at the focal distance from a lens, so that from any point of the former only parallel rays fall on the apparatus, and these when leaving it fall on a second lens which concentrates the parallel coherent rays at particular points of its focal plane. Naturally the interference fringes produced by multiple reflection or refraction cannot be separated from one another by this method. The first lens is superfluous if the sun or a bright sky is used as light source. If Jamin's apparatus is considered with the first plate in the position of its mirror image in the second, as in the case of Mach's arrangement, it reduces to the simple arrangement of Fig. 162. Here the reader must imagine two beams of light coming from the point,

Fig. 162.

the one, however, passing first through air and then through a plate of double the thickness of the actual Jamin plate, the other passing first through the double plate and then through the air. When the plates are inclined slightly, the single luminous point splits up into two which produce interference. Quincke * experimented with Jamin's apparatus and improved it by silvering the rear surfaces of the plates, while Ketteler † used it to investigate the colour scattering of gases. I have also carried out many experiments with this apparatus. The four-plate apparatus has been employed by L. Mach.‡

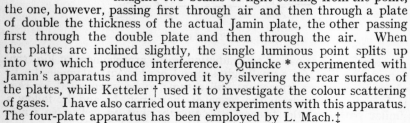

' Quincke, *Pogg. Ann.*, Vols. 132 and 145.

† Ketteler, " Beobachtungen über die Farbenzerstreuung der Gase," Bonn (1865).

‡ L. Mach, " Weitere Versuche über Projektile," *Sitzb. d. Wiener Akad.*, Vol. 105 (July, 1896) ; also, " Optische Untersuchungen der Luftstrahlen," *ibid.*, Vol. 106 (Dec.. 1897).

Spectral resolution had already been used by Newton to establish interference at large path difference, and Wrede * investigated spectrally the linear region of glitter obtained when a layer of mica is bent into a cylindrical form. He ascribed the channelled spectrum so obtained to interference between light reflected from the front and back faces. Poggendorff † indicated the important bearing of this experiment on the theory of interference. Fizeau and Foucault ‡ also investigated interference at large path difference, principally on account of interest in the coherence question. For example, the light emitted, say, to-day and to-morrow from the *same* light source can never be considered coherent, for all coherence is lost after only a very short interval. The question which concerned Fizeau and Foucault was whether it were possible to determine the path difference at which two beams ceased to be coherent or, in other words, to produce visible interference. At first they produced a large path difference by displacing *one* of the Fresnel mirrors. The fringes were formed on a narrow slit and the light transmitted was spectrally

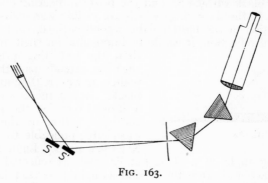

FIG. 163.

resolved (Fig. 163). The light reflected from thicker glass plates, and that transmitted by thicker crystalline plates placed between Nicols, was also investigated. If λ and λ' were two different wave-lengths, which were contained exactly n and n' times respectively in the total path difference, then $n\lambda = n'\lambda'$. Supposing that they counted m dark bands in the spectrum between the wave-lengths λ and λ', then $n' = n - m$, and $n = m\lambda'/(\lambda' - \lambda)$. They found visible interference even with a path difference of about 4000 wave-lengths. At greater path differences the bands in the spectrum become so numerous and at the same time so faint that it is impossible to count them. The latter is quite easily explained by inhomogeneity of the spectrum and is no indication of a commencement of incoherence. Stefan,§ following a similar principle, later obtained indications of interference by

* Wrede, *Pogg. Ann.*, Vol. 33.   † Poggendorff, *Pogg. Ann.*, Vol. 41.
  ‡ Fizeau and Foucault, " Sur le phénomène des interférences entre deux rayons de lumière dans le cas de grandes différences de marche," *Ann. de chim. et phys.*, Vol. 26 (1849).
  § Stefan, *Sitzb. d. Wiener Akad.*, Vol. 50, p. 392.

means of the Talbot fringes for still greater path differences up to 15,560 wave-lengths of the H line.

Further advance in the theory of the Newton's rings was made by Poisson * who noticed an incompleteness in Fresnel's theory in that only rays reflected once at the first and second surfaces of the air gap had been considered, these being of unequal intensity and consequently incapable of complete extinction, which is not in agreement with the fact that the monochromatic rings are in reality alternately bright and completely dark. He drew attention to the fact that light reaches the eye also after 3, 5, 7 . . . reflections in the air gap, and Fresnel then completed this part of the theory and showed that for reflected light the new theory gave perfectly black minima at the same positions as before.

While Newton had not found any material obstacle in his theory of "fits," Fresnel † demonstrated its untenableness by means of the following experiment. He placed a glass prism P (Fig. 164) on a thin lens L whose under side was blackened with pitch, the lens also lying on the black surface SS and the prism projecting over the edge of the lens. If the dark rings which are visible were caused only by the transmission of the light by the second surface, that is with the suppression of reflection, it would be impossible for them to be darker

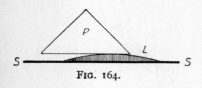

FIG. 164.

than the reflecting prism surface where it extends past the lens ; in reality, however, they are perfectly black. Arago, moreover, conceived a crucial test for the necessity of the joint action of the two rays, especially applicable to the case of Newton's rings. Light incident at the polarizing angle on a plane parallel plate is reflected both from the first surface and from the second as light polarized in the plane of incidence. Thus, if a thin lens is laid on a metallic mirror and the combination is viewed, at the polarizing angle for glass, through an analyser with its plane of polarization perpendicular to the plane of incidence, the light reflected from both lens surfaces is extinguished, but that from the metal remains. *No* fringes, however, are visible. Hooke had already pointed out that reflection at the second surface was a necessary property of a lamina which exhibited colours, and this can also be proved in the above case by blackening the metal surface.

Other effects can also be observed with the Newton arrangement, apart from the rings investigated by Newton. Thus Knox,‡ in 1815, observed, in the case of a lens which lay between two plane glass plates, diffuse bands in addition to the rings belonging to either lens surface, the bands being straight when the curvature of both lens

---

* Fresnel, " Œuvres complètes," " Controverse avec Poisson," pp. 183, etc., p. 239.
† Fresnel, " Œuvres complètes," Vol. 1, pp. 51, 133, 252.
‡ Knox, *Phil. Trans. Roy. Soc.*, 1815, pp. 161-181.

surfaces was the same. Van der Willigen * noticed these fringes in the case of a *single* plane glass plate and a *single* lens, and Stefan † saw some new fringes appear in the Newton lens combination when a crystalline plate with or without Nicols was suitably interposed between the eye and the lenses. A correct clue to the explanation of all these effects which, as varied as they may seem, are analogous to Brewster's, had already been given by Thomas Young.‡ Thus if the two rays of light coming from a particular spot of the glass surface bounding the air-gap of the Newton system, having had a path difference a impressed, interfere once more at a path difference b, for example by being reflected back again to another part of the air-gap, instead of two interfering rays there are now four and two of these have a path difference $a - b$. The fringes in question appear at places where $a - b = w$, say. If the light from the system of Newton's rings is, for example, reflected back from the uppermost glass surface at oblique incidence on to the surfaces bounding the air-gap itself, the rings are seen doubled and in addition there are a number of straight fringes which follow the regions of constant path difference. The latter are still visible even when the ordinary ring system is obliterated by interposing a small ring of paper between the lenses, since it is

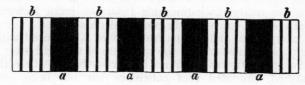

FIG. 165.

possible for the interference at a path difference $a - b$ to be visible when that at a path difference a or b is quite invisible on account of its magnitude.

Incidentally, I have considered these effects from another point of view.§ The spectrum of the light which is subjected to interference at a path difference a will exhibit a system of fringes. A second interference at a path difference b will produce a second fringe system, and so on. If the two systems are quite dissimilar and both too fine to make any appreciable difference to the spectrum, the unresolved light will not be coloured in any way, but if, however, the two systems are very nearly identical, coincidences and alternating variations appear along the fringes, somewhat after the manner of acoustical beats (Fig. 165). At the dark regions of coincidence more light is extracted from the spectrum than at other points and, if the

* Van der Willigen, " Ein System von geradlinigen Fransen gleichzeitig mit den Newtonschen Ringen," *Pogg. Ann.*, Vol. 123 (1864).

† Stefan, " Über eine Erscheinung am Newtonschen Farbenglas," *Sitzb. d. Wiener Akad.*, Vol. 50 (1864), pp. 135 and 395 ; *Pogg. Ann.*, Vols. 123 and 125.

‡ Brewster, *Phil. Trans. Roy. Soc.* (1838), p. 73 ; Young, *ibid.* (1802), p. 387. " Lectures on Natural Philosophy," p. 369.

§ E. Mach, " Optisch-akustische Versuche," Prague (1873) ; also, *Pogg. Ann.*, Vol. 150.

regions are sufficiently widely separated, a slight coloration of the unresolved light will be produced. In this way the invisible interference at large path difference may be rendered visible by subjecting the light to a second nearly equal retardation. It is obviously immaterial in what way the second fringe system in the spectrum is produced. Interference, for example, at the edges of the Newton lens system may also be made visible by looking at the reflected light through absorbent media (e.g. potassium permanganate, solutions of didymium salts, nitrogen peroxide) which produce dark absorption bands in the spectrum, or the colours in different parts of the spectrum of the incident light may be extinguished by mechanical means. If the interference effects at large path difference are arranged for projection on a screen, the fringes will be visible on looking at the screen through some similar interference apparatus which produces an approximately equal path difference.

The following is the simplest type of experiment of this kind. A small piece of card is held horizontally above a portion of the Newton lens system, which is also horizontal, so that sunlight is reflected from the glass on to the under side of the card. The image of the latter formed by reflection in the glass will now exhibit Knox fringes. With the type of lenses described on pages 151 and 152 all the effects just referred to are easily distinguishable from the main Newton's ring system and may be conveniently projected on a screen.

When interference at large path difference is produced with white light or light of a mixed colour, the spectrum of the light after passage through the apparatus will contain numerous bands where the light is extinguished, provided that coherence has not been destroyed, otherwise there will be no fringes at all. There is a possibility, however, that the fringes may be present but be too fine and close together to be distinguished. If thus some test could be found by which a spectrum with dark fringes of this type could be distinguished from an ordinary continuous spectrum, the range over which it is possible to establish the presence or absence of coherence could be extended much farther than has hitherto been possible. It is not possible to employ an interference method, since, although the production of interference at a further path difference a equal to the former does introduce visible fringes, there are in addition to rays of path difference $2a$ rays of a resultant path difference O which will interfere whether they result from previously impressed equal differences of a or not. The determination of the path difference at which incoherence becomes appreciable would signify a material advance in our knowledge of the process of light emission.

While Newton, Young, and Fresnel were quite conversant with the fact that if homogeneous light is employed Newton's rings may be followed up to high orders of path difference, it was Fizeau who made the first earnest attempt to reach the limits of visibility.* He chose a suitable lens for the upper component and a plane glass or metal plate for the lower one (Fig. 166), the distance apart of the

* Fizeau, *Ann. de Chim.*, Vol. 26 (1849) ; *Pogg. Ann.*, Vol. 119, p. 95.

PLATE VII

THOMAS YOUNG, M.D., F.R.S.

Engraved by G.R.Ward, from a Picture by Sir Thomas Laurence, P.R.A.

two being adjustable by a micrometer screw. A small totally-reflecting prism was placed in the focus of the lens and reflected light from a sodium flame down on to it, the light passing through the air gap in a practically normal direction and returning to the observer's eye placed near the prism. The whole surface of the lens is in this case seen covered with black and yellow rings which close into and disappear in the centre on separating the lens and plate, new rings appearing at the outside. By means of a mark on the glass each ring may be counted as it passes towards the centre, the path difference increasing by one wave-length, or the separation of lens and plate by half a wave-length, between the consecutive rings. A measurement of wave-length by means of the micrometer screw is thus possible. When about 500 rings have thus passed, the rings are less visible, at 1000 once more distinct, and so on in a periodic manner until when 10,000 have passed the visibility practically ceases. By means of a particularly homogeneous illumination Fizeau was able to count as many as 50,000 rings, for which the air gap was about 15 mm. Fizeau explained the periodic appearance and disappearance of the rings simply by assuming the presence of two wavelengths in sodium light which cause fluctuations in intensity after the manner of beats. The final disappearance, however, Fizeau was inclined to attribute to the commencement of incoherence. The fact that with light sources of higher temperature the fringes are *more* visible makes this explanation improbable, since it would be expected that at higher temperatures the phase changes would be more rapid. The origin of the disturbance may be sought for elsewhere. In Fig. 146 two cones of light arriving at the eye from one point of the glass

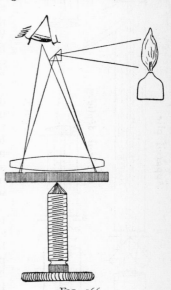

FIG. 166.

are indicated. So long as the air gap is very small, it may be assumed that the individual rays of the cones have equal path differences in spite of varying obliquity. Observation with a microscope, however, with which larger cones are utilized, will suffice to show that even with the ordinary arrangement for the production of Newton's rings the colours are very faint and unsaturated, and thus with greater thickness of air gap the aperture of the pupil is sufficient to make the effects indistinct. Lummer and also Exner have indicated that the dimensions of Fizeau's arrangement are compatible with such an explanation of the cessation of visibility.

Fizeau also replaced Newton's plane parallel plate by one which was not perfectly flat. In this case it is obvious that all the adjacent parts of the plate in question, for which the thickness of air gap is

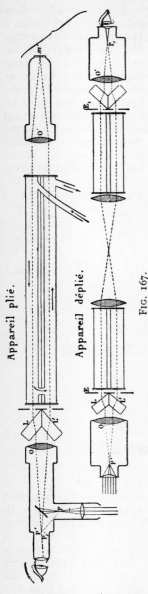

Appareil plié.

Appareil déplié.

Fig. 167.

constant, will indicate a uniform brightness, and the plate thus shows curves of equal thickness, which correspond to the contours on a contour map. If the air gap between an upper plane glass plate and a lower polished plate to be tested is arranged so as to be slightly wedge-shaped, the now approximately straight fringes undergo a shift when the lower plate is warmed. Fizeau used this arrangement to determine the coefficient of expansion.

Further advance was made in the theory of the Newton lens combination through the investigations of Sohncke and Wangerin.* We only need indicate here that the theory is no longer so simple if consideration is taken of the fact that the bounding surfaces of the air gap are not strictly parallel, in which case the rings do not appear situated exactly in the upper surface. If a point source is used to illuminate the arrangement, the interference effects may be followed with a magnifying lens, as M. P. Joubin † has shown, far out into the adjoining space ; in fact interference is visible in all places where the two beams are superposed.

Fizeau devised an original type of interference apparatus capable of serving a special purpose.‡ From Fig. 167 it will be seen that both rays traverse the apparatus over approximately the same path, but in reverse order and direction. The fact that the successive media are different does not influence the result, but when the tubes indicated in the figure are filled with water which is made to circulate in the directions shown with a speed of 7·07 metres per second, the one ray moves *with* this motion and the other *against* it. In this way the influence of the motion of the medium on the speed of light may be investigated. Fizeau states that with

* Sohncke and Wangerin, *Pogg. Ann.*, 131 (1867), 497 ; *Wied. Ann.*, 12 (1881); 20 (1893).

† M. P. Joubin, *Pogg. Ann.* (1872).

‡ Fizeau, " Sur une expérience relative à la vitesse propagation de la lumière," *Ann. de Phys.*, 29 (1849); " Sur les hypothèses relatives à l'ether lumineux, etc.," ; *ibid.*, 33 (1851); *Compt. Rend.*, 33 (1851), 349 ; *Ann. de Chim. et phys.*, Ser. 3, 54 (1859), 385.

a tube 3 metres long he observed a fringe shift of 0·00500 mm. (0·41λ) (c'est-a-dire près d'une demi frange).

J. J. Müller * considered it to be necessary, as a result of interference experiments similar to those to which Fig. 167 refers, that the wave-length, and therefore the speed of light, should depend on the intensity. That the wave-lengths radiated by luminous bodies do undergo variations with the luminosity is scarcely to be doubted, but the assumption of a variation of velocity with intensity in air-filled space is refuted by the far more exact experiments of Lippich.† This experimenter chose an arrangement similar to that of Fig. 167 and found not the slightest trace of fringe shift when a plane smoked glass plate was interposed in the two beams so that one beam was reduced in intensity at the beginning of its path and the other at the end. This information is important, since it follows that, at least for light propagated in air-filled space, the accelerations are thus proportional to the displacements to a high degree of accuracy, whether the latter are of a mechanical, electrical, or chemical nature.

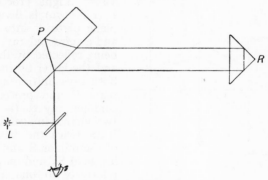

FIG. 168.

Nowadays simpler and more convenient arrangements may be chosen for these experiments. One of these will be evident from Fig. 168. By replacing the thick plane plate P by a thin one in conjunction with a plane mirror placed behind it, and the single refracting prism R by two, the two light paths may be separated as far as one wishes.

Some peculiar interference curves were observed by Haidinger ‡ and rediscovered by Lummer § after they had been forgotten. A simple example will serve to explain their nature. Suppose an extended source of monochromatic light LL (Fig. 169), e.g. a sodium flame, is viewed through a plane parallel plate. The rays which proceed from a *single* point *a* have too different path differences for

---

* J. J. Müller, *Pogg. Ann.*, 145 (1872), 86.
† Lippich, " Über die behauptete Abhängigkeit der Lichtwellenänge von der Intensität," *Sitzb. d. Wiener Akad.*, Vol. 172, Part II (1875).
‡ Haidinger, *Pogg. Ann.*, 63, 67, 68, 75, 91.
§ Lummer, *Inaugural-Dissert.*, Berlin (1884) ; *Wied. Ann.*, 23 (1884), 48-84.

visible interference to be produced on uniting in the eye to form an image, but rays which proceed in parallel directions from different points *ab* are split up by the plate into pairs of parallel rays of equal path difference, which are brought to the same point of the retina by an eye focussed for infinity. If *rs* is the optical axis of the eye, the interference curves of equal inclination, as they were termed by Lummer, appear, in the case of the orientation of Fig. 169, as circles perpendicular to *rs*. When the plate is not perfectly plane parallel the curves have deformations and variations in brightness which are made apparent by moving the plate (without varying its inclination). Lummer used this arrangement to trace small imperfections in the plate which were no longer detectable by Fizeau's method. He also investigated the curves of large path difference which are visible to an eye focussed for infinity when light from a sodium flame is successively reflected, at approximately equal angles, from two similar plane plates having an arbitrary inclination.

An important form of interference apparatus is that due to Michelson.* Light proceeding from L (Fig. 170) is divided by the plane plate P into a reflected and a refracted ray, the former being reflected by the mirror S_1 and the latter by the mirror S_2, both rays uniting again at the plate P and proceeding as a common ray to the eye. The two virtual images L_1 and L_2 of L are twice the distance apart of the mirror S and the virtual image of S_2, and may be shifted relatively to one another and also be transposed by moving S_1. If L_1 and L_2 are only a very short distance apart, rings similar to Newton's rings may be seen with white light, only it is evident that the greatest path difference is at the *centre*.

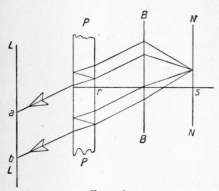

FIG. 169.

In this case the light source L obviously must be limited in extent (e.g. point source) for the effects to be visible. If L_1 and L_2 are coincident, a slight rotation of the mirror S_1 is sufficient to place them side by side and to change the fringes into straight ones. In this case the light source L may be also in the form of a slit parallel to the fringes. Let a lens Λ be now interposed between the extended light source L and the plate P, so that L is at its focus (Fig. 171). Λ_1 and Λ_2 represent the virtual images of the lens and should lie one immediately behind the other. If Σ_1 is a principal ray which emerges from a point σ of the source L and traverses the optical centre of the lens, all the rays leaving the lens which originate in σ will be parallel to Σ_1,

* Michelson, " Interference Phenomena in a New Form of Refractometer," *Phil. Mag.*, Ser. 5, 13 (1882), 236, 242 ; *Amer. Journ. of Science*, 33 (1882), 395 ; *ibid.*, Supplement to Vol. 7 (1883), 534 ; *Phil. Mag.*, Vol. 46, p. 395.

and the plane wave-front W_1 is perpendicular to the whole beam. The corresponding elements for the second virtual image of the lens are denoted by Σ_2, W_2. Since the light is in the same phase at m_1 and m_2, the path difference of the rays Σ_1, Σ_2, in common with all the other similar pairs of rays of the whole beam is therefore 2D cos a, where D is the distance apart of mirrors S_1, S_2 and a the angle of inclination of the beam to the axis of the lens. If monochromatic illumination is employed, on looking through a telescope focussed for infinity, with its axis parallel to the axis of the lens images, interference curves in the form of circles perpendicular to the telescope axis are visible, these being similar to those with the Lummer arrangement. The curves are visible even at very great differences of path.

Michelson's apparatus has considerable advantages for many purposes : facility of adjustment, any desired separation of the beams,

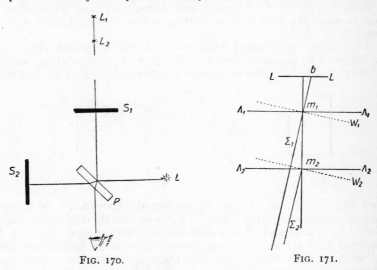

FIG. 170.   FIG. 171.

and a path difference which it is possible to increase at will in many of its applications. This form is not, however, suitable in every case. Michelson's form can be obtained from Mach's (Fig. 158) by replacing the two plates P, P by a *single* plate and arranging the two mirrors so that the incident rays are reflected back approximately along their original paths. If it is desired to study an interposed substance which is non-homogeneous, and upon which the eye must thus accommodate, parallel light cannot be used for this purpose and the substance may not be traversed *twice* by the rays. Actually I had Michelson's arrangement in view for the purpose of experiments on air-waves, without knowing of *his* apparatus, but then found an apparatus analogous to Jamin's more suitable.

With his own apparatus Michelson was able to distinguish interference for light of the red cadmium line with path differences up to nearly half a metre. Interference was visible at a path difference of

20 cm., using light of the green and blue cadmium lines. Michelson was thus in a position to evaluate the metre in terms of the wave-lengths of the red, green, and blue cadmium light, a very important piece of work. This was done as follows : an etalon was constructed which had as nearly as possible a length of 10 cm., and eight other standards of length were also made, such that each was half the length of the preceding one. The last, which may be referred to as I, was 0·39 mm. long, and the number of wave-lengths contained in its length was determined by actual counting. The other standards were then found in terms of the shorter ones.

The standards were of the form indicated in Fig. 172, and were provided with reflecting surfaces A, B, whose distance apart defined the length referred to above. On substituting one of these standards for the mirror S_1 in the apparatus of Fig. 170, the image of S_2 could be made to coincide first with A and then with B and the number of rings crossing the field of view, corresponding to a shift from A to B, counted.

To compare a standard with one of double its length (Fig. 173), the image of S_2 was made first to coincide with a and a', then with b ; the shorter standard was then moved backwards so that S_2 now coin-

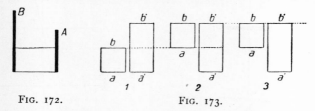

FIG. 172.   FIG. 173.

cided with a. If, on shifting S_2 backwards, coincidence of S_2 took place simultaneously with b and b', $a'b'$ was exactly double the length of ab. Any difference was evaluated in wave-lengths. It may be remarked that coincidence was always determined with white light and with straight fringes, since in these circumstances a zero path difference can be very readily and accurately recognized. By actual counting, the shortest standard gave 121,235 fringes for red cadmium light. It follows directly that

> 1 m. = 1553163·5 wave-lengths of red cadmium light.
> 1 m. = 1966249·7   ,,   ,, green ,,   ,,
> 1 m. = 2083372·1   ,,   ,, blue   ,,   ,,

This description, although somewhat brief, has been included since it is in this direction that the chief interest and practical impor-tance of the theory of interference are to be found.

Michelson was, in addition, guided by important theoretical investi-gations. He was the first to recognize that the final disappearance of Fizeau's interference fringes was not due to a cessation of coherence, but to the characteristic structure of sodium light. He found that the visibility V of an interference formation is given by

$$V = (i_1 - i_2)/(i_1 + i_2),$$

where i_1 denotes the brightness of the maxima, i_2 that of the minima, these necessarily being functions of the path difference and the distribution of brightness in the spectrum " line " utilized. From a theoretical investigation of this interdependence, assuming several distributions of intensity in the spectrum line, it was possible for him to estimate conversely the structure of the line from the visibility of interference. Fig. 174 gives examples of the relation in

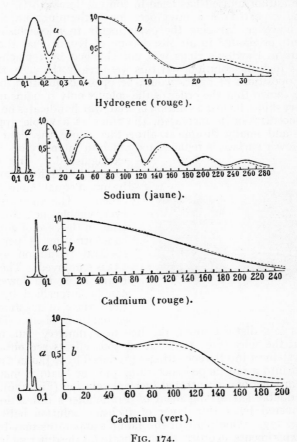

Hydrogene (rouge).

Sodium (jaune).

Cadmium (rouge).

Cadmium (vert).

FIG. 174.

question for yellow sodium and red cadmium light. Cadmium light proved the most advantageous for this purpose.

One consequence of this is that light is coherent for much greater path differences than Fresnel and Fizeau had ever believed. If Michelson could observe interference for path differences as great as $\frac{1}{2}$ metre when a spark source was employed, it must be assumed that with sources of lower temperatures coherence extends much farther. In any case, the limit of coherence has not been reached, since the visibility of interference is limited by other causes, such as the imperfect homogeneity of the light. It may be found possible, however, to *sift the light actually by interference itself* and make it more adaptable to the requirements.

A large variety of applications of the interference refractometer has already been considered and in conclusion it may be permissible to mention an application to the investigation of anomalous dispersion which the author himself has tried in conjunction with G. v. Osnobischin * and repeated on a later occasion with minor improvements, without, however, bringing the experiments to a conclusion.† The experiments originated in an observation of Kundt that the order of the colours in Newton's rings was not changed by replacing the air layer by a fuchsine solution. If this were really the case, the fundamental propositions of optics would be open to question, but it can be readily shown that the order of the colours only remains unchanged when a very dilute fuchsine solution is used, which indicates no anomaly. If the concentration is increased, the rings as a whole appear very indistinct and finally disappear altogether, since the light reflected from the lower surface is reduced too much in intensity or completely

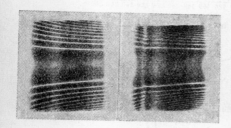

extinguished. The condition for good visibility, namely, two beams of equal intensity, is thus absent. The anomaly is, however, visible, not directly it is true, in the case of considerable concentration (5 per cent.) if spectral resolution as in Fig. 133 is employed. The reflected beam from the lower surface can be intensified by silvering the surface in question, as suggested by L. Mach. This makes the effects less distinct along the line of symmetry but more pronounced at the sides (Fig. 175). Analogous effects are obtained if a vertical system of interference fringes produced by a Jamin's apparatus is resolved into a fan-shaped spectrum, and one beam is made to traverse a thin layer of concentrated fuchsine solution (Fig. 176), or if one slit of the double slit arrangement of Fraunhofer's diffraction experiment is covered by a thin layer of fuchsine solution between glass plates (Fig. 177). One plate of the Jamin's apparatus may be silvered for these experiments, in order to compensate for the different intensities. There is yet another artifice applicable to either the diffraction experiment or Jamin's. Polarized light is used, and one beam is made to traverse a quartz plate of right-handed rotation and the other an equal plate of left-handed rotation. The loss of intensity in one beam can now be compensated by viewing the effects through a Nicol turned so that the resultant intensities are equal.

* Osnobischin, " Versuche über anomale dispersion mit Hilfe der Interference, angestellt im Prager Physik. Institut.," *Carl Rep.*, Vol. 11 (1875).
† Cf. also E. Mach and J. Arbes, *Sitzb. d. Wiener Akad.*, Vol. 92, Part II (July, 1885).

While these experiments are well adapted to qualitative demonstration of the anomalous effects, they are not very useful for quantitative purposes, for with low concentration of fuchsine solution the retardation is too small for the best results, and thick or highly concentrated layers extinguish the incident light completely in exactly the spectral region of most effect, and any equalization device is naturally useless. The best way is to flow an alcoholic solution over a glass plate so as to obtain a solid layer and cover it with a second plate, first covering it with oil so as to make the whole optically uni-

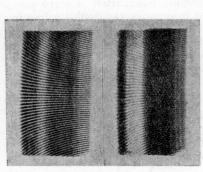

DE G H   DE G H
FIG. 176.

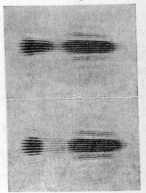

FIG. 177.

form. In this case one beam traverses fuchsine, oil, and glass, and the other only oil and glass. Results thus obtained are not strictly comparable with those found with the liquid fuchsine. Perhaps others will be able to improve the method.*

* The above figures were originally contained in a publication on anomalous dispersion, now out of print, which I prepared in the summers of 1892 and 1893 in the Prague Laboratory in collaboration with my assistants Cölestin Krupka (now professor at Vienna) and Father Karl München, S.J., later professor at the Stella matutina in Feldkirch.

CHAPTER X

POLARIZATION

BARTHOLINUS,* in a short yet significant publication of sixty pages which appeared in 1670, was the first to describe the double refracting Iceland spar or calcite. He referred to its rhombohedral form, its electrification by friction, its resistance to chemical action, and in particular to the peculiar refraction of light occurring in this crystal. If it is laid on a sheet of paper marked with points or dashes † and viewed from directly above the surface PQRS (Fig. 178), each point

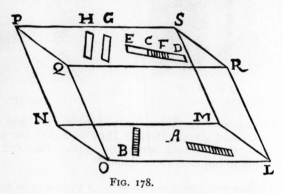

FIG. 178.

appears double, in reality with one image undisplaced and the other shifted in a particular direction by an amount proportional to the thickness of the crystal. The direction of shift is that of the bisector of SRQ, where R is the corner formed by the three faces bounded at R by equal obtuse angles, and the sense is from R towards the opposite corner P. The images of a short line having this direction partly coincide if sufficiently long, the perpendicular direction being that in which the separation is greatest. On turning the crystal, keeping it at the same time resting on the paper, one image remains stationary while the other, which also appears more distant, rotates about the former in a circle. Bartholinus at once recognized that the latter image must be due to an unusual type of refraction, since this rotation of the image is not produced by a plate of glass when turned

* Erasmi Bartholinus, " Experimenta crystalli Islandici disdiaclastici quibus mira et insolita refractio delegitur," Hafniae (1670).
† *Loc. cit.*, pp. 11, etc.

relatively to the paper. He also determined the refractive index in the case of the ordinary image by Kepler's method.

Twenty years later the subject was again taken up in Huygens' " Traité de la lumière." * Huygens found that the results obtained by Bartholinus required little alteration, but he made valuable progress with observation and theory. Since a detailed account of Huygens' work appears in a later chapter, it will only be necessary here for us to concern ourselves with what is of importance to the questions at issue. Huygens experimented with sunlight as illuminant and observed the passage of the rays through the crystal directly. The so-called principal section of the crystal is the plane through the bisector of the angle SRQ perpendicular to the surface SRQ, this plane incidentally containing the edge RL. If the upper surface of the crystal is covered by a sheet of paper provided with a small aperture at b (Fig. 179), sunlight incident perpendicularly on this surface along ab is divided into two rays which are contained in the principal section

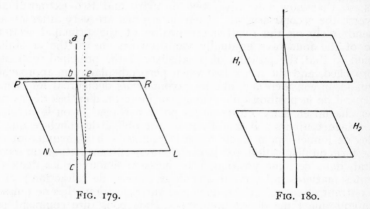

FIG. 179.   FIG. 180.

(denoted by RLNP). The component bc passes through the crystal wholly without refraction, whereas the other " extraordinary " ray bd is deflected towards RL, but emerges parallel to the former.† If, inversely, d were a luminous point or mark on the paper on which the crystal rests, it would give rise to two similar rays dba and def in the reverse direction, by which an observer looking down at the crystal would see a double projection of d on the upper surface, one at e by ordinary refraction, and another at b by extraordinary refraction, this being in accordance with the observations of Bartholinus. To explain the double refraction, Huygens assumed two separate waves and, for these, two different media. The ordinary refraction resulted from a spherical wave in the ether, but the extraordinary from a spheroidal wave which was propagated both through the ether and through the molecules of the substance. His own observation, however, laid difficulties in the way of this explanation. Thus, if two similarly oriented calcite crystals are placed one behind the other in sunlight, the ordinary ray emerging from the first is propagated as the ordinary ray in the second and similarly for the extraordinary ray from the first, the effects being the same as for a crystal of double the thickness.* The behaviour is unchanged when one of the principal sections indicated in Fig. 180 is rotated through 180° so that the crystal surfaces are no longer similarly oriented but still have their principal sections parallel. Huygens concluded from this that the emergent ordinary ray no longer behaves as ordinary sunlight and has lost the power to be influenced by matter possessed in extraordinary refraction. He conceived a similar behaviour for the extraordinary ray. A further experiment revealed to him the weakness of this conception, for when the principal sections are mutually perpendicular the ordinary ray of the first crystal traverses the second as the extraordinary ray, and conversely, and with the principal sections inclined at any other angle each ray from the first crystal is separated in reality into two rays, so that now four rays, two ordinary and two extraordinary, traverse the second crystal. Their intensities are very different and depend solely on the relative orientation of the principal sections. Two of the four rays gradually vanish when one of the crystals is turned so that the position of parallelism of the principal sections is approached, and the other two when perpendicularity is approached. " Quand on considere icy, que les rayons *ce, dg* demeurent les memes, il depend de la position qu'on donne au morceau d'en bas de les partager chacun en deux, ou de ne les point partager, là ou le rayon *ab* se partage toujours ; il semble qu'on est obligé de conclure que les ondes de lumière, pour avoir passé le premier cristal, acquieront certaine form ou disposition, par laquelle en rencontrant le tissu du second cristal, dans certaine position, elles puissent émouvoir les deux differentes matieres qui servent aux deux especes de refraction ; et en rencontrant ce second cristal dans une autre position, elles ne puissent émouvoir que l'une de ces matieres. Mais pour dire comment cela se fait, je n'aye rien trouvé justqu'icy que me satisfasse." He was thus contented to leave the matter for others to investigate.†

It is remarkable how Huygens had stood at the threshold of a great discovery though not fully aware of the fact and unable to obtain a clear grasp of the situation. A double barrier resulting from the nature of his initial speculations lay before him ; on the one hand he constantly thought that light waves were analogous to (longitudinal) perfectly symmetrical sound waves, a circumstance which would render him incapable of explaining the properties of light which are nowadays apparent, and on the other hand there was the obstacle, a necessary consequence of the latter, that if a wave which is similarly constituted in all directions perpendicular to its motion is to be transmitted in two different ways, this may only occur in two different media. Such were the apparently insuperable difficulties which confronted Huygens.

Newton was far more courageous in his discussion of the effects

---

* *Loc. cit.*, p. 88.   † *Loc. cit.*, p. 91.

observed by Huygens. He had not personally made any exhaustive
experimental investigation, but he describes the effects in question in
detail at the conclusion of his " Opticks." With the happy manner,
peculiar to his genius, of adapting his ideas to the realities of the case,
he summed up the problem with the question : " Annon radiorum
luminis diversa sunt latera, diversis proprietatibus congenitis prae-
dita ? " * a question which does, indeed, actually contain the solution
to the problem. The very manner in which Newton developed the
idea of lateral asymmetry of the rays renders its inherent nature
apparent. Thus the rays which traverse a calcite crystal are refracted
in an exactly similar manner on traversing a second similarly oriented
crystal, so that the ordinary and extraordinary rays must differ speci-
fically, and also both be already contained in the incident ray, for if
their properties were initially bestowed by modification at refraction,
they would have to appear at *each* new refraction. Newton may have
had in mind a resolution or division of the ray. From the experiment
with crossed principal sections Newton concluded that the two rays
only differ with respect to position, since by changing the orientation
of the principal sections each ray is able to assume the rôle of the
others. It followed that each ray must possess a property *a* on two
opposite sides, and another property *b* on the two mutually perpendicular opposite sides. He could understand why Huygens was unable to surmount the difficulties in his path, since pressures and
" motions," he says, could only be propagated in an isotropic medium
uniformly in all directions. Moreover, even if Huygens *had* known
that the rays do not receive their properties initially at refraction but
are present *before* incidence, his difficulties would not have been
lessened. Newton thought that the four sides of a ray were probably
endowed with forces which exhibited polarity, like magnetic forces
for example, which could interact with the particles of matter in a
large variety of ways, according to the differences in the latter, thus giving a possible explanation of the asymmetric behaviour of the rays and
of the respectively strong and weak double refractions in calcite and
quartz. One pair of opposite sides of a ray was to be considered
endowed with forces of one polarity and the perpendicular pair with
forces of the opposite polarity.

Newton here takes care to proceed along the lines of the views
expressed at the beginning of the " Opticks." † In experimental
science, namely, little regard is to be paid to hypotheses, and the
invention of obscure qualities for each phenomenon in particular is
not to be encouraged. It is another proposition, however, to endeavour to express many phenomena in terms of a few properties which
scarcely admit of direct observation but are discoverable by analytical methods ; this is of real value and results in a gradual acquire-
ment of a deeper and broader knowledge of nature. Newton deduced
the present-day view that the polarized components may be considered
present in the light before it enters the calcite, and that they differ

* Newton, " Optice " (1719), Quaestio 26, p. 361.
† *Loc. cit.*, pp. 409, 412, 413.

from one another only with respect to their orientation. In following his original intention, however, he expresses everything in terms of hypothetically invariable, *material* properties, and here he departs from the abstract representation of reality, at the same time showing *his* peculiar bias.

The asymmetry of light rays recognized by Newton became evident a century later under quite different circumstances to another investigator, Malus.* Arago † tells of the remarkable fate of this man, who endured the plague in the Egyptian campaign, and in the confusion of war wrote a dissertation on the constitution of light from caloric and oxygen. On his return to France, he published a paper on analytical optics and another on the refractive indices of opaque bodies, both being, like the former, of little significance. An announcement of a proposed prize by the Paris Academy for a mathematical theory of double refraction directed him towards some of his most fruitful labours. While engaged upon this problem at his house in the Rue d'enfer, one evening he was looking through a calcite crystal at the reflection of the setting sun in a window of the Luxembourg Palace and was astonished to see for certain orientations only *one* image instead of two, the ordinary and the extraordinary images disappearing in turn on rotating the crystal. His first conclusion was of a modification of the light by the atmosphere. In the meantime, however, the sun had set, and the observation could not be repeated as before. Malus thus allowed light from a candle to be reflected first from a water surface and then from a glass surface and tested it with a calcite crystal. Conversely, light was also subjected to reflection after it left the calcite crystal. On the night of his original observation he had thus discovered the essential features of what, in consideration for the views that Newton had already expressed, is termed " polarized " light. An account of his experiment of 1808 was first published in 1809, the following being an excerpt of some of its principal features.

Sunlight which has undergone reflection or refraction is in general indistinguishable from direct sunlight, but in certain circumstances, for example after passage through a doubly refracting medium, it is endowed with permanent distinguishing features. Such light behaves no longer as direct sunlight in a second doubly refracting body and, moreover, quite differently according as the two principal sections are parallel or perpendicular. It is also apparent that all solid and liquid transparent, and even opaque, bodies effect a modification of the light. Light reflected from a water surface at an angle of $52° 45'$ is transmitted by calcite having its principal section parallel to the plane of incidence simply as an ordinary ray, and, when the principal section is perpendicular, as an extraordinary ray (Fig. 181). If, also, the light transmitted by calcite is allowed to undergo reflection at this angle from a water surface, the principal section of the calcite being parallel to the plane of incidence, the ordinary rays are to a certain extent reflected, while the extraordinary rays all enter the water completely

---

* Malus, " Mémoires de Physique et de chemie de la societe d'Arcueil," Paris (1809), Vol. 2, pp. 143, etc., 254, etc. See Appendix.
    † Arago, " Œuvres," " Notices biographiques," Vol. 3, p. 113.

without reflection. Reflection may thus be utilized to produce the characteristic modification of light as well as to detect it (Fig. 182).

The most effective angle of reflection for the production of the modification is different for each substance and is, in general, greater, the greater the refractive index. We shall, following Malus, call the modification "polarization" and the most effective angle, the "polarizing" angle. Light polarized by reflection is defined as "polarized in the plane of incidence," and the plane itself is called the "plane of polarization." Malus now observed that, if light

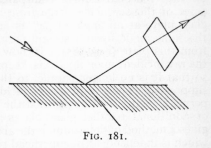

FIG. 181.

is reflected at the polarizing angle from the first surface of a plane parallel plate, the same occurs also at the second surface (Fig. 183). The sines of the polarizing angles for both cases thus bear the same ratio as the refractive index. For a more convenient verification,

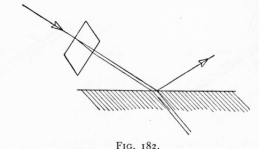

FIG. 182.

Malus later used a prism of the form shown in Fig. 184, in which the ray reflected from the second surface emerges perpendicular to the upper surface, and thus with its polarization unchanged. The complete polarization of this ray is easily proved by subjecting it to

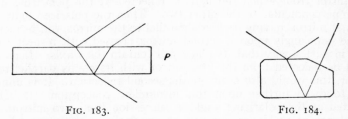

FIG. 183.   FIG. 184.

another reflection. We shall not discuss further here the behaviour of the rays reflected in doubly refracting crystals, but only mention that Malus noticed an anomalous behaviour of metals with respect to polarization in contrast with transparent substances.

The second publication gives a few points of a supplementary nature. In the case of simple reflection, forces allied to those which produce double refraction must be operative, thus making it possible for rays reflected from a transparent substance to assume the character of those which emerge from calcite. If a ray is incident on a glass plate at an angle of 54° 35′ and, after reflection, is incident at the same angle upon a second parallel plate, the ray is reflected also from this plate (Fig. 185). If, now, the second plate is rotated about the ray incident upon it as axis, keeping the angle of incidence constant, so that it is no longer parallel to the first, the ray reflected from it is suppressed when the planes of incidence for both plates are mutually perpendicular. In this position the ray is transmitted by any number of additional parallel glass plates without loss by reflection, which gives a method of determining the absorption by transparent substances which is independent of superficial reflection.

Polarized light behaves at reflection in an essentially different manner from ordinary light. Whereas the reflected intensity of ordinary light increases with increasing angle of incidence up to grazing incidence, that of light reflected at a second mirror after polariza-

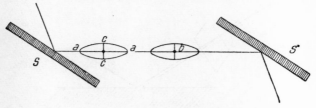

FIG. 185.

tion at a first with its plane of incidence perpendicular to that of the second, indicates, with increasing angle of incidence at the second mirror, a minimum at the polarizing angle and a further increase as the angle is increased. To obtain a clear conception of the processes involved, Malus assumed each particle of light to be provided with three distinguishing axes, a in the direction of the ray, b parallel to the mirror from which the light is reflected at the polarizing angle, and c perpendicular to the other two. Then the polarized light from the first mirror, having its b axis parallel to the mirror, will be incident at the same angle upon a second mirror, crossed with respect to the first, in such a way that its plane will contain the c axis. If no light could be reflected from the first mirror with its c axis parallel to the mirror, this would also occur at the second reflection. It is unnecessary to dwell further upon this incomplete conception. If light is reflected at the polarizing angle in succession from two mirrors with the planes of incidence inclined at an angle a, then, according to Malus, the intensity of the final reflected light is to that of the incident light as $\cos^2 a : 1$. This important result holds similarly for two calcite crystals whose principal sections are inclined at the angle a. Malus does not lay claim to having discovered the cause of these polar-

PLATE VIII

E^{NNE} L^{IS} MALUS

(1775 - 1812)

ization phenomena, but to have shown the nature of their interdependence and to have displayed them in a form amenable to mathematical calculation.

Towards the end of 1809, Malus recognized that not only reflected light, but also refracted light, showed traces of polarization. For, while light reflected at the polarizing angle from a glass plate is polarized completely, the corresponding refracted rays exhibit this property to a lesser extent. If, however, several parallel glass plates are placed one behind the other (Fig. 186), the final refracted light is almost completely polarized and, moreover, the reflected and refracted rays behave like the ordinary and extraordinary rays of calcite, that is to say, each exhibits the peculiarities appropriate to the other on being turned through 90°. The same observation was made at about the same time, although perhaps less completely, by Biot.

If, following Malus, it is assumed that in ordinary light as many b axes as c axes are contained in any line perpendicular to the direction of the ray, and at reflection a selection of light particles having definite orientations takes place, it follows that the remainder of the light which escapes reflection will also show traces of polarization. If a

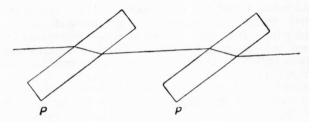

Fig. 186.

substance existed which reflected *one half* of the light at the polarizing angle, the other refracted half must, according to Arago, likewise be completely polarized in a reverse way after a single refraction, that is, be capable of supplementing the reflected half to form unpolarized light. Arago deduced the law, as a sequence to Malus' observations, that the quantity (not the fraction) of polarized light contained in the refracted ray must be exactly the same as that in the reflected ray.

Malus' discovery constituted an important advance. Up to that time the polarization or asymmetry of light had always been considered a special property of doubly refracting substances, and it was on account of its appearance in quite new and simple circumstances that the independent nature of polarization was first recognized, and a clear perception of it as an independent property of light first obtained. The consequent broadening of ideas was not to be underrated. While Kepler had become acquainted with reflection without refraction, Malus had discovered a refracted ray without a corresponding reflected ray. In this way the most elementary conceptions were affected by the newly obtained ideas and remoulded.

The climax of Malus' discoveries was that of the so-called cosine square law which he saw fit to deduce from the point of view of mechanical conceptions of the turning of light molecules by the forces of reflection and refraction. It is probably not incorrect to assume that another consideration was also suggested by his *material* conception of light, and was most likely to be his real source of information.

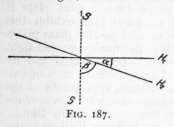

FIG. 187.

Let the principal sections H_1, H_2 of two calcite crystals include the angle a (Fig. 187), and let SS be a plane perpendicular to H_1. An ordinary ray of unit intensity emerging from H_2 is transmitted in H_1 as an ordinary ray of an intensity which is a function of the angle a, and as an extraordinary ray whose intensity is the same function of the angle β, since either ray is distinguishable from the other only by its relative rotation of 90°. In any case, however, the sum of the intensities (the quantities of the light substance) must be unity. This holds when cos a is chosen as the function of a, for

$$\cos^2 a + \cos^2 \beta = \cos^2 a + \sin^2 a = 1.$$

Arago, moreover, found the consequences of this law confirmed by photometric experiments and used it as the principle of his polarization photometer. It is thus obvious that the conception of light as a substance, in as far as it advocated a correct and important conception of the invariability of *quantity*, was a useful one, and the adaptability of this hypothesis could not be altogether useful.

The knowledge of polarization was materially advanced by the labours of Brewster,* though his views have not in every case been confirmed by the subsequent developments in optics. Brewster conceived the ordinary unpolarized light to consist of two perpendicular, polarized, components of equal intensity which, in fact, would be obtained by recombining the two types of ray emerging from calcite. Polarized light was thus obtained by separating the two components by double refraction. The two polarized components could also be relatively inclined at an angle other than a right angle, which constituted partially polarized light, the coincidence of the components giving complete polarization, as when produced by reflection or refraction. A third manner of producing polarized light, discovered by Brewster, consists in absorbing one of the components, for example by transmission through agate. He noticed that a plate of agate,† cut perpendicular to its cleavage plane, transmitted no rays polarized perpendicular to the latter if the thickness were great enough. The transmitted light was thus polarized in a plane parallel to the cleavage plane. A similar peculiarity was discovered almost simultaneously by Biot and Seebeck in the case of tourmaline cut parallel to its axis ; this transmits only the rays polarized perpendicular to the axis, the others being absorbed. Biot constructed a tourmaline prism having

---

* D. Brewster, " Treatise on Optics," London (1831).
† Brewster, *loc. cit.*, p. 182 ; *Edinburgh Encyclopædia*, Vol. 15, pp. 600, 601 ; *Phil. Trans. Roy. Soc.* (1819), p. 146.

its refracting edge parallel to the axis and observed two images, one colourless and the other greenish, on looking at a needle through the prism in the neighbourhood of its edge, this showing the existence of double refraction.   The green image, which was formed by light polarized parallel to the axis, was more faint the farther away from the edge of the prism the light passed.

Brewster's conception of partially polarized light was in conflict with that of Arago, who considered it to be a mixture of unpolarized and polarized light.   According to Biot, unpolarized light was formed by a superposition of polarized light having every possible orientation of its plane of polarization perpendicular to the direction of the ray.

Whereas Malus had not succeeded in discovering any relation between refractive index and polarizing angle, Brewster * was able to show from numerous observations that the tangent of the polarizing angle is equal to the refractive index.   Thus

$$\tan p = \mu, \text{ or } \sin p/\cos p = \sin p/\sin p',$$

and therefore $\cos p = \sin p'$, which indicates that, for complete polarization of the reflected ray at the polarizing angle, the reflected and refracted rays are mutually perpendicu-
lar (Fig. 188).   By means of this tangent law (Brewster's law), Brewster concluded that on account of dispersion the polarization produced in the refracted beam could never be so complete as in the case of double refraction, since the law is not simultaneously fulfilled for all colours.   In fact, he obtained brilliant colour effects when he used glasses or other media of large dispersion.   Brewster independently discovered polarization by

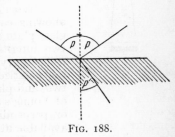

FIG. 188.

refraction in glass plates practically at the same time as Malus and Biot, and deduced laws corresponding to those discovered by Malus. He also performed detailed experiments on polarization by successive reflections and refractions at any given angle of incidence.

In a letter dated 1st January, 1814, Fresnel † requested his brother to procure for him Haüy's " Physik " and some publications dealing with polarization, so that he might learn something of the matters with which he himself could make so little progress.   After only two years Fresnel was in a position to further the knowledge of polarization by an investigation in collaboration with Arago.‡   Both investigators first wished to know whether polarization had any influence on interference effects, but their experiments at first gave negative results, light from a source emitting polarized light producing the same effects as if it were unpolarized.   Fresnel then endeavoured to obtain interference from the two images produced by means of

* Brewster, *loc. cit.*, pp. 169, etc.
† Fresnel, " Œuvres complètes," Vol. 1, Introduction, p. xxix.
‡ Arago, *loc. cit.*, p. 129.

calcite, but no fringes were visible, even when the inequality in wave-length of the ordinary and extraordinary rays was compensated for by interposing a suitable glass plate in one of the beams.   Two calcite crystals of equal thickness, placed one behind the other with principal sections crossed, for which the compensation must have been very exact, were also of no effect.   This fortunate variation caused Fresnel to surmise that rays polarized perpendicularly to one another are incapable of interference.   This he at once confirmed by remembering that a thin plate of gypsum or quartz appears colourless against the blue sky,* although between calcite plates it shows colours which Fresnel considered to be interference colours.   Arago † considered a more direct proof desirable.   He therefore proposed to polarize the

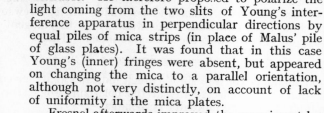

light coming from the two slits of Young's inter-ference apparatus in perpendicular directions by equal piles of mica strips (in place of Malus' pile of glass plates).   It was found that in this case Young's (inner) fringes were absent, but appeared on changing the mica to a parallel orientation, although not very distinctly, on account of lack of uniformity in the mica plates.

Fresnel afterwards improved the experiment by allowing each of the two beams to pass through a glass plate at the polarizing angle and utilizing the two internal reflections.   Arago then thought of using a crystalline plate transmitting only one of the polarized rays (e.g. tourmaline), dividing it in two, and placing one portion before each of the slits of Young's apparatus, with their axes either parallel or perpendicular.   Since such a crystal was not available at the time, the pile of mica strips was used.   Fresnel covered the two slits with a single plate of gypsum, and later with a single quartz plate of about 1 mm. thickness cut parallel to its axis, in which case the rays transmitted by double refraction do not differ in direction, but have a path difference of a few wave-lengths.   To visualize a

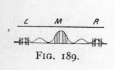

Fig. 189.

particular case, assume that quartz has been used.   The ordinary rays passing through both slits form a symmetrical fringe system in the centre of a screen or the focal plane of a magnifying lens, and the ex-traordinary rays produce a similar system.   Both are identical and coin-cide on the screen.   Since the extraordinary rays in quartz are retarded with respect to the ordinary rays, Fresnel thought that the extra-ordinary rays E_R coming from the right-hand slit in conjunction with the ordinary rays O_L from the left-hand slit must produce a fringe system towards the right at R (Fig. 189), that is, if they are *capable* of inter-fering, and a similar system would be found at L formed by E_L and O_R. This was an error on Fresnel's part, since it is at once obvious that here there are simply two identical fringe systems as observed by

---

* Fresnel, " Œuvres complètes," Vol. 1, pp. 523, etc.
† Arago, " Mémoires scientifique," Vol. 4, p. 381.

Young, produced one by the ordinary and the other by the extraordinary rays and superposed. Both types of ray have, indeed, a path difference, which, however, varies, not with the position on the screen, but with the *colour*, which is what occurs in the case of chromatic polarization effects.

This mistake did not prove important and even had a favourable action on the continuation of the investigation. For, to test his views, Fresnel divided the quartz plate in two and placed one portion over each slit so that the axis of the quartz was, say, horizontal for the right-hand, and vertical for the left-hand slit. The dissimilar rays from the two slits were now polarized in a parallel direction, while the similar rays were polarized perpendicularly. Fringe systems now appeared near R and L, but not at M, that at R being produced by the interference of E_R and O_L, which were polarized in the same direction, and that at L by E_L and O_R. On the other hand at M only O_R and O_L, or E_R and E_L, would be able to give visible interference, but this is excluded by the fact that they are polarized perpendicularly. Immediately the axes of the quartz were inclined at 45° instead of 90°, all three fringe systems appeared simultaneously, the middle one being more distinct since it consists of two systems superposed. The interference effects are only invisible when the planes of polarization are arranged at right angles, and any appreciable departure from this condition brings them into view. The separation of the two side fringe systems depends on the thickness and the degree of double refraction of the crystalline plates, and Arago at once recognized * that the above experiments could be made use of for the quantitative investigation of weak double refraction.

Arago then performed the following experiment. One of the two similar piles of mica strips was placed in front of each of the slits of Young's apparatus in such a way that light was transmitted at the polarizing angle, one pile having a vertical and the other a horizontal, plane of incidence. With a thin quartz plate, cut parallel to its axis and placed over the slits with its axis inclined at 45° to the horizontal, it would be expected that the ordinary rays from both slits would give a central fringe system and the extraordinary rays another similar one. In reality this did not happen, and the further result was obtained that light which emerges from sources polarized in two perpendicular directions cannot be made to interfere by subsequently making the planes of polarization coplanar. Fresnel † was easily able to modify his experiment in which two crossed quartz plates were placed one over each of the slits of Young's apparatus so that he obtained the same result. If light polarized at 45° with respect to the axis of the quartz (e.g. by a pile of mica strips) was allowed to fall on the two slits, only the two side fringe systems were visible to the naked eye. When, however, a calcite crystal was held in front of the eye, with its principal section inclined at 45° to the axis of the quartz, all three fringe systems could be seen in each of the images it produced.

---

* Arago, " Mémoires scientifique," Vol. 1, p. 132.
† Fresnel, " Œuvres complètes," Vol. 15, pp, 386, etc. ; Vol. 18, p. 521 ; and Vol. 19.

On removing the pile of mica from the slits, the central fringes disappeared.   Thus only light polarized in parallel directions is capable of interference, and light which is initially polarized in perpendicular directions and subsequently brought to the same plane, only when it has come from the same polarized beam.   In a variation of this experiment, using a *single* plate of quartz to cover both slits, Fresnel fell into the same error as before.   Here this is to a certain extent pardonable since, when the experiment is performed according to Fresnel's method, the observer thinks that side fringes are visible, these, however, being, as I have indicated on another page, no true interference fringes.   Incidentally Fresnel also used a mirror device instead of the double slits, and interposed the crystalline plates one in each beam, thus making the effects more brilliant.   Since now the conditions under which polarized light can interfere were exactly known, Fresnel was able to perform his experiment with the crossed calcite crystals, which had previously given a negative result.   If thus polarized light from a point source is allowed to fall on this combination with its plane of polarization inclined at 45° to the principal section of the first crystal, and the light emerging from the second is made to pass through a third calcite crystal for example, which is oriented so that its planes of polarization are inclined at 45° to the principal section of the second crystal, fringes are obtained as distinct as those with the ordinary Fresnel mirror experiment with unpolarized light.   In leaving the consideration of such less important experiments, it may be mentioned that in the form of a footnote Fresnel indicated hesitatingly the conception of transverse vibrations, to which he did not yet venture to express definite adherence.   The phenomena of chromatic polarization also often engaged his attention, being introduced here and there among the above-described experiments, but, as he had not altogether discovered their origin, they appeared somewhat unfamiliar to him and led him to evolve certain postulates which later proved unnecessary.

The results of the Fresnel-Arago experiments were summarized as follows :—

1. Under the conditions in which ordinary light rays exhibit destructive interference, two rays of light polarized in perpendicular planes indicate no trace of any interaction.

2. Rays polarized in the same plane interfere like unpolarized rays, the effects being identical in each case.

3. Rays originally polarized in perpendicular planes may be subsequently brought to the same plane of polarization without attaining the ability to interfere.

4. Rays polarized in perpendicular planes and brought to the same plane interfere like unpolarized rays if they originate in the same polarized beam.

A fifth proposition has reference to one of the above-mentioned postulates which is later found superfluous.

In the above-mentioned publications, an explanation of the colours of thin laminæ of mica and gypsum in polarized light, which had in the meantime been discovered and studied, is entered into.   It will, therefore, be necessary to consider here a few of the most important of these effects. In the course of his experiments on Newton's rings in polarized light * the idea occurred to Arago to view a mica lamina against the bright sky through a calcite crystal. He was surprised to find the two images differently coloured, the intensity of coloration varying also with the time of day and region of the sky. The fact that the light from the sky had thus proved of different polarization in different regions and times of the day led him to interpose the mica between a polarizing mirror and calcite, which made the coloration extraordinarily brilliant.

If the piece of mica was perpendicular to the light coming from the polarizing mirror, it was found that there were two perpendicular directions in the mica which had the property that when either contained the plane of polarization the mica was completely without effect. For any other position of the mica, it had, according to Arago's expression, a " depolarizing " action, since the calcite always indicated two images, even for those orientations of the principal section with which, using the mirror alone, only one image was apparent. The two images showed colours which were complementary, since in the region where they were superposed the colour was white. On turning the mica in its own plane, the hue of the coloration remained the same, except for the two positions of no effect, and only the degree of saturation varied, the latter being greatest when the above-mentioned two directions formed an angle of 45° with the plane of polarization of the incident light and with the principal section of the calcite. The light depolarized by the mica differs from ordinary unpolarized light since in the former the different colours are affected by unequal amounts. The coloration depends on the thickness of the mica, which is made evident by using a mica wedge which shows coloured bands parallel to its edge. Gypsum behaves similarly to mica. Since substances known to be doubly refracting behaved like mica, Arago supposed that mica also was doubly refracting. He thought he had discovered an experimental means of detecting weak double refraction even in those substances which are only obtainable in small fragments, although he was not quite certain of this, since he found that flint glass, which is non-crystalline, also indicated colour effects in these circumstances. Doubtful points such as these would, however, be removed by further experiments. Arago † also observed these colour effects in a similar way with thick quartz plates cut perpendicular to their axes. While the effects were unaltered by rotating the quartz about its axis, turning the analysing calcite caused a whole series of colours to pass, the colour of one image always being complementary to the other. Arago called the whole group of phenomena by the name of *polarization colorée* (chromatic polarization). A rapid succession of similar observations followed.

In 1813 Brewster ‡ independently observed a series of effects

---

* Arago, " Mémoire sur les couleurs des lames minces," *Mémoires d'Arcueil* (1817), Vol. 3 ; " Œuvres complètes d'Arago," Vol. 10.
  † Arago, " Mémoires scientifique," Vol. 1, pp. 402, etc.
  ‡ Brewster, *Phil. Trans. Roy. Soc.* (1814), pp. 203, 211.

similar to those found by Arago, and discovered the axial system of colours obtained with topaz, while Wollaston found the ring system of calcite, Biot, Seebeck, and J. Herschel also making further discoveries. Brewster * in 1818 recognized the connexion between the optical and crystallographical properties of uniaxial and biaxial crystals. Arago found that the effects with quartz were due to a rotation of the plane of polarization by the quartz ; this was investigated quantitatively by Biot, who discovered a right-hand and left-hand rotation, the relation of which to the crystallographical properties was recognized by J. Herschel.† In 1815 Biot ‡ found a rotation of the plane of polarization in liquids.

Biot § rendered great service in the development of the knowledge of chromatic polarization, and carried out many important observations and accurate measurements. The phenomena in question exhibit a few marked, general, characteristic features. If a gypsum or mica lamina placed between two mirrors functioning as polarizer and analyser is imagined to be capable of increasing gradually in thickness, the mirrors remaining unchanged, the same colours appear in a periodic succession, but gradually get less saturated and finally merge into white. With the mirrors mutually perpendicular and with very thin laminæ, the colour at the commencement is black, while with the mirrors parallel it is white. The analogy with Newton's rings by reflected and transmitted light is here complete to the extent of the appearance (with a few rare exceptions) of the *same* colours. On gradually rotating the analysing mirror from the perpendicular to the parallel position, the colour likewise gradually changes into the complementary. When the principal section of the lamina is either parallel or perpendicular to the plane of polarization, the lamina has no effect, while the 45° position gives the most marked coloration. All these data find a natural place in Biot's theory of dynamic polarization (polarisation mobile), which resulted from their consideration and was an imitation of Newton's theory of " fits."

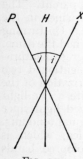

FIG. 190.

Biot imagined that the particles of a ray polarized in the plane P (Fig. 190), immediately after entering the plate with principal section H, commence oscillating about the latter with equal excursions to either side, so that the ray appears periodically polarized along P and along X. The periods are considered to vary with the colour, as in Newton's theory. The moment the ray reaches the second surface of the plate, the oscillations cease and the analysing mirror records the plane of polarization occupied by each colour at the instant of leaving the plate. For oblique passage through a crystal the rays

* Brewster, " On the Laws of Polarization and Double Refraction in Regularly Crystallized Bodies," *Phil. Trans. Roy. Soc.* (1818).
† J. F. W. Herschel, " Vom Lichte," Tubingen (1831), pp. 581, etc.
‡ Biot, *Le bulletin de la société philomatique* (Dec. 1815).
§ Biot, " Traité de physique experimentale et mathematique," Paris (1816), Vol. 4, pp. 317, etc.

must assume other periods of oscillation, in order that the results may agree with the effects observed by Brewster, Wollaston, and others. It must be assumed that in a thicker crystal the oscillations of the plane of polarization gradually come to rest, since in this case the emergent light always indicates only two fixed planes of polarization independent of the thickness. This alleged dissimilar behaviour of thin and thick crystals, as well as the impossibility of determining the boundary between the two properties or the nature of their transition, constitutes an essential weakness of Biot's theory. Further experimenting led Biot into fresh difficulties. He found that very thick crystalline plates with crossed principal sections also exhibit colours which correspond to the difference of the thickness, facts which could only be explained along the lines of the above views by means of new and very ingenious assumptions, into which it would not be worth while to enter.

In the *Quarterly Review* of 1814, Young * reviews the researches on polarization, and expresses the view that Biot's theory may well serve the purpose for which it was devised, namely, to explain the phenomena of one particular branch of optics, but may not be at all consistent with the other optical theories. The interference principle has many merits, and even if it be incapable of explaining polarization, it may be equally applicable to all cases of recurrent colours. He shows that, in a doubly refracting crystalline plate which exhibits a particular polarization colour, the path difference between the ordinary and extraordinary rays is constant, as for a Newton's ring of a definite colour. On the other hand he was unable to explain why the two perpendicularly polarized rays only interfere under certain conditions. Brewster, in 1815, declared the impossibility of explaining polarization by means of waves. In an article on " Chromatics " in the *Encyclopædia Britannica* of 1817, Young † endeavoured to approach an explanation of polarization by means of the assumption of transverse waves. According to the article it must be assumed that we are concerned with oscillations in a direction oblique to that of the ray. The production of a feeble transverse motion by the concurrence of two longitudinal waves of approximately the same direction and half a wave-length path difference is discussed. Young, however, considers the adoption of an " imaginary transverse vibration " not as a physical explanation, but only as a means for representation. Again, in 1827, Young, in a supplement to Arago's article on polarization (*Encyclopædia Britannica*), returns to the physical difficulties connected with the conception of transverse waves. He considered that the ether, to be capable of propagating such waves, must not only be extremely elastic, but also be a *solid*.

As early as 1816, Fresnel, when at work on the interference of polarized light,‡ also maintained an active interest in the problem of

---

* Young, " Review of Malus, Biot, Seebeck, and Brewster on Light," *Quarterly Review* (April, 1814), Vol. 11, p. 42 ; also, " Miscellaneous Works," London (1855), Vol. 1, p. 260.

† *Ibid.*, p. 279, from the supplement to the *Encyc. Brit.* (1817).

‡ Fresnel, " Œuvres Complètes," Vol. 1, pp. 79, etc. (vii-x).

Arago's chromatic polarization.   He recognized the colours of crystalline plates as interference colours, conditioned by the path difference
between the ordinary and extraordinary rays, and communicated this
opinion to Arago, who had drawn his attention to Young's article
of 1814.   Fresnel had discovered, independently of Young, that the
thickness of a crystalline plate corresponding to a particular colour
could be calculated beforehand from the wave-length and the refractive
index, and that the result was in exact agreement with the measurement of Biot.   The question as to the rôle played by polarization,
which Young had left unsolved, he found a difficult one, though at
least it was apparent that for his interference experiments and for
Arago's colour effects the same principle was in operation.   Thus he
had no hesitation in contrasting his theory, which was based solely
on facts, with that of Biot, which was full of hypotheses.   He criticized the weaknesses of the latter theory : Why should the behaviour
of thin crystalline plates be so completely different from that of thick
plates, or why should the plane of polarization, which according to
Biot's own experiments oscillates to so great an extent, suddenly
become fixed ?   Fresnel's interference experiment proved that, even
with very thin plates, the light emerged with
two fixed planes of polarization.   Fresnel thus
assumed that the incident light polarized in the
plane P is split up by the crystal according to
the cosine square law of Malus into two components parallel and perpendicular to the
principal section H, and that the light reflected from the analysing mirror with plane of
reflection R is the fraction of the components
resolved according to the same law, this being
capable of interference.   He found that Biot's
formulæ were to a certain extent applicable, so

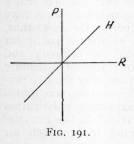

FIG. 191.

that the latter's work was by no means useless.   The fact that the same
plate, that is to say the same path difference, gave a complementary
coloration for the parallel and perpendicular positions of the mirrors
caused Fresnel some hesitation.   He was, however, reassured by
considering that light was only resolved by the crystal, and thus,
according to the principle of *vis viva*, which was introduced on discarding Malus' material conception of light, a loss of light on the one
hand must mean a gain in intensity elsewhere.   Here also he found
the same mysterious phase difference of half a wave-length as elsewhere,
as for example in the case of Newton's rings, which he thought would
be explained when a fuller knowledge of the nature of polarization
and double refraction had been obtained.   As a general rule, he
found, with consideration of Biot's results, that to determine the
colour, a half wave-length is to be added to the path difference if the
deflection of the polarized components from their original direction
has occurred through a double rotation in the same sense (as in Fig.
191).   This was an essential advance beyond the conceptions of Biot.
    In 1816 it had occurred to Fresnel * that rays of light polarized

* Fresnel, " Œuvres complètes," Vol. 1, Introduction, p. xiii ; and " Theorie de la
lumière," Section 2.

in perpendicular directions behave analogously to mutually perpendicular forces. He communicated this observation to Ampère, and both soon arrived at the conclusion that all interference effects with polarized light were easily explicable if it could be assumed that the vibrations were transverse. Fresnel, however, was able to deduce as little from this hypothesis as his predecessor Young. In the first instance, to explain polarization he postulated a ray with oblique vibrations having feeble transverse components. What was the part played by the longitudinal vibrations in this case, however, which had up to that time proved so convenient and had been assumed by Fresnel to be the essential constituent ? The whole subject was thus laid aside until several years later an absorbing problem led him back to it. A letter of 29th April, 1818, from Young to Arago,* whose contents became known to Fresnel through Arago, may have contributed towards this. Young compared the ether with an infinitely long transversely vibrating string. Fresnel expressed the obvious criticism that Young had not elucidated the possibility of such a motion in a liquid, and when towards the year 1821 he was able to show how this could occur, he confessed without hesitation to the theory of transverse vibrations, which proved of such value. How difficult a step this was is evident from the fact that his collaborator Arago explicitly declined responsibility for it. That part of their joint work which contains the matter relevant to this theory appeared in 1821 in the *Annales de chimie* under Fresnel's name alone.

Fresnel's conception of the ether † which first seemed to justify the assumption of transverse vibrations was an atomic one. The atoms of a liquid, he considered, were not to be conceived as *entirely without* positions of stable equilibrium, but only to be imagined as having these positions in much closer proximity than in a solid. The active disturbance is then transmitted over a series of equilibrium positions and the particles are then *easily displaceable*, while for small displacements the state of stable equilibrium is not in any way destroyed, and the particles are set into vibration about their position of rest by the elastic forces. The longitudinal waves in such a medium are again introduced when the repulsive forces are assumed very great. In this case a pressure is propagated much faster than the transverse vibrations. The latter are produced by the elastic displacements relative to each other of the layers perpendicular to the direction of propagation. According to this theory the ether is conceived as an incompressible fluid which under these conditions behaves like a solid body.

With the assumption of transverse vibrations, all the difficulties which prevented Arago's phenomena from being correctly understood disappeared. The vibrations must, on account of symmetry conditions, be either in the plane of polarization or perpendicular to it. In most cases the choice of the one or the other does not matter, but for certain cases, for reasons to be mentioned later, Fresnel chose the

---

* Fresnel, " Œuvres complètes," Vol. 1, Introduction, p. lviii.
† *Ibid.*, Vol. 2 ; " Theorie de la lumière," pp. 50, etc.

latter assumption. If a (Figs. 192, 193) represents the direction of the displacements in the incident light, and if b and c represent the same for the components of the vibration in the crystal plate resolved respectively parallel and perpendicular to the principal section, it is obvious that, for an analysing mirror crossed with respect to the polarizer, d and e indicate opposite phases while, for a parallel setting of the analyser, the phases are identical. The enigma which occupied the attention of Biot and Fresnel had thus been solved.

Each point of a luminous substance vibrates at each instant only in *one* particular plane, but these planes are different at successive instants for a particular point, and different at the same instant for neighbouring points. Thus unpolarized light is composed of a super-position of polarized rays, since an unpolarized beam can be regarded as consisting of a collection of polarized rays in each of which the plane of polarization is rapidly varying.

The process of polarization by reflection, double refraction, etc., thus does not consist of an *excitation* of a particular mode of vibration, but only in the selection of special directions of vibration. The

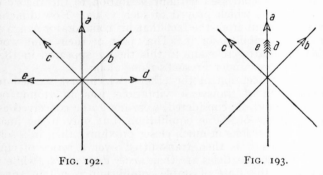

FIG. 192.   FIG. 193.

cosine square law of Malus is a self-evident consequence of the resolution of the vibrations in association with the principle of *vis viva*, by which the light intensity is measured by the square of the velocity (or amplitude). The Fresnel-Arago laws of interference of polarized light likewise readily follow from the assumption of transverse vibration, for motions which are mutually perpendicular can have no effect on one another. Fresnel does not mention that the two perpendicular, polarized, components of ordinary light are incoherent, but this would follow from the nature of his views.

As we have seen, great difficulties had to be overcome before the nature of polarization could be thoroughly explained. This was, no doubt, the reason why workers of such renown worked on this problem, and the cause of the tardy nature of its solution. It would thus be worth our while to go into the nature of these difficulties. Here it is best to adopt the naïve attitude of the beginner, to which even the great investigator must succumb with respect to an entirely new problem. It was while attending the grammar school (gymnasium) that I first heard of the transverse vibrations of which light must consist. This view made a very strange, phantastic, and unsympathetic impression on me, without my knowing the actual cause. When I tried, with the aid of my memory, to obtain a clearer view of the matter, I had to confess that I felt instinctively the impossibility of transverse vibrations in so readily movable (displaceable) a medium as air, and thus more so for the ether, which I considered must be still more rarefied and easily displaceable. Malus' mirror, which when turned about the polarized ray as axis at one time reflects and at another not, soon brought me a steadfast conviction of the existence of transverse waves capable of propagating light. The question of mechanical possibility was quite forgotten, being altogether insignificant compared with the resulting explanation of actual facts. The sequel to, and usage of, this conception alone finally seemed to justify it. Others, as students, may probably have had similar experiences. This, it seems to me, has also occurred in the history of optics. It is one question, what actual property of light it is that makes itself evident in polarization, and quite a different one, whether this property may be (mechanically) explained or further reduced. The fact that these two questions have not always been clearly distinguished has often had a retarding action on the progress of optics. This is obvious even with Huygens. Newton clearly set forth the facts of polarization, as far as they were known in his time, and distinctly separated from them the explanation. Malus did the same, but in Fresnel's time the necessity for such a separation was no longer so clearly recognized by investigators. The Fresnel-Arago interference experiments indicate, as an actual fact, *that the periodic properties of light behave like geometrically additive elements of a two-dimensional space* (a plane perpendicular to the ray), and this is true whether it can be explained or not. There was no need for Fresnel to keep back this important discovery since he thought that he had found a mechanical explanation, this being of a very hypothetical nature, whereas the matter to be explained is in no wise hypothetical. Newton behaved in a similar manner when he did not announce the law of inverse squares in the case of gravity because he was unable to explain it.

The knowledge of polarization was increased by yet another experiment carried out by Fresnel in 1817. If the light transmitted by a calcite crystal and then reflected from a glass or liquid surface was investigated by means of a second calcite crystal, each of the four resulting images vanished once in succession, no matter how the principal section of the first crystal was oriented with respect to the plane of reflection. This indicates that polarized light remains polarized after reflection, no matter in what direction the plane of polarization of the incident light may lie. In general only the azimuth of the plane of polarization is altered. This result was overlooked by both Malus and Biot. If the reflecting surface had no polarizing action, and only effected that modification of light which is an intrinsic part of reflection itself, and reproduced all vibrations symmetrically, the plane of polarization of the reflected light, Fresnel considered, should be the mirror image of the plane of polarization of the incident light. If the plane of polarization is either parallel or perpendicular to the plane of incidence, this position is also retained by the reflected light, only a variation in intensity being effected.   By resolving a polarized beam according to the cosine square law of Malus into these two planes, and regarding the components as equivalent to the unresolved beam, any particular case can be interpreted in terms of the two simplest cases.

Light polarized at 45° with respect to the plane of incidence was investigated.   For perpendicular incidence no change of the plane of polarization was evident.   On increasing the angle of incidence, the plane of polarization of the reflected light approached the plane of incidence, with which it coincided at the polarizing angle.   Increasing the angle of incidence further, the plane of polarization moved in the reverse direction, until at grazing incidence it was again identical with that of the incident light.   For a given polarization azimuth of the incident light, the azimuth of the reflected light thus varied with the angle of incidence.   Light reflected from the front and back surfaces of a coated glass plate, after grazing incidence with a polarization azimuth of 45°, proved to be polarized respectively in perpendicular directions, the total light from the glass in front behaving like that passing with an enormous path difference through a calcite crystal.

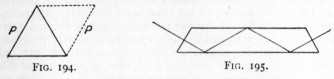

FIG. 194.   FIG. 195.

Metals have, for incidence other than perpendicular or grazing, an appreciable depolarizing action.

These experiments naturally led to an investigation of reflection at the second glass-air surface of a glass plate.   In order to be able to work at all angles of incidence, Fresnel first chose a prism, then combined two prisms (Fig. 194), and finally manufactured rhombs of appropriate shapes.   Light whose plane of polarization was inclined at 45° to the plane of incidence also remained completely polarized after reflection, provided that the limit of total reflection was not yet reached.   For total reflection, a partial depolarization could be detected by means of a calcite crystal.   The region of Newton's blue fringe was coloured since the limit of total reflection and of depolarization was not attained simultaneously for all colours.   For a further increase in the angle of incidence beyond the limit of total reflection, the extent of depolarization at first increases rapidly and then falls off gradually until at grazing incidence no depolarization is detectable. The depolarization effected by total reflection can be removed by a second reflection at the same angle of incidence, but with the plane of incidence perpendicular to the first ; with the planes parallel, however, the extent of depolarization is increased and may be made complete by two, three, or four total reflections (Fig. 195), according to the refractive index of the glass and the angle of incidence.   In this case for any position of the principal section the two images are equally intense. Light which has been completely depolarized by two reflections is again partially polarized after a third exactly similar reflection, and after four such reflections (in the same plane) is again completely polarized, but in a plane perpendicular to the original one. Six reflections in parallel planes produce complete depolarization once more, and eight reflections complete polarization again in a plane parallel to the original.

Light depolarized by total reflection is essentially different from ordinary light, since the latter cannot be transformed by several total reflections alternately into polarized and depolarized light, but maintains throughout its characteristic symmetric behaviour. Light depolarized by these means produces, like polarized light, colour effects in crystals, and here again distinguishes itself from ordinary (unpolarized) light.

By a more accurate study of the colour effects produced in gypsum or quartz plates, cut parallel to their axes, by light depolarized by total reflection, Fresnel was able to give an important explanation of the nature of the depolarization. Since the light emerges after two total reflections in a rhomb parallel to its initial direction, the colours indicated by gypsum both in the direct polarized light and in the depolarized beam may be conveniently observed and compared simultaneously through a *single* calcite crystal, and a convincing proof of their difference obtained. If the axis of the gypsum is parallel to the plane of incidence of the rhomb, the colours correspond to a greater path difference than if polarized light had been used and, when the axis and plane are crossed, a less path difference is apparent, this increased or decreased path difference being a quarter wave-length different from that for completely polarized light. From this we may conclude with Fresnel that polarized light incident at 45° to the plane of incidence of the rhomb is split up by the two total reflections into two components polarized respectively parallel and perpendicular to the plane of reflection, and that these have a path difference of a quarter wave-length due to reflection, this path difference consequently being present before the components enter the gypsum plate. A single total reflection thus produces a path difference of an eighth of a wave-length. If the gypsum is fixed to the analysing calcite crystal with its axis inclined at 45° to the principal section of the latter, and both are rotated together, no colour variation is apparent, whereby the perfectly symmetrical behaviour of the " depolarized " light is manifest. When polarized light is incident at 45° to the axis of a crystalline plate cut parallel to its axis, and afterwards passes through a Fresnel rhomb whose plane of reflection is inclined at 45° to the crystal axis, on turning the analysing calcite crystal, colours appear which vary continuously and occur twice over in a complete revolution, as with the case of quartz cut perpendicular to its axis.

With the aid of his conception of transverse vibrations, Fresnel was easily able to show that his completely depolarized light was compatible with the idea of circular vibrations, which might consist of either right-hand or left-hand circular motions. If the path difference of the two components differs by either $\frac{1}{4}\lambda$ or $\frac{3}{4}\lambda$, the vibration is in general elliptic ; for $\frac{1}{2}\lambda$, however, the vibration is linear with its plane of polarization perpendicular to that of the light incident on the rhomb. Arago's effects in quartz plates cut perpendicular to their axes, Fresnel was able to explain by the interference of two opposite circular vibrations which are propagated along the optic axis with slightly different velocities, that is with a peculiar type of double refraction along the axis of the quartz. Fresnel considered in the same way the rotation of the plane of polarization in liquids, and succeeded also in both cases in demonstrating directly the existence of double refraction.

Elliptic polarization was also discovered in another manner. Malus originally thought that metals had no polarizing action on light, but later he supposed that the light was polarized both in and perpendicular to the plane of reflection, a view which Fresnel was inclined to adopt. Brewster found, without being aware of Malus' work, that light reflected from metals is to a great extent polarized in the plane of incidence. In 1815 he discovered the property possessed by silver and gold of modifying the light by repeated reflection in such a way that investigation with a calcite crystal indicates two rays of complementary colours polarized in perpendicular directions. According to his conception, which he himself recognized must be erroneous, these metals behaved like doubly refracting plates of a definite thickness, an error made by Biot also. Brewster soon saw that the modification introduced by metallic reflection comprised a new type of polarization intermediate between ordinary (linear) and circular polarization, to which he gave the name of elliptic polarization. When unpolarized light is reflected from a metallic surface, the light polarized in the plane of incidence is always of greater intensity than that polarized in the perpendicular direction. This difference is least for silver and greatest for steel. By repeated reflections the reflected light may be made completely polarized in the plane of reflection ; for this purpose eight reflections from steel, at an angle between 60° and 80°, and thirty-six from silver will suffice.

To investigate the influence of repeated reflection on polarized light, Brewster made use of two small parallel plates which could be rotated on a goniometer and be placed as close together as he pleased. One of the rays of a rotatable calcite crystal was arranged so as to fall on the plates, and the ray emergent after several reflections to and fro was investigated with a second calcite crystal. Light polarized either parallel or perpendicular to the plane of incidence was not altered by this process, but for any other orientation of the plane of polarization new characteristic effects appeared. With silver and gold, the analysing calcite indicated two images of complementary colours, which appeared most brilliant when the plane of polarization of the incident light was inclined at 45° to the plane of reflection ; the colour, moreover, varied with the angle of incidence and the number of reflections. Similar, though less marked, effects may be observed with other metals.

Let light polarized at 45° with respect to the plane of incidence be incident at an angle of 75° on a steel plate. The reflected light differs

PLATE IX

FRANÇOIS ARAGO.

both from linearly polarized and unpolarized light, and produces different colours in a crystalline plate than are given by the former. The colours correspond to an increase or decrease of path difference of approximately a quarter wave-length, and after 2, 4, 6 . . . similar reflections the light is completely polarized, while after 3, 5, 7 . . . reflections it exhibits the same characteristics as after a single reflection. The light after a single reflection thus somewhat resembles circularly polarized light. With two reflections in glass, however, light polarized at $+ 45°$ to the plane of incidence is changed to circularly polarized light, and two further reflections give linear polarization at $- 45°$, whereas light polarized at $+ 45°$ and reflected once from steel at $75°$ is changed to linearly polarized light at $- 17°$ by a second similar reflection.

The successive approach of the plane of polarization of the reflected light to the plane of incidence as the number of reflections increases explained, according to Brewster, the complete polarization of ordinary light in the plane of incidence by many reflections, since Brewster regarded ordinary light as equivalent to the sum of two components polarized at $+ 45°$ and $- 45°$.

CHAPTER XI

THE MATHEMATICAL REPRESENTATION OF THE PROPERTIES OF LIGHT

Up to the present we have intentionally considered only those properties of light which follow immediately and obviously as a result of observation and experiment. That white light is a composition of differently refrangible constituents, that it is periodic, and that it may also be asymmetric could scarcely be regarded by anyone, even after the most precise consideration, as otherwise than an expression of facts. It is true that the unequal refrangibility, the asymmetry, and the periodicity of a light ray cannot be directly recognized when the ray enters the eye, as can, for example, colour and brightness, but the step from the observation to the conception is a very small one and is logically unavoidable. The periodicity of light rays is not observable like the periodicity of a water wave ; its periods in time and space are too short. Also the periodicity of a *single* ray is in any case unobservable, for it only becomes evident when *two* rays meet. In order merely to state a fact, one would have to say : periodic variations in brightness appear at the concurrence of *two* rays. This would evidently be inconceivable if each single ray were at each instant and at all points identically constituted, or if the rays did not acquire quite distinct characteristics in the first instance by their actual concurrence. The conception of the periodicity of a *single* ray is thus the only one in harmony with actual fact and with a consistent, sound, ordered, and logical reasoning. In no case can it be regarded as a self-consistent discovery. Polarization and periodicity must, since Fresnel and Arago have demonstrated the dependence of interference on polarization, be considered as related, and this can only be the case if the periodicity is conceived as two-dimensional and transverse, as Fresnel finally supposed. The principles so far obtained arc thus based on the analysis of the facts of experience rather than on hypotheses.

It must also be recognized, however, that a preconceived opinion, or a hypothesis based on similarity, may also be very favourable to the development of knowledge, as more can be solved by means of it than a consideration of mere data affords. Deductions from hypotheses lead to observation, and these soon indicate the merit of the hypotheses.

Young's and Fresnel's corresponding assumption that light depended on (mechanical) vibrations and that these were like those of the pendulum, was an actual hypothesis, which was more than actual facts would directly indicate. Fresnel assumed that the acceleration towards the equilibrium position of an ether particle with a displacement u is of the form

$$au + bu^2 + cu^3 + \ldots ,$$

which reduces for small displacements to the first term. We may thus write

$$\frac{d^2u}{dt^2} = -au,$$

the solution of which is

$$u = m \sin \sqrt{a}\,t + n \cos \sqrt{a}\,t.$$

If the time is counted from the instant of passing through the equilibrium position, the simple form

$$u = m \sin \sqrt{a}\,t$$

is obtained, where m is the amplitude and $\sqrt{a}$ determines the period.

A few transformations, originally used by Fresnel, will simplify the application of these formulæ. If, commencing with a sine vibration, the time is counted from an instant θ later than that at which the particle, moving in a positive direction, passes through the equilibrium position, then, writing r for $\sqrt{a}$,

$$u = m \sin r(t + \theta)$$
$$= m \cos r\theta \sin rt + m \sin r\theta \cos rt.$$

The single-termed formula is thus transformed quite simply into one containing two terms. Denoting the amplitudes thus :—

$$m \cos r\theta = p,$$
$$m \sin r\theta = q,$$

we have for the reverse transformation

$$p \sin rt + q \cos rt = \sqrt{p^2 + q^2}\, \sin r(t + \theta),$$

where

$$\tan r\theta = q/p.$$

From this the superposition (summation) of two sine vibrations of the same period and direction follows quite simply. Suppose a vibration $a \sin rt$ coincides with a second $b \sin r(t + \theta)$; then by the above

$$a \sin rt + b \sin r(t + \theta) = (a + b \cos r\theta) \sin rt + (b \sin r\theta) \cos rt.$$

Regarding the bracketed terms on the right-hand side as the amplitudes of the vibrations $\sin rt$ and $\cos rt$, by similarity with the previous expression, this is equivalent to

$$\sqrt{a^2 + 2ab \cos r\theta + b^2}\, \sin r(t + \tau),$$

where

$$\tan r\tau = \frac{b \sin r\theta}{a + b \cos r\theta}.$$

The square root expression represents the amplitude of the resultant vibration. According to Fresnel, the combination of vibrations of the

same amplitude and direction is analogous to the combination of forces.
If a, b (Fig. 196) represent the amplitudes of the two components, and
$r\theta$ the angle between them, then the amplitude of the resultant vibration is given by the third side of the triangle. This varies with the
angle $r\theta$, the phase difference, intermediately between the values
$a + b$ and $a - b$ or, if a and b are equal, between $2a$
and 0.

The light intensity, that is, the physiological optical
action, Fresnel considered as determined, by the *vis viva*
of the waves, in accordance with his energy conception of
light which now replaced the *material* conception. For
equal periods and wave-forms this *vis viva* is proportional
to the square of the amplitude.

As Fresnel had decided in favour of transverse vibrations, the problem of combining two relatively oblique
vibrations presented itself, and this was found to give a
very simple explanation of the properties of circularly and
elliptically polarized light.

The hesitation to which reference has already been
made had prevented the acceptance of the hypothesis of
transverse waves for quite long enough. Fresnel had been

FIG. 196.

repeatedly led to believe and to declare that perpendicularly polarized rays behave like perpendicular forces. This is clearly
manifest in the case of circular or elliptic polarization by total reflection, the total intensity of which is not affected by the phase difference between the polarized components.

We will now illustrate Fresnel's results by means of a useful geometrical representation. First of all let us resolve a uniform circular

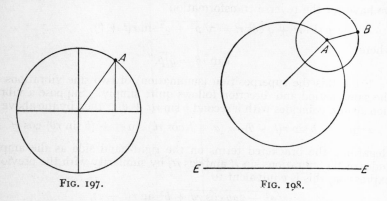

FIG. 197.   FIG. 198.

motion along two mutually perpendicular diameters. These components
will consist of simple harmonic vibrations of equal periods and amplitudes,
or of sine vibrations, for the accelerations under which they occur are
in each case proportional to the distance from the centre. Both
vibrations have a relative phase difference of a quarter vibration.
In this way a distant observer with his eye situated in the plane of the

circle will see the uniform motion as a sine vibration, or the projection of the motion on any plane perpendicular to the plane of the circle will be a linear sine vibration (Fig. 197).

If to one sine vibration a second one of the same period is added, a point A (Fig. 198) can be imagined as executing a uniform circular motion with a second point B revolving about it simultaneously in the same direction in a circle. The resulting motion is again circular,

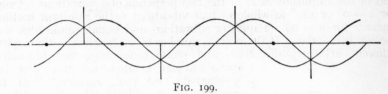

FIG. 199.

and its projection is still a sine vibration corresponding with the Fresnel construction of Fig. 199. Let the time be denoted by the abscissæ and the displacements of a sine vibration by the ordinates, and let two such vibrations be superposed. The algebraic summation of the ordinates gives, in agreement with the foregoing considerations, a sine vibration of the same period, but with an amplitude varying with the phase displacement between $2a$ and 0. The same diagram holds also for two waves travelling along the same straight line, only instead of the abscissæ referring to time, they will now indicate distance. If the two waves are imagined to be travelling in opposite directions with the same velocity, it can be seen that the ordinates of symmetry in the construction (the maximum ordinates) remain fixed during the motion and only vary in magnitude. The positions of zero displacement likewise remain fixed. In this way a very clear illustration of *stationary* waves is obtained.

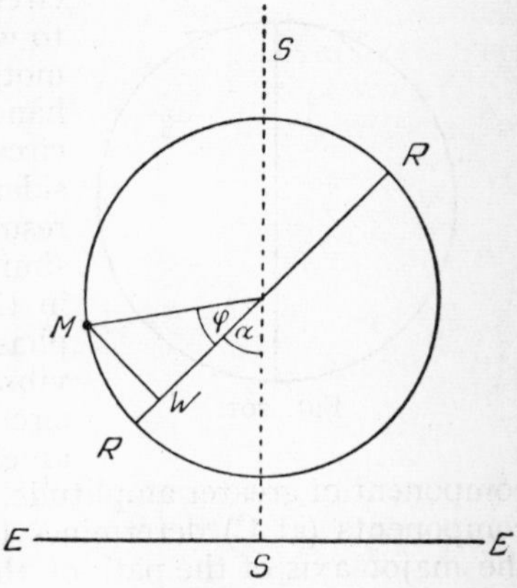

For the case of combinations of vibrations of equal period which are relatively inclined at an angle, we will first consider two perpendicular vibrations having a phase difference of a quarter vibration, which by the

FIG. 200.

above will give a circular motion of the same period. If the phase difference remains unchanged, but the ratio of the amplitudes is altered, the vibration curve becomes an ellipse. The same thing occurs when the directions of the components are inclined obliquely.

Suppose a point M (Fig. 200) describes a circle uniformly and its motion is projected by rays parallel to SS on to the plane EE perpendicular to the paper. If M is also made to move up and down perpendicular to the paper in such a way that its displacement in this direction is proportional to sin ϕ, that is to its distance from a fixed diameter RR, a second perpendicular sine vibration of the same period is produced, and it will be seen that M moves in a plane section of the right cylinder standing on the circle as base. This section is an ellipse, and the projection of the combined motion on EE is in general also an ellipse. The phase difference is shown by the angle a. An ellipse will result for any arbitrary value of the angle a between RR and SS and of the amplitude ratio of the two perpendicular vibrations. Only for $a = 0°$ or $180°$ (a whole or half vibration) is the resultant motion linear; for $a = 90°$ (a quarter vibration) and equal amplitudes the motion is circular. If there are a number of coplanar vibrations with different arbitrary directions and phase differences, two mutually perpendicular components may first be evaluated, and their resultant will in general be an elliptic vibration, with a circular vibration as a particular case.

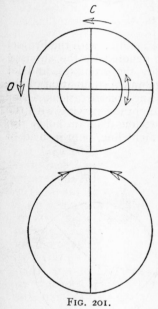

There are thus three types of polarization—elliptic, circular, and linear—of which the first is the most general and the others may be regarded as special cases of the first. Each type may be combined either with itself or with each of the others, but without producing any new type. An important case is the combination of two circular vibrations, on account of the use to which it was put by Fresnel. A circular motion may either be right-handed or left-handed in direction. If two left-handed circular vibrations are combined, a consideration of Fig. 201 will show that their resultant is another circular vibration of similar direction. Its amplitude depends in the same way upon the amplitudes and phases of the components as with linear vibrations. On the other hand, opposite circular motions of amplitudes a, b produce an elliptic vibration in the direction of the component of greater amplitude. The conjunction of the phases of the components (at C) determines the direction and magnitude $(a + b)$ of the major axis of the path of the vibration, and the opposition (at O) the magnitude $(a - b)$ of the minor axis. When the amplitudes are equal, the resultant vibration is a linear one, as is obvious from a direct consideration, the direction of vibration being the line of symmetry of the phases. From these considerations it is thus evident that both the other types of polarization can be represented by a combination of light executing circular vibrations. Similarly, elliptically polarized rays may readily be combined so as to give any type of polarization we please. We will return to such cases later.

Fresnel's formulæ provide a convenient means for following quantitatively the action of different cases of interference and polarization,

FIG. 201.

as the following example will illustrate. If the period is denoted by T, a consideration of the above formulæ shows that $rT = 2\pi$ and $u = a \sin 2\pi t/T$. A wave of wave-length λ which has traversed an additional distance D superposes on the displacements of the former a displacement $a \sin 2\pi(t/T - D/\lambda)$, and the amplitude of the resulting vibration is, according to the above formula,

$$a \sqrt{2 \left(1 + \cos \frac{2\pi D}{\lambda}\right)}.$$

Whenever the cosine argument is equal to an odd multiple of π, that is, when D/λ assumes one of the values $1/2, 3/2, 5/2, \ldots n + 1/2$, the amplitude becomes zero and extinction results. For values of the argument which are even multiples of π, that is, for the integral values of $D/\lambda = 1, 2, 3, \ldots, n$, there is maximum reinforcement. We will now consider a beam of white light divided into two beams of equal intensity with a path difference D imposed, and afterwards spectrally resolved. The effects described in an earlier chapter can now be established directly, from the formula. If λ denotes the wave-length of the extreme red of the spectrum, and is assumed to be contained exactly 100 times in D, this point of the spectrum indicates maximum brightness. Considering now a gradual transition of the wave-length to one-half of the value, this final value will be contained in D 200 times, and in the region between there will be 99 maxima with 100 intermediate extinctions. If the extreme red wave-length is contained 1000 times in D, there will be 999 maxima and 1000 dark bands in the region between this wave-length and that of one-half the value. The number of dark bands thus increases with the path difference in a manner exactly determinable. If D/λ has a definite value, say p, which corresponds, for example, to a dark band, and D is increased in some way, λ must also increase in the same proportion, if p is to remain constant, which means that, with increasing path difference, the dark bands shift from the violet towards the red end of the spectrum. Keeping the path difference constant or the fringes stationary, on changing from one fringe to its next neighbour towards the red, the number of wave-lengths corresponding to the particular fringe contained in the path difference will decrease by unity. If we put $D/\lambda =$ constant, then $d\lambda/dD = \lambda/D$, which indicates that the fringes shift with increasing path difference more and more slowly the greater the latter becomes. The fringes thus become continually denser in the spectrum as the path difference is increased. With regard to the spectral effects produced by doubly refracting plates placed between polarizer and analyser, similar considerations will apply. The expression D/λ has merely to be replaced by the term $(\mu' - \mu) \cdot D/\lambda$, to which, for polarizer and analyser set perpendicularly, $1/2$ has to be added, as occurs in the case of Newton's rings already considered. In the last expression μ' and μ are, of course, the two refractive indices and λ the wave-length in air.

When Fresnel adopted the sine form for the periodicity of light, he endeavoured at the same time to give a mechanical explanation for his assumption. He was thus concerned here again, as in the question of transverse vibrations, with two *distinct* problems in one. This finds some sort of explanation in the fact that interference data do not give any direct conclusion as to the nature of the periodicity or of the vibration form. The sine form recommends itself on account of its simplicity, and the simplicity of the mechanical hypotheses which suffice for its explanation seemed to Fresnel to warrant such an assumption. Fresnel was here in a similar position to that of Galileo with regard to the law of acceleration. The latter is not directly obvious from data. After deliberation Galileo thus concluded that his assumptions were correct from the correspondence between his deductions and actual fact. Fresnel proceeded in a similar manner ; from his assumption of the sine form, which contained hypotheses which were not altogether proved, he developed a comprehensive theory of diffraction and its agreement with the facts of experience was held to be a point in favour of the correctness of the underlying assumptions.

The periodic nature of light is evident directly from the facts of interference, and it now remains to be seen whether the latter will give any clue as to the form of the periodicity. If a surface placed at different distances r_1, r_2, r_3 from a point source of light assumes a brightness i_1, i_2, i_3 respectively, the degree of brightness may be defined by the equation $i_1 r_1^2 = i_2 r_2^2 = i_3 r_3^2 =$ constant. Surrounding the source with a concentric sphere of area F, which is illuminated with a brightness i, Fi may be considered as the invariable light *quantity* emitted by the source. The physiological origin of brightness may thus be completely ignored, and a direct physical measure of quantity, either a chemical or energetic one, be specified. This was first effected with appreciable exactitude after the time of Fresnel. If we assume that the measure of quantity or brightness is now determined, photometric measurements alone of the change in intensity of the interference field with path difference should disclose the form of the periodicity. For photometric observations to be possible the fringes would have to be produced by homogeneous light and be broad enough for regions of approximately uniform brightness to be divided off. Such measurements would give, if Fresnel's assumption is correct, and if the intensity for zero path difference is unity, an intensity of $1 + \cos 2\pi D/\lambda$ for a path difference D. Presupposing, with Fresnel, the energetic conception of light, not necessarily a mechanical one, and measuring the intensity by the kinetic energy or *vis viva*, which, if the period is not varied, is proportional to the square of the amplitude, the vibration form $u = \sin 2\pi t/T$ is the only one agreeing with the above intensity relation. A more complicated periodicity, representable by a Fourier series—

$$u = \sin \frac{2\pi t}{T} + \sin \frac{4\pi t}{T} + \sin \frac{6\pi t}{T} + \ldots$$

leads, as may be realized, to another intensity relation for the interference field. If light is considered as a *material* substance, great difficulties are met with. The mere periodicity can then only be justified by assuming two materials of opposite qualities to alternate in the ray, somewhat like positive and negative electricity. Both these materials must be given the power of exciting the retina when either is in excess, and the power must disappear when both are present in equal quantities. Without going further into these difficulties, it may be remarked that even this *material* theory was capable of gradual adaptation to the facts and of developing fresh knowledge, as was evident by its use in the hands of Malus. Newton's theory is not a pure material theory, but contains a kinetic element.

Even if no photometric measurements are possible, both elementary considerations and also a more exact investigation of the interference field obtainable with homogeneous light will show that preference is to be given to the form $\sin 2\pi t/T$. Suppose we assume a periodicity representable by a Fourier series which, in addition to the fundamental vibration determining the colour, contains partial vibrations of 2, 3, 4, . . . n times the frequency. It is then obvious that if the fundamental vibration is extinguished by interference on account of the path difference, this is not in general the case for the vibrations of shorter periods. Complete extinction is only possible with forms containing only the odd partial vibrations. Thus in general in the interference of homogeneous light, in addition to principal maxima and

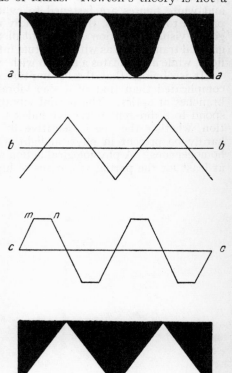

Fig. 202.

minima, secondary maxima and minima are to be expected. Even for those cases in which the terms of the series are so numerous that the individual secondary maxima are indistinguishable, the light distribution in the interference field will vary appreciably as soon as there is much departure from the form $\sin 2\pi t/T$. Suppose, for example, the periodicity is given by the curve *bb* (Fig. 202). If two such curves are superposed and their ordinates algebraically summed, the time variation of the vibration resulting from the interference is given by the curve *cc*, where *mn* corresponds to the path difference. For a path difference corresponding to half a period, the peaks and hollows of the zig-zag curve are cut off by equal amounts, so that the resulting curve coincides with the axis. If the path difference is still further increased, the same curves again occur in the reverse order with respect to time, and as mirror images of the former. Over the regions where the curve consists of inclined straight lines, the velocity, and thus the *vis viva* is everywhere the same, being zero in the horizontal portions *mn*. The light distribution in the interference field for a path difference increasing from left to right is shown at *dd*, whilst *aa* represents the distribution according to Fresnel's sine relation. If these black and white figures are fastened to cylinders, *aa* and *dd* being placed parallel to their axes, then on rapidly rotating the cylinders they will give a visual indication of the light distribution. The figure *aa* shows gradual transitions, as with an actual interference field for homogeneous light, while *dd* indicates a system with very sharp maxima and minima.

It is obvious that the assumption of a different periodicity more complicated than that of a sine vibration is inconsistent with other branches of optics. The partial vibrations of higher frequency correspond to a different refractive index than for the fundamental vibration, whether the eye is sensitive to them or not. They can then hardly be present in physical light which has been made spectrally homogeneous. A physiological action appears to be likewise excluded, at least for the partial vibrations of higher order.

CHAPTER XII

THE FURTHER DEVELOPMENT OF THE KNOWLEDGE OF POLARIZATION

THE previous historical survey places us in a position to give an account of polarization in a systematic and more detailed manner. Before the time of Malus, the only case of polarization known was that associated with double refraction. Malus showed that polarization was also produced by reflection and by ordinary (repeated) refraction. Polarized light was produced, and recognized or analysed, successively by the calcite crystal, glass mirror, pile of glass plates, tourmaline, etc.

First of all we will describe a clearer and more advantageous form of Malus' reflection experiment. The lens L (Fig. 203) condenses a

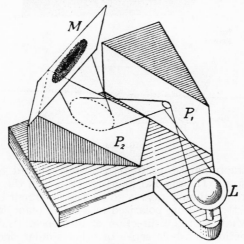

FIG. 203.

beam of sunlight into a cone, the axial ray of which strikes the black glass mirror P_1 at an angle of 56° to the normal. The reflected beam impinges at the same angle on the second mirror P_2, which has its plane of incidence perpendicular to that of the first, and is thence reflected on to the ground glass screen M. The latter will exhibit a dark patch decreasing in brightness towards the centre, which is perfectly black and corresponds to the ray which undergoes two reflections at the polarizing angle in perpendicular planes. For the other rays the extinction is less complete.

Many of the original observations may be repeated quite conveniently by using a calcite crystal. The knowledge of chromatic polarization was certainly greatly increased by this means, because the two images were obviously complementary when they coincided. There are certain cases, however, in which it is desirable to have a large field of view produced by only one of the two polarized rays. This requirement was first fulfilled by the construction by Nicol of the Iceland spar prism with which his name is now associated.

To manufacture a "Nicol" prism a calcite rhombohedron of length about three times its thickness is first produced by cleavage (Fig. 204). The end faces, which form an angle of 72° with the longer edges (AB, CD) are ground off at an angle of 68° with the latter, and perpendicular to the plane which is parallel to the principal axis and to AB, CD. The crystal is then cut in two along a plane perpendicular to this last plane and to the end faces, and the two parts are cemented together again with Canada balsam. The layer of this substance

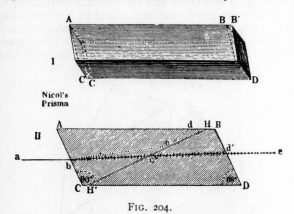

Fig. 204.

allows the extraordinary rays to be transmitted, but totally reflects the ordinary rays. The angular aperture for which the extraordinary rays are free from ordinary rays is 30°. The divergent emergent light is also not strictly speaking polarized in a single plane, but in a plane varying somewhat with the direction of incidence. Subsequently to Nicol's construction, a whole series of other similar ones arose, each with the object of attaining greater perfection in some particular direction, or conditioned by the increasing scarcity of calcite and considerations of economy in material. A description of them here would be superfluous, and the Nicol will be exclusively utilized. It follows from Nicol's construction that the plane of polarization of the light transmitted by the prism is that of the long diagonal of the end face ; this may also be discovered by actual experiment.

Since in the sequel the properties of doubly refracting substances will often come under consideration, it will be well first to describe a few simple experiments pertaining to such media. A well-formed transparent quartz crystal may be used as a prism by allowing the light to pass through the faces *a, c* as is indicated in Fig. 205. It is customary to grind down the faces *a, c, e* so that the others disappear. With such a prism, whose refracting edge is parallel to the crystallographic principal axis, the following observations can be made by investigating the transmitted sunlight or light from a lamp with a Nicol. The spectra produced are two in number and are partially superposed, the light of each spectrum being polarized. The plane of polarization in the less deviated spectrum, which corresponds to the smaller refractive index and consequently the greater velocity in the quartz, is parallel to the principal axis. For the other spectrum the plane of polarization is perpendicular to the axis. On the other hand, a quartz

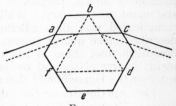

FIG. 205.

prism which is cut so that its axis is perpendicular to the refracting edge and parallel to the base, only produces *one* spectrum when light is transmitted parallel to the axis (Fig. 206). In this case no polarization will be indicated on investigation with the Nicol, and the velocities in the quartz are also equal. In other cases two spectra emerge from the prism, in which the plane of polarization of the less deviated spectrum is parallel, and that of the other perpendicular, to the axis.

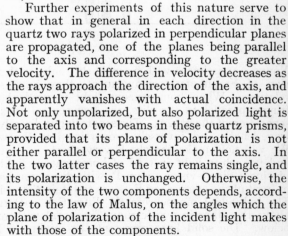

FIG. 206.

Further experiments of this nature serve to show that in general in each direction in the quartz two rays polarized in perpendicular planes are propagated, one of the planes being parallel to the axis and corresponding to the greater velocity. The difference in velocity decreases as the rays approach the direction of the axis, and apparently vanishes with actual coincidence. Not only unpolarized, but also polarized light is separated into two beams in these quartz prisms, provided that its plane of polarization is not either parallel or perpendicular to the axis. In the two latter cases the ray remains single, and its polarization is unchanged. Otherwise, the intensity of the two components depends, according to the law of Malus, on the angles which the plane of polarization of the incident light makes with those of the components.

If the angles of the prisms of Figs. 205 and 206 are assumed to be decreased until they approach zero, the separation of the rays also decreases until the rays finally coincide in spite of the different velocities and planes of polarization. We may thus infer that a plane quartz plate cut parallel to its axis also transmits two rays polarized in perpendicular planes and having different velocities.

For quartz, the refractive index of the faster ray is 1·547, while that of the slower varies according to its inclination to the axis from 1·547 to 1·556.

Similar observations may be made with calcite prisms. Calcite exhibits much stronger double refraction than quartz, but the ray with its plane of polarization parallel to the axis has in this case the smaller velocity. The larger refractive index has the constant value 1·654, while the smaller varies from 1·483 to 1·654. More exact experiments will show that, in the case of rays which traverse quartz parallel or almost parallel to the axis, a modification of the above statement is necessary. While quartz behaves optically in a more complicated way than calcite, experiments with quartz have been described since quartz prisms are more easily procurable free from blemishes than those of calcite. Moreover, in the following experiments quartz plates and wedges, etc., will often be used and a knowledge of the behaviour of this material is thus advantageous.

The experiments on the interference of polarized light will now be given a form in which the results may be more readily appreciated. A telescope F$_1$ (Fig. 207) has its eyepiece replaced by a screen, provided with a slit S, placed in the focal plane of the objective. Sunlight enters at S and falls on a second screen, having a slit Σ parallel to S, placed over the objective of a second telescope F$_2$, through the eyepiece of which the diffraction fringes formed in the focal plane are observed. The latter are similar in appearance to those found in

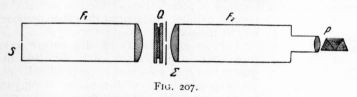

Fɪɢ. 207.

Young's experiment with a single slit, only, with the present application of Fraunhofer's arrangement, they have simpler dimensional relations. When homogeneous light is used the minima are dark fringes parallel to the slits, the two central ones having double the separation of the others. The separation is directly proportional to the wave-length and inversely proportional to the width of the slit Σ. We will now make the slit S very short, i.e. equivalent to a point, and use white light instead of homogeneous light, at the same time placing a direct-vision prism P, with dispersion parallel to the slit Σ, in front of the eyepiece of F$_2$, so as to retain the visibility of the fringes. The individual monochromatic diffraction patterns now appear one above the other in a spectrum (Fig. 208a) with red above and violet below. The solid lines represent the minima. If the slit Σ is increased to double the width, the fringes contract to half the separation (Fig. 208b) or, considering Fig. 208a, new fringes appear in the positions of the dotted lines. If the widening of the slit is imagined to be effected by placing an exactly similar slit immediately to one side of it, the fringe system represented by the dotted lines may be conceived as due to the interference of the light from the right- and left-hand halves of the slit. For either half alone simply produces a system represented by the solid lines at the same place in the focal plane.

If the light from the two halves were incoherent, the superposition would only produce the same effects in greater intensity. That such a view is correct is shown by placing a Jamin's compensator over the slit Σ in such a way that the latter is divided into two equal parts by the line of intersection of the two inclined plates. By turning the compensator, the dotted system, which depends on the path difference between light from the two halves, can be displaced, while the solid line system remains stationary. Bearing these remarks in mind, the following experiments will be readily understood.

First we will satisfy ourselves that the effects illustrated in Fig. 208 are unaltered by placing a Nicol over the slit S with any orientation, that is, by using polarized instead of ordinary unpolarized light. When the polarization of the light is everywhere identical, the interference thus occurs as usual.

 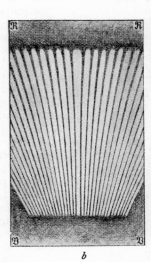

a   b

FIG. 208.

We will now remove the Nicol, and substitute a specially constructed quartz plate in front of the slit Σ. This plate consists of two portions, taken from the same plate of quartz of about 1 mm. thickness cut parallel to its axis, which are placed in contact along an edge so that the axes in the two pieces are respectively parallel and perpendicular to the latter, and the whole is cemented together with Canada balsam between two good plane glass plates.* The line of contact is arranged so that the direction of the axis, say for the left half of Σ, is horizontal, and for the other half vertical. The light entering is now polarized both in horizontal and vertical directions, for the left-hand half the vertically, and for the right-hand the horizontally, polarized components respectively having the greater retardation. The quartz

---

* Dr. Steeg u. Reuter, of Homburg vor der Höhe, have produced such perfect quartz plates that the plane glass plates may be dispensed with.

device thus acts like a Jamin's compensator, only in opposite sense for the two directions of polarization. The fringe system corresponding to the half slit widths is now seen as before undisplaced, but the dotted system is doubled, one system being displaced obliquely to the left and the other to the right (Fig. 209). The interference is between the rays having the same plane of polarization only, and the system displaced to the left corresponds to vertical polarization, and that displaced to the right to horizontal polarization. This is made evident by viewing the fringes through a Nicol placed over the eye-piece, when only one of the oblique systems will be seen if the plane of polarization of the Nicol is either vertical or horizontal. The light polarized in perpendicular directions does not interfere, since no symmetrical fringe system is observable as in Fig. 208. This type of system would have to be produced by this interference, since the horizontally polarized light of the right half is retarded by exactly the same amount as the vertical component of the left half.

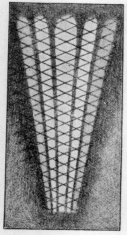

FIG. 209.

The non-interference of perpendicularly polarized light is also evident from the following experiment. The quartz device is displaced so that the whole of Σ is covered either with the portion of horizontal or of vertical axis, the effects being now indistinguishable from those produced with unpolarized or with polarized light of any orientation. The quartz, however, transmits light polarized parallel to its axis, which produces the interference pattern of Fig. 208b, and also light polarized in the perpendicular direction, which is retarded with respect to the former by several wave-lengths, and more so for violet than for red. Nevertheless no interference of the two kinds of light is apparent. This does not originate in the perpendicularity of the displacements of the light vibrations alone, for when a Nicol with its plane of polarization inclined at 45° to the quartz axis, which resolves displacements into the same plane, is placed over the eye-piece, the effects are not altered in any way. It must, therefore, be concluded that the two perpendicularly polarized components, into which the light is separated, are incoherent.

We will now replace the quartz so that the right-hand half of Σ is covered by a portion with axis vertical and the other half by a part with axis horizontal, and in addition place a Nicol N in front of S. According as the plane of polarization of N is vertical, horizontal, or inclined at 45°, the fringes which are seen are respectively the oblique system displaced to the left, the similar one displaced to the right, or in the last case, both of them together, but in no instance is the symmetrical dotted system of Fig. 208a visible.

Suppose the Nicol in front of S has its plane of polarization inclined at 45° to the horizontal. With the plane of polarization of the eyepiece Nicol either vertical or horizontal, naturally only the vertical or horizontal components from the quartz are transmitted, producing only the systems displaced to right or left. When the eyepiece Nicol is turned parallel to that at S, the symmetrical fringes also appear. The horizontally polarized rays from the right half of the slit and the vertically polarized rays from the left have equal retardations and are resolved into the same plane by the second Nicol; they are also coherent since they come from the same source, and thus the whole area of the slit may be considered as producing similar coherent polarized rays, which give the symmetrical system of Fig. 209. In a similar way the vertically polarized light from the right may be taken with the horizontal component of the left to produce the same system. Since, however, all the rays are coherent and have been resolved into the same plane, it must be remembered that the former pair is retarded with respect to the latter by a number of wave-lengths varying with the colour, being greater for violet than for red.

This retardation produces the horizontal dark bands of Fig. 210.

There is a slight modification in the case for which the two Nicols are crossed. Taking the components resolved into one plane in pairs, the members of the pairs have a respective phase difference of half a wave-length, independent of the colour and the deviation through diffraction. The minima of one pair coincide with those of the others, and thus remain when the light is considered as a whole. The symmetrical fringe system has thus maxima where in the previous case there were minima. The components of each half of the slit also receive a phase difference of half a vibration on account of the crossing of the Nicols, this difference being additional to the path difference dependent on the colour, and remaining when combined effects of all the components are considered for each half of the slit. The horizontal bands in the spectrum are thus for crossed Nicols intermediate in position between those for parallel Nicols.

FIG. 210.

The effects just described naturally appear in succession when the eyepiece Nicol is rotated. Figs. 209 and 210 illustrate the five different systems of fringes which appear either simultaneously or in succession. Fresnel did not make use of any spectral resolution for his experiment, and consequently could not readily distinguish the various systems from one another. He thus regarded the effects produced by superposition of two fringe systems, which belong to the class of subsidiary fringes occurring with Newton's ring system, as a special type of fringe system.

These experiments would be simplified if, instead of crossed quartz, crossed tourmaline could be utilized, as it transmits only the one component. It is very difficult, however, to procure tourmaline sufficiently homogeneous for the purpose, whereas good clear quartz is comparatively easy to find. The experiments are easy to carry out, but have the objection that on account of the small light intensity they are only suitable for subjective observation. They also postu·late, for an exact analysis at least, a knowledge of the theory of diffraction, which must be regarded as a disadvantage where a logical sequence is required.

The most important result appearing in the above experiments is that *the perpendicularly polarized components into which unpolarized light is separable are mutually incoherent.*

This view, which was so laboriously established, nowadays appears quite natural and almost self-evident. So long as it was assumed that there were phase changes caused by the action of irregular disturbances on the light, the presumption of which was scarcely avoidable with a mechanical conception of the nature of light, such a view must exert its influence when the periodicity was recognized as transverse and two-dimensional. When once it was assumed that the light vibration did not occur in a fixed plane containing the ray, but in one which was variable, a change both in intensity and phase must occur in the polarized components of the vibration obtained by resolution into any two perpendicular directions, and these changes must be independent of each other in each component, if the variations of the vibration plane are not to follow some incomprehensible rule. Vibrations in a *definite* plane, however, always resolve into two perpendicular components in planes fixed with respect to the first in such a way that the changes in phase and intensity occur similarly in both components, so that the latter both appear coherent.

We will now consider the phenomena of chromatic polarization. The key to the understanding of these effects is given by the laws formulated for the interference of polarized light, and conversely the phenomena have led back to the same laws. These facts have revealed themselves here and there in different forms. The manner in which Arago, in consequence of experiments on Newton's rings, discovered the first facts of chromatic polarization, his qualitative experiments, and Biot's measurements of the thickness of the plates corresponding to definite colours, all indicated the analogy between the already known colours of thin plates and the newly-discovered colours. In fact, Biot's theory of mobile polarization is also modelled on Newton's theory of "fits," and both theories represent quite well, if not perfectly, the effects for which they were devised. The dependence of colour on the path difference of the rays in plates exhibiting only simple refraction, and on the path difference of the perpendicularly polarized rays in doubly refracting plates was recognized by Young, and it was only necessary for Fresnel to take a final step, an important one nevertheless, and remove the inconsistency which still remained between the two parallel conceptions. The knowledge of a *transverse, two-dimensional periodicity* and of the *incoherence* of the *perpendicularly* polarized components of ordinary light renders *consistent* the details of important branches of optics—interference, polarization,

the colours of thin laminæ, chromatic polarization, and double refraction.

Retaining the above-mentioned analogy, it is possible to give a
concise but clear description of the phenomena of chromatic polarization. Newton used spherical surfaces for studying his interference
effects, since they were easily obtainable and also permitted an easy
calculation and measurement of the thickness of the air gaps. Naturally this was not essential, and a wedge-shaped air gap, or one whose
thickness varied from point to point in a known way, would have been
equally effective. We shall use a wedge of a doubly refracting substance to study chromatic polarisation, and the effects observed will
correspond, so to speak, with a sector or radial portion removed from
Newton's lens system. The wedge is cut so that the crystal axis is
either parallel or perpendicular to the sharp edges. A Norrenberg's
polariscope will be used to investigate the effects. This consists of a

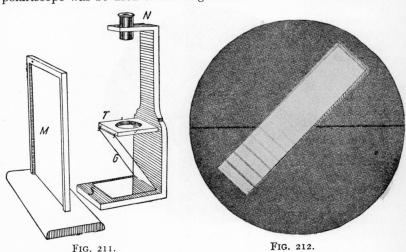

FIG. 211.   FIG. 212.

support for the Nicol N (Fig. 211), a platform T whose centre is cut
away and is covered by a glass plate to support the object under
investigation, and a polarizing glass plate G held in position by the
platform at an angle of 35° to the vertical, all arranged in a vertical
sequence. The light from the sky, reflected vertically downwards by
the inclined plate, is completely polarized and is reflected from the
amalgam mirror S vertically upwards through G and T without change
in polarization. If direct light from the sky is unavailable, owing,
for example, to the horizon being obscured by trees or buildings, a
vertical ground glass screen M may be placed in front of the apparatus.
We will now place on the platform T a quartz wedge about a centi-
metre wide and a few centimetres long, with axis parallel to its long
edge, the latter being arranged at 45° to the plane of polarization of
the incident light. At its thin end the thickness of the wedge is
reduced to a minimum while the thicker end is about 1 mm. thick.

If the Nicol N is turned so that it is at positions of maximum brightness or darkness, that is so that it is parallel or perpendicular to the
plane of polarization, the thin end of the wedge exhibits brightly-
coloured bands (Fig. 212) which run parallel to the sharp edge. Traversing the wedge from the thin to the thick end, the colours follow
in the same order as with Newton's rings on passing from the centre
outwards. If a definite point of the wedge is kept in view, it will
easily be seen that for parallel and perpendicular positions of the
Nicol the colours are complementary. Towards the thick end the
colours became fainter and merge into white. This thicker end, or a
thicker plane plate of quartz cut parallel to its axis, is also darker
than the remainder of the field of view when viewed through a Nicol
with its plane of polarization parallel to that of the incident light, and
the reverse is the case in the perpendicular position. As in the case
of Newton's rings, for the thick parts interference occurs for so many

FIG. 213.

colours at once that no further coloration is produced. Thus, since
in the light transmitted by the Nicol certain colours are extinguished,
but are present in the light which is totally reflected in the Nicol,
and conversely, one-half of the light is contained in the transmitted
beam and the other half in the reflected. This explains the relative
brightness of the thick end of the wedge and the surrounding field.

An actual quartz wedge obviously cannot be ground down to zero
thickness, but the effects corresponding to zero thickness may be
shown by using Biot's method of superposing another crystalline plate
with its axis at right angles to the former. Two opposite prism faces
of a natural quartz crystal are ground away so that a plate with axis
parallel to its faces is obtained with a thickness of about $\frac{1}{2}$ mm. If
this plate is placed over the wedge at the region exhibiting bright
colours in such a position that the latter entirely disappear (Fig. 213),
a summation of the effects has been obtained, and the axes are parallel.
When the plate is placed in the perpendicular direction at a part of the

wedge where its thickness equals that of the plate, brightly coloured bands now appear where previously, with wedge or plate alone, none were visible.   A subtraction has been effected, and the place where the thicknesses of wedge and plate are equal behaves as if the thickness were zero.   On either side of this region the combination behaves as if the thickness increased uniformly.   The fringes are the same distance apart as for the wedge alone.   When the planes of polarization of the incident light and the Nicol are parallel, the region corresponding to zero thickness is bright (white), being dark when the planes of polarization are perpendicular.   As in the first case the incident light is recombined by the Nicol in exactly the same way as it was split up by the wedge into components, and in the second case merely recombined in an opposite sense, the intensity of illumination of the region of zero thickness will not be different from that of the surrounding field.   Thus in this respect also the combination behaves as if the thickness were actually zero.   The colour sequence is the same as in Newton's rings ;   with planes of polarization parallel the colours commence with white in the middle (the symmetry line) as for Newton's rings by transmitted light, and with the planes of polarization perpendicular, with darkness, as for the rings by reflected light.

The preceding results are confirmed by spectral analysis.   A blackened card provided with a narrow slit is laid on the platform T so that the slit is inclined at 45° to the plane of polarization, and the quartz wedge is placed so that its coloured fringes are intersected perpendicularly by the slit.   A black cardboard cone placed on the platform and reaching up to the Nicol may be used to screen off stray light from the side.   If the ground glass screen is illuminated by sunlight, and the slit is viewed through a direct vision prism placed above the Nicol, which is rotated into either the parallel or perpendicular positions, a spectrum exactly similar to that with Newton's rings is seen. The wedge may also be placed with its edge parallel to the slit, so that the whole length of the latter corresponds to the same thickness. If the wedge is then pushed across the slit so that, for example, the portion above the slit increases in thickness, the spectrum being viewed at the same time, the dark fringes can be seen entering at the violet end and passing across to the red, with continually increasing density as the path difference correspondingly increases.   These effects may also be shown, only with less variety, with a quartz plate cut parallel to its axis.   A rotation of the Nicol shows that in passing from a parallel to a perpendicular position the dark fringes take the place of the previous bright regions.

This practically exhausts the similarities between chromatic polarization and the interference of ordinary light, and it remains to describe the effects which constitute the distinguishing features of chromatic polarization.   While the colours of thin plates on the one hand are independent of the orientation (rotation in their own plane), the effects in crystalline plates on the other hand are extremely variable.   Let the quartz wedge be placed on the platform T with the planes of polarization of incident light and Nicol either parallel or perpendicular.   When the wedge is turned in its own plane, the colours are seen to become stronger and fainter but, so long as the Nicol is not turned, each particular point of the quartz retains the same hue. The greatest saturation of the colours occurs when the quartz axis is inclined at 45° to the plane of polarization of the incident light, since here the two interfering beams are of equal intensity. When the quartz axis is either parallel or perpendicular to the plane of polarization, the colours are completely extinguished, as now only one beam is present so that interference is impossible.

Now let the axis of the wedge be inclined at 45° to the plane of reflection R (Fig. 214) of the glass plate. The two beams of equal intensity may be denoted by OA, OB. If ON represents the plane of polarization of the Nicol, it is obvious that the beams are transmitted in like sense by the Nicol so long as ON remains in the quadrants AOB or COD. When ON bisects the quadrants the components along ON are equal, and the saturation is complete ; for other positions it is

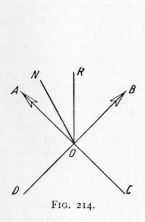

FIG. 214.

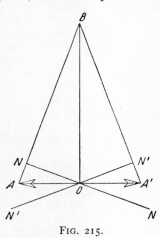

FIG. 215.

weaker. If ON passes into the quadrants BOC or DOA, the components of OA, OB along ON act in opposite sense and the colour changes to the complementary, saturation again being greatest when ON bisects the quadrants. The coincidence of ON and OA or OB means absence of colour on account of the disappearance of interference.

We will now consider the most general case in which the quartz axis is inclined to the plane of reflection R at any angle. The magnitude and direction of the components in the quartz may be represented by OA, OB (Fig. 215). The plane of reflection R thus lies parallel to the diagonal through O of the rectangle constructed about AO, OB. Let AB be joined and the corresponding triangle OA'B be drawn. If the plane of polarization ON or ON' of the Nicol is oriented so that it is at right angles to either AB or A'B, the action of both components is obviously equal. In both cases the saturation is complete, with the difference that in the first case the components are in like sense, in the second case in opposite sense. The colours for the two cases are thus complementary. The orientations of the Nicol for absence of colour are now AA' and OB, and the Nicol placed in the quadrant AOB or the opposite quadrant gives a colour complementary to the corresponding position in the quadrant A'OB or its opposite quadrant. The positions NN and N'N' of the Nicol for maximum saturation are no longer perpendicular. If a is the angle between R and OB, both NN and N'N' are obviously inclined to AA' at the same angle a.

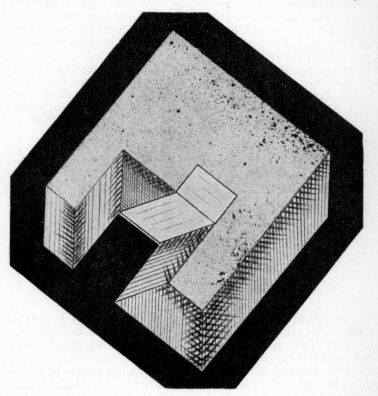

FIG. 216.

ON and ON' thus include the angle $2a$. It is useful to compare with this Biot's ideas on mobile polarization.

As has already been mentioned, Fresnel discovered circular polarization while continuing Malus' experiments on the internal reflection from glass plates and endeavouring to extend the observations into the region of total reflection. For the latter purpose an ordinary plane parallel plate is not applicable, since any light entering the front face, even at grazing incidence, at the most is only incident on the back face at the critical angle of total reflection. Fresnel thus constructed parallelepipeds of various kinds, of which the most useful will be considered here. The usual mounts for these parallelepipeds are very inconvenient for many experiments. It is advisable, therefore, to embed the parallelepiped loosely in a simple cork mount, the under side of which is illustrated in Fig. 216. With such a mount there is the advantage that there is a clear path for the light immediately to one side of the parallelepiped, so that the direct and modified fields of view may be compared. It is still better to cement larger glass plates on the incidence and emergence faces of the rhomb, whereby the necessary stability may be attained without reducing the field of view. If such a Fresnel rhomb F is placed on the platform T of the polariscope (Fig. 211) so that the plane of reflection R of the incident light is at 45° to that of the rhomb, as indicated in Fig. 217, the light emergent from the upper face after two reflections at 45° is found to exhibit quite new characteristics. When the Nicol is rotated the brightness remains unchanged, while that of the surrounding field shows a gradual change from a maximum for the parallel position to a minimum for the perpendicular position. The light emergent from the rhomb

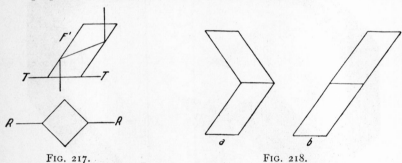

FIG. 217.   FIG. 218.

thus has properties which differ from those received by simple reflection or by refraction in calcite. It also differs from unpolarized light, since if the quartz wedge is placed on the upper surface of the rhomb, and the Nicol is turned at 45° to the axis of the quartz, bright colours are visible. When the mirror S of the polariscope is covered with a sheet of white paper and the plate G is removed, so that the illumination is now unpolarized, the colours vanish. The unpolarized light from the white paper is not affected by the Fresnel rhomb, but is transmitted without alteration. Returning to the original arrangement, and adding another rhomb with its plane of reflection parallel to the first, as in Figs. 218a or b, the light is retransformed to linearly polarized light. The new modification of light is thus essentially different both from linearly polarized and unpolarized light ; it has the property in common with the former of producing interference colours, but corresponds with unpolarized light in that it behaves quite symmetrically on all sides. Let Q (Fig. 219) represent the surface of contact of two Fresnel rhombs placed one on the other with their planes of reflection R'R' parallel. Let RR be the plane of

reflection of the glass G, and NN the plane of polarization of the Nicol. The incident light polarized in RR, after passing through *both* rhombs, is again linearly polarized, its plane being that of NN. If, now, the upper rhomb and the Nicol are turned together through the same angle without relative motion, the lower rhomb remaining fixed, the light does not vary in intensity. The upper rhomb thus has exactly the same action no matter what its relative orientation to the lower, and the light leaving the lower rhomb is *laterally similarly constituted in all directions*. It is useful in this last experi-ment to place the upper rhomb so that the surfaces Q do not completely cover each other, so that the action of the one rhomb may be compared with that of the other. The ex-periments are performed more conveniently with a quarter-wave plate which will be de-scribed below. Now let the wedge be laid on the upper surface Q of the lower rhomb

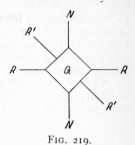

with its axis along R'R'. When the Nicol is turned together with the wedge, the rhomb remaining fixed, the interference bands of the wedge turn also, without changing in colour or position. This, too, shows that the new modification behaves in the same way in all directions.

The relation of the new modification to linearly polarized light is disclosed by a more detailed consideration of the quartz interference

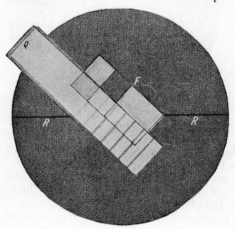

Fig. 220.

colours. The axis of the quartz wedge, as we know, is parallel to its longer edge, which is thus parallel to the plane of polarization of the faster ray. Let the wedge be placed on the Fresnel rhomb so that its surface is partly on and partly off the rhomb, and its axis is parallel to the plane of reflection of the latter. Let the plane of polariza-tion of the incident light be RR (Fig. 220). Where the wedge covers the rhomb, the fringes appear displaced by a quarter of their distance apart towards the thicker end of the wedge. The superposition thus gives the same effect as a shift of the wedge alone from the thin towards the thick end, and the wedge thus has its apparent thickness reduced by the rhomb. The light emergent from the glass thus consists of two perpendicular, polarized components which are parallel and perpendicular to the quartz axis; before entering the quartz they have a path difference of a quarter period, but in the opposite direction to that impressed by the quartz. Light incident at 45° to the plane of reflection of the rhomb is thus split up by two reflections in the latter into two components of which that polarized in the plane of incidence is retarded by a quarter period with respect to the perpendicular component.

All the effects obtainable with the Fresnel rhomb are attributable to this property. The rhomb may be replaced by a crystalline plate cut parallel to its axis which imparts a phase difference of a quarter

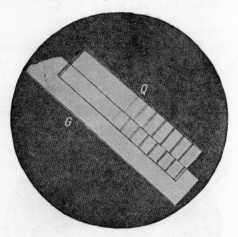

FIG. 221.

vibration to the two components, the more retarded of which is to be considered as a plane of reflection of a Fresnel rhomb. Such a quarter-wave plate is readily obtainable by cleaving a piece of mica. If a sheet of the latter of greater than the required thickness is placed on the platform T, the planes of polarization of glass and Nicol being either parallel or perpendicular, and is oriented to give colours of the greatest saturation, the two components transmitted by the mica are polarized in planes at 45° to the plane of the incident light. The mica is then made rectangular by cutting it perpendicular to these directions and is split thinner and thinner until when placed over or under the quartz wedge, as in Fig. 221, it produces the same effects as a Fresnel rhomb combined with the quartz wedge. In this case the mica plate shifts the quartz fringes towards the thicker end of the wedge. If the mica is cut long and narrow as in Fig. 221, its longer edge corresponds to the plane of reflection of the rhomb. Such a quarter-wave plate may be combined either with a rhomb or another similar plate, and all the above experiments be performed, provided that it is remembered that the longer side of the plate corresponds to the component of greater retardation and to the plane of reflection of the Fresnel rhomb.

Let RR (Fig. 222) again be the plane of polarization of the incident light and R'R' the plane of reflection of the rhomb.   If the Nicol is given a complete rotation, the unobstructed field of view exhibits a maximum brightness for the position RR and complete darkness for NN, while the face of the rhomb remains equally bright for all orientations, one-half of the light being transmitted by the Nicol and the other half reflected.   A mica quarter-wave plate VV laid on the rhomb with its longer side parallel to its plane of reflection increases the path difference from $\frac{1}{4}\lambda$ to $\frac{1}{2}\lambda$ and orients the plane of polarization along NN so that the region where mica and rhomb appear superposed is fully bright for the position NN.   If VV is turned through 90° without displacing anything else, the latter region becomes completely dark.

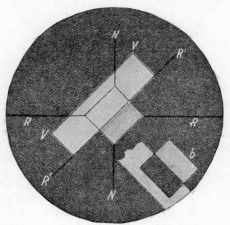

FIG. 222.

Consider now two rhombs FF and F'F' (Fig. 223), mounted in a convenient way for many purposes by attaching one side of each to a block of wood, placed on the platform T in such a way that two edges of the square end faces are in contact, as indicated in the figure which shows a horizontal projection of the rhombs.   RR represents as before the plane of polarization of the incident light, and the plane of reflection of FF is turned through an angle of 45° anti-clockwise with respect to RR, and that of F'F' through the same angle in the opposite direction.   These directions may be indicated respectively by − 45° and + 45°.   The end faces of both rhombs do not exhibit any change of intensity with the orientation of the Nicol, so that both beams of light behave in all directions as if identical and are indistinguishable by *this* means.   Now let a quarter-wave plate VV be laid across the end faces so that about one-half of each is covered by the plate and its longer side is parallel to RR.   Turning the Nicol into the direction

NN, that is — 45° from RR, the covered portion of FF now exhibits maximum brightness, that of F'F' complete darkness, the brightness of the uncovered portions remaining, of course, unchanged. If the Nicol is turned through 90°, the brightness of the covered portions is interchanged.

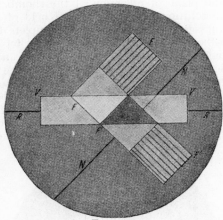

FIG. 223.

A Fresnel rhomb, with its plane of reflection inclined either at — 45° or + 45° to the plane of polarization of the incident light, thus produces light which, although it behaves in all directions as if identical, nevertheless exhibits a kind of right- and left-handed property. The light from both of the above rhombs is transformed to linearly polarized light after passage through a quarter-wave plate ; in the first case (rhomb FF), however, the plane of polarization is inclined at — 45°, in the second at + 45°, to VV, the direction of the more retarded component, and this is true for any orientation of the mica with respect to the rhombs. Even without the confirmation by views already obtained from other sources, these data alone would have produced the impression that here one is concerned with a rotation or a kind of screw motion.

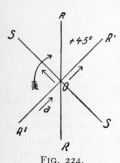

FIG. 224.

These effects are easily explicable when considered from Fresnel's standpoint. Imagine a beam of light linearly polarized in the plane RR (Fig. 224) to be directed vertically upwards from the plane of the paper, and let R'R' be the plane of polarization of the more retarded component emerging from a Fresnel rhomb or a quarter-wave plate. This component may be regarded as shifted a quarter vibration behind the plane of the paper. When the less retarded component is in a phase corresponding to a passage through the equilibrium position O of SS in the positive direction, the other component, instead of being in the same phase, has a maximum displacement a in R'R' in the negative direction. It thus follows that the vibration in the upward directed ray is circular, in a clockwise direction when viewed from a position in advance of the ray, in which case it is called a right-handed circular vibration, the ray being right-handed circularly polarized. If Fig. 224 is turned completely over by rotation through 180° about RR as axis, a left-handed circular vibration results.

Light which is circularly polarized is separable into two linear components having a phase difference of a quarter vibration, vibrating along two perpendicular diameters. Considering in Fig. 225 a right-handed circularly polarized ray to be moving from the paper towards the reader, and to be incident upon a quarter-wave plate having its more retarded component, say, along R'R', instead of light in the phases a, b being recombined, the phases are b, c, owing to the retardation of the plate, and the resulting linearly polarized light has its plane of polarization in a direction inclined at 45° to R'R'. This orientation is obvious from consideration of the figure. For left-handed circular polarization the plane of polarization would be in the perpendicular

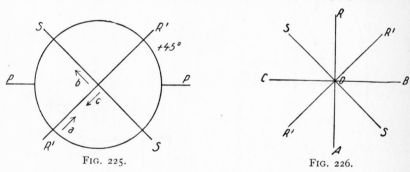

FIG. 225.   FIG. 226.

direction. The Fresnel rhomb and the quarter-wave plate may thus be used not only for producing right- and left-handed circular polarization, but also for testing the direction of the rotation in a given circularly polarized ray.

If the inclination of the plane of reflection of a rhomb varies appreciably from $\pm$ 45° with respect to the plane of polarization of the incident light, or if the angle of incidence of the totally reflected light is changed, or only a *single* total reflection utilized, the emergent light loses its characteristic of an identical behaviour in all directions. A variation in brightness is noticeable on turning the Nicol. This type of polarization was called by Fresnel " elliptical."

Let RA (Fig. 226) represent the plane of polarization of the incident light and R'R' the plane of reflection of the Fresnel rhomb. If the inclination of R'R' varies from $+$ 45°, the right-handed circular motion changes to right-handed elliptical. It remains right-handed so long as R'R' is in the quadrants ROB, COA, and RR' is the direction of the major or minor axis of the vibration according as the angle ROR' is less or greater than $+$ 45°. For ROR' = 0° or 90°, the light is linearly

polarized respectively along RA or BC.   In a similar way the light is
left-handed elliptically polarized when R'R' lies in the quadrants BOA,
ROC, with the special cases of linear and circular polarization as before.
All the varieties of elliptical polarization may be both produced and
analysed by means of a Fresnel rhomb or a quarter-wave plate.   The
directions of the axes of the vibration are given by the positions of the
Nicol for maximum and minimum brightness, and the ratio of the axes
by effecting a transformation into linearly polarized light.   If a quarter-
wave plate is arranged so that the plane of polarization of its more
retarded component is parallel to the plane of polarization of the Nicol
when in the position of maximum brightness (Fig. 227), linear polarized light emerges from the plate with its plane of polarization inclined
at an angle $+ \phi$, say, to this plane of the Nicol, the elliptical polarization being right-handed.   The opposite case is obvious.   If the major
axis OA = A, the minor axis OB = B, then tan ϕ = B/A.

Instead of a rhomb, let a totally reflecting prism in which the light

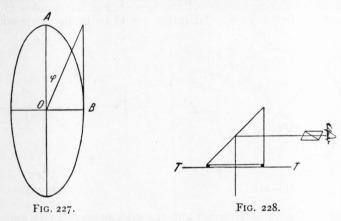

FIG. 227.   FIG. 228.

only experiences a *single* reflection be placed on the platform T, and
be observed through the Nicol from the side (Fig. 228).   The relative
retardation of the two components is here smaller, but can be demonstrated by the same methods.   Actually, it was with this arrangement
that Fresnel commenced his observations, being led to the construction of the parallelepipeds with the object of both increasing the
relative retardation and rendering the emergent light parallel to the
incident.   The light from the prism is found to be linearly polarized
when the plane of reflection is parallel or perpendicular to the plane
of polarization of the incident light, and in all other cases elliptically
polarized.   Using the notation of Fig. 226, a simple consideration will
show the following to hold.   So long as R'R' remains in the quadrants ROB, COA (Fig. 229), the light is right-handed elliptically polarized, but if it enters BOA, ROC, the polarization changes to left-handed
elliptical.   For R'OR = 45° the major axis of the ellipse coincides
with RA and the minor axis simultaneously attains its greatest possible value.   For positive complementary values of R'OR the ellipses,

whose major axes no longer coincide with RA, are symmetrical with respect to RA.   As R'OR deviates from 45° the ellipses become narrower and degenerate for R'OR = 0° or 90° to straight lines, each of which coincides with RA.   A similar argument holds for the other pair of quadrants.

As a means of producing circular or elliptical polarization, the quarter-wave plate is not so perfect as the rhomb.   While the latter with white light imparts, if not exactly, very nearly an identical polarization to each colour, the quarter-wave plate is unable to produce a relative retardation of $\frac{1}{4}\lambda$ for all colours simultaneously on account of the difference in wave-lengths.   The retardation must, therefore, be made exact for the central and brightest part of the spectrum and be left approximate for the remainder.   If circularly polarized light is produced by means of a quarter-wave plate, it is found that, although the brightness does not vary with the azimuth of the Nicol, the hue is yellowish for one pair of opposite quadrants and bluish for the other pair.

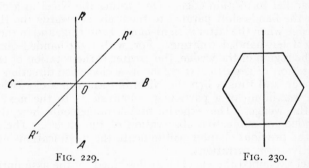

FIG. 229.   FIG. 230.

The discovery of circular and elliptical polarization increased the importance of crystal phenomena and their colour effects in particular. Some further types of these will now be considered.   If a plate of quartz cut perpendicular to its axis (Fig. 230) is placed on the platform T of Fig. 211, it appears coloured and the colour changes in a continuous manner with a rotation of the Nicol, but remains unchanged when the quartz itself is rotated in the plane of the platform.   The experiments of Arago and Biot indicate that this effect is due to the rotation of the plane of polarization, which is greater for the more refrangible part of the spectrum than for the less refrangible part. If right-handed quartz * is used, the colours thus appear in the order, red, yellow, green, blue, violet, purple, when the Nicol is turned in a direction which is clockwise to the observer, and reappear in the same order as the rotation is continued.   For left-handed quartz the order is reversed.   The colours are obviously spectrally impure, since those which lie in adjoining parts of the spectrum have only slightly different rotations and are transmitted with various intensities by the Nicol.

* I.e. quartz for which the rotation of the plane of polarization is clockwise when viewed from a position in advance of the ray.—Tr.

As a further experiment, a practically homogeneous region of an extended spectrum may be projected on the ground glass screen, in which case it will be seen that, as the spectral region is changed to a more refrangible one, the Nicol must be turned still farther in a clockwise direction to bring it again into the position of maximum or minimum brightness. Now let the spectral slit, direct-vision prism, and cardboard cone again be used, and the ground glass screen be illuminated by sunlight. A spectrum containing dark bands, increasing in number with the thickness of the quartz, is now observable. When the quartz is right-handed, the bands shift towards the violet as the Nicol is turned in a clockwise direction. This method is particularly convenient for accurately determining the rotation corresponding to the Fraunhofer lines. It also forms reliable means for finding the direction of rotation in a specimen of quartz when the latter no longer exhibits distinct coloration on account of its thickness. Using a wedge-shaped quartz plate cut perpendicular to its axis, and viewing it through the Nicol, coloured bands are seen traversing the quartz parallel to its thin edge. On turning the Nicol in a clockwise direction the bands shift parallel to themselves towards the thick end of the wedge when the latter is right-handed rotating, and in the reverse direction if left-handed rotating. For, with right-handed quartz, the thicker the region of the wedge, the greater is the rotation of the plane of polarization of a particular colour in a clockwise direction (viewed from above), and thus, when the Nicol is turned in a clockwise direction, the maximum of a particular colour shifts to the next thicker part of the wedge. The experimental arrangements here described are intended for subjective observation of the effects. The descriptions in the previous chapter will indicate the modifications necessary for objective demonstrations.

Fresnel explained the effects just described by the assumption that a linearly polarized ray entering the quartz along the axis divides itself into two opposite circularly polarized rays of slightly different velocities, which thus emerge with a relative path difference. In air the oppositely polarized rays again have the same velocity, and thus produce once more a linearly polarized ray which, however, has its plane of polarization inclined to that of the incident light. If the necessary assumptions are made concerning the dependence of velocity on colour and direction of rotation, all the details of the observed effects may be exactly accounted for. In right-handed quartz the rays which are right-handed polarized are faster than the left-handed, and the difference is greater the greater the refrangibility of the ray in the spectrum. Fresnel was then able to prove experimentally the actual existence of two rays of opposite circular polarization propagated along the axis with different velocities, and the method was later refined by V. Lang. The matter on pages 221 and 222 relating to the propagation of light in quartz must thus be modified in this respect. Fresnel's theory is easily put to the test, and all its hypotheses and conclusions drawn from it are found to be confirmed by observation. Suppose right-handed circularly polarized light is produced by a Fresnel rhomb and a right- or left-handed quartz plate is laid upon the rhomb.

No colours are visible in the region where the plate covers the rhomb, for any position of the analysing Nicol, which is to be expected, since in this case one of the interfering rays is absent. Another test is as follows : A quartz plate cut perpendicular to its axis is laid on the platform T and on it is placed a rhomb with any orientation. The right-handed circularly polarized rays leaving the quartz are transformed into linear, with plane of polarization inclined at $+ 45°$ to the plane of reflection of the rhomb, and the left-handed circularly polarized into linearly polarized rays at $- 45°$. In fact the quartz, where it is seen through the rhomb, presents the appearance of a plate cut parallel to its axis with only two hues, whose greatest saturation occurs for two mutually perpendicular settings of the Nicol at $+ 45°$ and $- 45°$ to the plane of reflection of the rhomb.

As illustrations of these effects two further experiments may be included. Suppose that the quartz wedge cut parallel to its axis is placed with its axis inclined at $- 45°$ to the plane of reflection of the polarizing mirror, and on it is laid a quarter-wave plate with the plane of polarization of the more retarded component parallel to the plane of reflection. The faster linear component in the wedge is then transformed into a right-handed, and the slower one into a left-handed, circularly polarized ray, and the wedge which is cut parallel to its axis behaves, where it is covered by the quarter-wave plate, similarly to a piece of right-handed quartz cut perpendicular to its axis. On turning the Nicol in a clockwise direction the bands in the part covered by the plate shift towards the thicker end of the wedge, while they remain stationary in the uncovered part of the wedge as long as they are still visible. It is obvious that with the proper modification of the arrangement left-handed quartz may likewise be imitated. As the inverse of this experiment, let a quarter-wave plate oriented at $45°$ with respect to the plane of reflection of the polarizing mirror be placed *underneath* a quartz wedge which is cut perpendicular to its axis. This causes the colours in the wedge to disappear, although not so perfectly as would be effected by a Fresnel rhomb. If the plate is placed *above* the wedge, the former having any orientation, the previously movable bands are made stationary and the colours become similar to those of a crystalline plate cut parallel to its axis.

Elliptical polarization is also produced in quartz, as later investigation indicated, by rays which traverse the quartz in a direction oblique to the axis. A still further modification of our mental picture of the behaviour of light in this medium is thus necessary. As, however, the angle the rays subtend with the axis is increased from zero, the two elliptically polarized rays merge very rapidly into linearly polarized rays with perpendicular planes of polarization. Thus for most purposes the conception already developed may be retained.

The effects which we have been considering may, in an exactly similar manner to that described on page 222, be illustrated by means of interference experiments with circular and elliptically polarized light. The slit $\varSigma\varSigma$ (Fig. 231) is covered by two quartz plates of equal thickness cut perpendicular to their axes, the right half with a right-handed, and the left half with a left-handed, specimen. There then passes through the right half a right-handed circularly polarized beam Rr and a left-handed one Rl, and the left half produces likewise two beams Lr and Ll. It must be remembered that the right-handed beam from the left-hand half, and the left-handed beam from the right-hand half are the more retarded. Omitting both the Nicols, the following is observable. The unpolarized light which enters $\Sigma\Sigma$ is divided in each piece of quartz into a right-handed and a left-handed circularly polarized component. Using the direct-vision prism as before, a fringe system running obliquely downwards to the left is seen ; this originates in Rr and Lr, being of the same resultant polarization and thus directly visible. Likewise Rl and Ll form a system running obliquely downwards to the right, and this is also directly visible. The interference of the right-handed circularly polarized beam with the left-handed is invisible through the direct-vision prism alone, since, for one reason, it merely produces linear polarization in a varying plane. There is, however, another reason, for even when the ocular Nicol is introduced, on rotating it the field of view remains quite unchanged, although a varying plane of polarization would necessarily be visible. It thus follows that the right- and left-handed circularly polarized components of equal intensity into which the light is divided by the quartz are in general incapable of interfering, that is to say, they are *incoherent*. This is also evident from the fact that a quartz plate cut perpendicular to its axis does not appear coloured when illuminated by unpolarized light and viewed through a Nicol, so that here, also, direct interference experiments and chromatic polarization experiments agree and afford a mutual explanation.

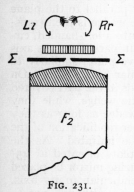

FIG. 231.

If in the previous experiment, instead of unpolarized light, right-handed circularly polarized light produced by a Nicol and quarter-wave plate is utilized, only the system which runs obliquely downwards to the left is obtained, and similarly, with the left-handed circular polarization, that which runs to the right. When light linearly polarized by a Nicol is incident on $\Sigma\Sigma$, the two circular components are now independent but, unless the ocular Nicol is used, still only the two oblique systems are visible. When the Nicol is interposed, the interference of the right- and left-handed circularly polarized light is rendered visible.

The beams Rr and Ll emerge from the quartz plates in the same phase. A deviation to the left by diffraction, however, makes the path of Ll shorter than Rr, and a rotation of the plane of polarization to the right is caused which for a path difference of $\lambda/2$ is 90°. Parallel Nicols will thus here produce a dark fringe. A similar symmetrical and coincident fringe system is produced by Rl and Lr. If the Nicols are set perpendicular, the respective positions of bright and dark fringes are interchanged. The beams Rr and Rl coming from *one* half of the slit, which produce the coloration of the quartz when placed in a polariscope, give rise with this arrangement to horizontal spectral fringes, a coincident system being produced by Lr and Ll. Here, again, the bright and dark fringes change places when the Nicols are changed from parallel to perpendicular positions. We have again five readily distinguishable fringe systems, which are exactly analogous to those of the experiments with quartz plates cut parallel to their axes.

Corresponding experiments may also be performed with elliptically polarized light. Imagine the two quartz plates cut perpendicular to the axis placed in front of the slit $\Sigma\Sigma$, a right-handed piece over the right half, and a left-handed piece over the left half. Now let the right-hand piece be turned through an angle ϕ about a horizontal axis perpendicular to the line of vision, and the left-hand piece similarly about a vertical axis also perpendicular to the line of sight. The rays transmitted by the quartz along the line of vision are, according to Airy, right-hand elliptically polarized with, say, a vertical major axis, and left-hand elliptically polarized with a horizontal major axis. The ratio of the axes is the same for both rays and the corresponding axes are mutually perpendicular. The two rays are, according to Stokes, oppositely elliptically polarized. The right-handed rays in the right-handed quartz and the left-handed in the left-handed quartz have, however, the greater velocity.

With this arrangement a similar series of experiments to those with the coplanar quartz plates may be performed, but here, in order that no disturbing effect may be introduced by light coming from the line of separation of the plates, a double slit must be substituted for the single slit. This removes the central rays, but does not affect the results. The light of similar polarization again interferes like unpolarized light, and the interference of two opposite elliptically polarized beams may be regarded as the interference of two perpendicular linear, and two opposite circular, vibrations. The result is, therefore, not a simple rotation of a plane of polarization, but an elliptical vibration whose major axis turns with the path difference, and whose minor axis varies between a maximum value and zero. Only in special cases does linear polarization result.

The oblique fringe systems, of which one alone appears when its corresponding elliptical polarization is used for the illumination of the quartz, are quite as distinct as in the previous cases. The symmetrical system, however, and the horizontal spectral fringes become faint in parts. This is the only important difference from the results with circularly polarized light. This last experiment is, in fact, the most general case, intermediate between the two former, and merges into the first when the inclination of the quartz with the direction of the light is increased (linear polarization), and into the second when the quartz is perpendicular to this direction (circular polarization). The most important result from the third experiment is, however, that *unpolarized light is divisible into two incoherent, oppositely elliptically polarized components of equal intensity.*

All the important results could have been deduced theoretically from the experiment of Fresnel's which establishes the incoherence of the two mutually perpendicular linear polarized components of unpolarized light.   For, if the phases of these linear components are not related according to any definite law, but may assume every possible difference with respect to each other, which, indeed, is the essence of incoherence, they also correspond to alternating right- and left-handed circular, and to alternating right- and left-handed elliptical vibrations.   The equal average intensity of the linear components has as a consequence the equality of the average of the circular and elliptical components and, in the latter case, the similarity of the ellipses and the perpendicularity of their corresponding axes.   From any of the three possible ways of representing unpolarized light the possibility of the other two ways may be deduced theoretically.

Beams of light having any arbitrary polarization may be made to show visible interference if they originate in the same polarized source. It is not necessary for this to be linearly polarized, although this is the simplest case ; it is clear that any definite relation between the

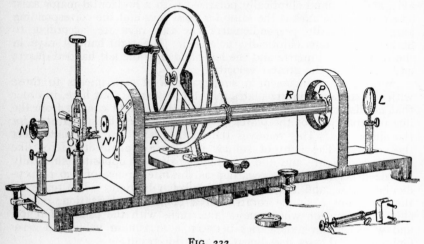

FIG. 232.

phases of the two components (one may be zero) of a beam of polarized light must of necessity occur also in the beams into which it is divided.

We will now give a brief survey of the results of our discussion of the different polarization phenomena.   This object is conveniently attained with aid of the apparatus shown in Fig. 232.   Here N denotes a large Nicol provided with a surrounding opaque screen, RR a tube about 50 cm. long and 4 cm. in diameter, supported between friction rollers so that it can be rapidly rotated by means of the large pulley and cord.   At N′ a Nicol, also provided with a screen, is fixed in the tube, and across it may be fixed either slits or rectangular diaphragms. The other end P of the tube carries, if necessary, a deviating crown glass prism of angle about 10°, or in addition a direct-vision prism, these also rotating with the tube.   A lens L of about 37 cm. focal length forms an image of the Nicol diaphragm on a screen, preferably one which is semi-transparent. First let the Nicol N be removed altogether, a rectangular diaphragm be placed on N', a crown glass prism at P, and a beam of sunlight sent axially through the tube. If the tube is now rapidly rotated, the light from the aperture of the diaphragm is deviated by the prism and, as the latter rotates, is carried round on the screen and simultaneously analysed. In fact, all the effects will now be seen simultaneously which with an ordinary polariscope are only visible in succession. Incident unpolarized light produces a uniformly bright, white circle on the screen. When the Nicol N is brought into action, so that linearly polarized light is incident on the rotating parts, the circle has maximum brightness along one diameter and is interrupted by a dark region along the perpendicular diameter. The former diameter corresponds with the plane of polarization of the Nicol N. The interposition of a quarter-wave plate between N and N', with the planes of its components inclined at 45° to the plane of polarization of N, produces circular polarization and makes the circle uniformly bright again over its whole area, with a yellowish hue in one pair of quadrants and a bluish hue in the other pair. A departure from the 45° position produces elliptical polarization with two diametrically opposite maxima and two similar minima which, however, are only completely dark when the inclination of the components of the plate to the plane of polarization of N is either 0° or 90°, in which cases the light is again linearly polarized.

The chromatic polarization effects of a crystalline plate cut parallel to its axis may likewise be exhibited. On placing the plate between N and N', with the plane of polarization of one of its components inclined at 45° to that of N, a ring is produced which is complementarily coloured in alternate quadrants, appearing a neutral white along the lines of separation of the quadrants. A quartz plate cut perpendicular to its axis, on the other hand, exhibits a ring in which the complete sequence of colours appertaining to quartz of this thickness appears twice and also indicates the direction of rotation of the plane of polarization. In spectrum form, also, the effects are easily followed. The rectangular Nicol diaphragm is replaced by a slit and the dispersion direction of the crown glass prism and of the direct-vision prism is set perpendicular to the direction of the slit. When using a rotating tube, the violet is arranged to lie towards the centre on account of its smaller intensity. With this arrangement, a broad spectral ring is obtained, violet at the centre and red on the outside. The crystalline plate cut parallel to its axis exhibits dark bands running perpendicular to the ring radii, the bands being more numerous the greater the thickness of the plate, alternating in the successive quadrants and vanishing at their intersections. The quartz plate cut perpendicular to its axis exhibits a spectral ring, across which dark spirals run, in a clockwise direction from the outer red to the central violet, if the quartz is right-handed and the effects are observed from the emergence side of the semi-transparent screen. Many other beautiful experiments which will not be dealt with here may be performed with this apparatus.

An important question is that of the relation between ordinary unpolarized and polarized light. Fresnel developed the view that unpolarized light consisted of a rapid succession of linear vibrations of every possible orientation of their plane of polarization, or of a collection of such linearly polarized rays placed side by side. So long as only one type of polarization is acknowledged, this conception is a very natural one, but immediately several kinds of polarization are recognized, and the elliptical as a general case including the others, it appears too restricted and arbitrary. Dove endeavoured to find experimental support for Fresnel's view by producing light from a rapidly rotating Nicol which in fact exhibited to the eye all the properties of natural unpolarized light and behaved like the latter towards a calcite crystal or a Malus' mirror with any orientation, and so on. Such a beam of light, it is true, is equivalent, as Airy observed, to two opposite circularly polarized beams of slightly different wave-lengths,

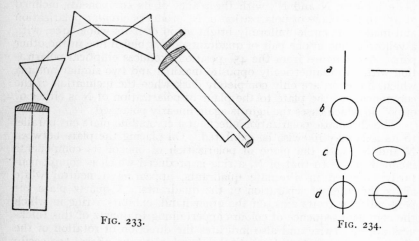

FIG. 233.   FIG. 234.

but practically it is not different from unpolarized light. Dove's experiment may be easily performed with the apparatus of Fig. 232.

A long time after Fresnel formulated his views, Stefan endeavoured to prove their correctness experimentally in the case of sunlight and light from a lamp. Though there was an error underlying his method, as Stefan himself later acknowledged, his experiment is nevertheless interesting and is thus worth describing. Stefan made use of a spectroscope of large dispersion, as illustrated diagrammatically in Fig. 233, and interposed between the prisms and observing telescope a thick plate of, say, right-handed quartz cut perpendicular to its axis, so that it covered the half of the telescope objective towards the side of the refracting edges of the prisms. If a glass plate of the same dimensions is substituted for the quartz, the whole spectrum appears intersected by a system of fine, dark interference fringes, the so-called Talbot bands. These are caused by the interference of the light from the two halves of the telescope objective, since the light passing through the right-hand half covered by the glass is retarded with respect to that from the other half.   If now the thickness of the quartz is chosen so that the plane of polarization is rotated through 90° for the Fraunhofer E line, say, then the following effects will be observed.   Light initially linearly polarized will exhibit no fringes near the E line on account of the 90° rotation (Fig. 234 *a*) ;   circularly polarized light will give the same interference effect as unpolarized (Fig. 234 *b*) ; elliptically polarized light will give an effect intermediate between these two, namely, an indistinctness of the fringes in the neighbourhood of the E lines (illustrated by Fig. 234 *c* and *d*).   Stefan actually found that for sunlight and light from a lamp the first case applies, and thus concluded that the latter consisted of linearly polarized light of constantly changing azimuth.   His mistake was as follows.   Although it is quite impossible for the 90° rotation to obliterate the interference when the rotations of the circularly polarized light are all in the same direction, an alternating left- and right-handed rotation, as in the hypothetical unpolarized light, will behave quite differently. In this case the left-handed constituent, when the 90° rotation is produced by a right-handed quartz plate, is retarded by half a wavelength more than the right-handed one, so that the fringes of either constituent, instead of coinciding, alternate in the critical region and consequently obliterate each other.   Thus in the second case, when right-handed circular polarization alternates with left-handed, the same extinction near the E line is produced as in the first.   This must, in any case, be true, if the two linear components of natural unpolarized light are incoherent, as has been proved.   It is also obvious that the third case, considered as a superposition of the two former, must give the same result.   Stefan's experiment thus merely verifies the principles already cited of the incoherence of the oppositely polarized components of unpolarized light.

A correct general conception of the nature of unpolarized light was first found by Stokes.   When polarized rays which originate in the same source are combined, the resulting effects, Stokes observed, are completely explicable by the data afforded by the work of Young and Fresnel.   New effects are produced, however, by the combination of independent polarized rays, that is, of rays from different light sources.   Stokes considered the most general case of such a combination.   He found that any mixture of such rays can be represented as a combination of unpolarized with elliptically polarized light.   This mixture is characterized by four constants, so that different mixtures with the same constants exhibit the same properties and are equivalent.   The deductions were simplified by the introduction by Stokes of the conception of oppositely polarized rays.   An elliptically polarized ray is transformed into an oppositely polarized one by rotating it through 90° about its direction in space and reversing its direction of rotation (i.e. right- or left-handed).   This definition comprises the opposite circular and linear vibrations as special cases.   It was then shown from the results of Fresnel, Arago, and Airy, those of the latter being critically modified, that at each double refraction, however it may occur, unpolarized light is split up into two independent oppositely polarized rays, a process characteristic of unpolarized light.

The relation of polarized to unpolarized light is discussed in a comprehensive publication by Lippich. In the end results in agreement with those of Lippich and Stokes were arrived at by Verdet, whose work, which is distinguished by its clearness and conciseness, we shall follow here. The characteristic properties of ordinary light are first, that it may be split up into two linear components of equal intensity in two perpendicular planes containing the direction of the ray, and second, that these components are incoherent. In practice this may be effected by means of a doubly refracting crystal, by a totally reflecting prism, or in other ways. Let us now, following Verdet, investigate the conditions which must operate for these properties to be fulfilled. Let the vibration components (Fig. 235) be $x = a \sin \phi$ and $y = b \sin (\phi + \delta)$, corresponding to the most general case of elliptical polarization. Resolving these along another pair of orthogonal axes inclined at the angle ω to the former, the new components are $x' = x \cos \omega + y \sin \omega$ and a similar equation for y' which we need not consider. By substitution of the values for x and y, it follows that

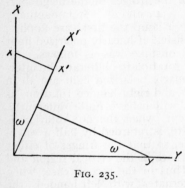

FIG. 235.

$$x' = (a \cos \omega + b \cos \delta . \sin \omega) \sin \phi + (b \sin \delta \sin \omega) \cos \phi.$$

The intensity of the x' component is obtained by squaring. and adding the terms in brackets, that is the amplitudes of $\sin \phi$ and $\cos \phi$, and is given by

$$a^2 \cos^2 \omega + b^2 \sin^2 \omega + 2ab \cos \delta . \cos \omega . \sin \omega.$$

Adding $a^2 \sin^2 \omega$ to the first term and subtracting it from the second, the expression may be written

$$a^2 + (- a^2 + b^2) \sin^2 \omega + 2ab \cos \delta . \cos \omega . \sin \omega,$$

which varies with ω for given values of a, b, and δ. If, however, many vibrations arrive in succession, a, b, and δ may vary in such a way that the mean value of the expression is independent of ω, that is,

$$\overline{a^2} + (\overline{-a^2 + b^2}) \sin^2 \omega + \overline{2ab \cos \delta} . \cos \omega . \sin \omega = \text{constant},$$

where the bars denote average values. The first term is constant, but the other two vary quite differently in $\sin^2 \omega$ and $\cos \omega . \sin \omega$ as ω is varied; thus the sum can only be constant when the coefficients of $\sin^2 \omega$ and $\cos \omega \sin \omega$ are independently zero. We thus have the equations:

$$\overline{a^2} = \overline{b^2},$$
$$\overline{ab \cos \delta} = 0.$$

This condition must also be fulfilled if all the phase differences δ receive a constant increment ϵ. Instead of the second equation we may thus write

$$\overline{ab \cos (\delta + \epsilon)} = \overline{ab \cos \delta} \cdot \cos \epsilon - \overline{ab \sin \delta} \cdot \sin \epsilon = 0.$$

Since ϵ is arbitrary, this can only be true if the coefficients of $\cos \epsilon$ and $\sin \epsilon$ are independently zero. Unpolarized light thus fulfils the three conditions :—

$$\overline{a^2} = \overline{b^2} \qquad . \qquad . \qquad . \qquad . \qquad . \qquad (1)$$
$$\overline{ab \cos \delta} = 0 \qquad . \qquad . \qquad . \qquad . \qquad (2)$$
$$\overline{ab \sin \delta} = 0 \qquad . \qquad . \qquad . \qquad . \qquad (3)$$

Since there are a very large number of ways of disposing the terms of a sum so that the latter has some definite constant value, the problem of representing unpolarized light is very indeterminate. If some particular type of vibration is, however, assumed, it is easy to find the corresponding one which compensates it to produce unpolarized light. Suppose, for example, that a vibration is given which is characterized by the constants a_1, b_1, δ_1 and appears m_1 times. It is necessary to find what are the values of a_2, b_2, δ_2, m_2 for the compensating vibration. The equations to be satisfied are :—

$$m_1 a_1{}^2 + m_2 a_2{}^2 = m_1 b_1{}^2 + m_2 b_2{}^2 \qquad . \qquad . \qquad (1)$$
$$m_1 a_1 b_1 \cos \delta_1 = - m_2 a_2 b_2 \cos \delta_2 \qquad . \qquad . \qquad (2)$$
$$m_1 a_1 b_1 \sin \delta_1 = - m_2 a_2 b_2 \sin \delta_2 \qquad . \qquad . \qquad (3)$$

Dividing the third equation by the second, it follows that $\tan \delta_1 = \tan \delta_2$, or either $\delta_1 = \delta_2$ or $\delta_2 = \delta_1 + \pi$. The assumption of the former transforms the second and third equations to $m_1 a_1 b_1 + m_2 a_2 b_2 = 0$, which, considered in conjunction with the first, gives $b_1 = 0$, $a_2 = 0$ (or $a_1 = 0$, $b_2 = 0$) as the only reasonable assumption. In this case $m_1 a_1{}^2 = m_2 b_2{}^2$.

A number of linear vibrations of amplitude a may thus be compensated to give unpolarized light by subsequent linear vibrations which are perpendicular to the former. The problem is, however, still indeterminate. If a value is assigned to the ratio of the amplitudes, then $m_2 = m_1(a_1{}^2/b_2{}^2)$; if on the other hand the number of the succeeding vibrations is stipulated, the amplitude ratio is determined by $a/b = \sqrt{m_2/m_1}$. In the case of $\delta_2 = \delta_1 + \pi$ the second and third equations give $m_1 a_1 b_1 = m_2 a_2 b_2$ or, squaring, $m_2 a_2{}^2 = m_1{}^2 a_1{}^2 b_1{}^2 / m_2 b_2{}^2$. If the first three terms of condition (1) are multiplied by the left-hand side of the last equation, and the last term of condition (1) by the right-hand side, and the products equated, the factor $(m_2 a_2{}^2 - m_1 b_1{}^2)$ may be extracted, the equating of which to zero makes the whole expression zero. It then follows that

$$m_1 b_1{}^2 = m_2 a_2{}^2,$$

and similarly $m_1 a_1{}^2 = m_2 b_2{}^2$. The two vibrations are thus opposite elliptical vibrations with axes a_1, b_1 and $b_1\sqrt{m_1/m_2}$, $a_1\sqrt{m_1/m_2}$ respectively. If one of the axes a_1, b_1 is zero, we have the previous case of opposite linear vibrations ; if $a_1 = b_1$, the vibrations are opposite circular.

It thus appears that, in general, unpolarized light must be imagined as a combination of elliptical vibrations. The ratio of the axes, their azimuth, and the directions of rotations of these vibrations are constantly changing, and, for unpolarized light to result, the variation must conform to certain conditions. These have their origin mainly in the fact that, within certain limits, every possible value of these elements defining the ellipses is equally possible and occurs equally often in a small interval of time. They are therefore fulfilled, provided no *special* conditions are in operation, by the luminous body itself. If a radiating particle is imagined to perform a perfectly irregular motion (Fig. 236), the two recombinable perpendicular components into which it is resolvable are not related according to any definite rule, but are incoherent. A simpler, yet similar, case is that in which the two-dimensional motion is one in which the elements are periodic with a definite period. The most simple case is that in which the vibration path is a simple ellipse, whose axes vary in magnitude and azimuth, the two sine components still being incoherent. Linear and circular vibrations as constituents of unpolarized light are not excluded, but represent very special cases.

FIG. 236.

A difference of opinion now existed as to whether the variations of the elements took place gradually or discontinuously. If perfectly monochromatic light is considered possible, a gradual variation is excluded, since this (according to Airy) would correspond to a combination of rays of slightly different periods of vibrations. Thus either in homogeneous unpolarized light the variation of the elements must occur discontinuously or such light cannot exist in nature, which was Lippich's assumption.

This view gains favour when the process of light emission is more closely considered. The duration of the light vibration is certainly vanishingly small compared with the length of time in which the particle is luminous under combustion in the flame, but the number of such particles simultaneously present is very large. Under these circumstances a discontinuous change in the phases is scarcely probable on physical grounds. If it is considered further that each emission process represents a contribution to the intensity, which is more quickly completed the more intensive and violent the process, this of itself suffices to exclude the possibility of perfectly homogeneous (monochromatic) light. For two vibrations of slightly different period may be considered as a single vibration of slowly varying amplitude. and this kind of variation itself may be interpreted as an inhomogeneity. This is illustrated by the formula

$$a \sin rt + a \sin (r + \rho)t = a\sqrt{2(1 + \cos \rho t)} \cdot \sin (r + \rho/2)t,$$

which is obtained similarly to that on page 211. If the left-hand side is regarded as representing the given vibrations, the formula explains the existence of beats ; if the right-hand side is regarded as the given expression, it indicates the existence of inhomogeneity owing to periodic variations in amplitude. If the latter varies still more quickly and in a more complicated periodic (or irregular) manner, it corresponds to the presence of a still greater number of vibration periods. This explanation of the broadening of spectral lines with increasing temperature and density of the luminous gas probably contains fewer hypothetical elements than those based on considerations of moving gas molecules and on Doppler's theory.

We will now consider an experimental illustration of the formation of unpolarized light from polarized constituents. A black piece of cardboard provided with a rectangular aperture is laid on the platform T of the polariscope of Fig. 211 and the aperture is covered by a quartz plate cut parallel to its axis, of a thickness great enough to produce no coloration. Let the axis be inclined at $- 45°$ to the plane of reflection of the polarizing mirror. Under these conditions the effects are not disturbed by the contrast of the field of view surrounding the quartz plate, and it is apparent that the quartz retains a constant brightness as the Nicol is rotated. The light thus exhibits an unpolarized character, and Brewster's expression that the quartz " depolarized " the light was well chosen. If, however, instead of the

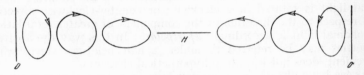

FIG. 237.

rectangular aperture, a screen provided with a slit is employed and the light spectrally resolved, a thinner quartz plate gives a few dark spectral bands and, by means of a rotated Nicol and the application of a quarter-wave plate, all the types of polarization can be shown to exist side by side in the region from one band to the next.

This also is easy to understand. In Fig. 237 the plane of polarization of the incident light is assumed vertical and that of the analysing Nicol horizontal. At the points D and D', which appear dark, the light is linearly polarized in a vertical plane, while half-way between D and D' there is a maximum brightness, and linear polarization in a horizontal plane. Passing from D towards the violet end of the spectrum to D', the path difference of the two components in the quartz increases gradually by a whole wave-length. With the given orientation of the quartz axis the following sequence of polarization occurs : right-handed elliptical with major axis vertical, right-handed circular, right-handed elliptical with major axis horizontal, horizontal linear, left-handed elliptical with major axis horizontal, left-handed circular, and left-handed elliptical with major axis vertical, after which the whole cycle is repeated. If the quartz is sufficiently thick, the bands contract together so that they are indistinguishable. The perfectly homogeneous constituents are then polarized, but the type of polarization changes very rapidly from colour to colour. A narrow spectral band, such as may in practice be separated out, will prove chromatically non-homogeneous but unpolarized, although it is composed of homogeneous polarized constituents.

Unpolarized light may be regarded as a special kind of polarization, which we will now more appropriately refer to as *indifferent* light instead of unpolarized, or natural light. This term calls to mind its perfectly indiscriminating lateral, or *homotropic* behaviour towards a rotated Nicol, as well as its inertness with respect to a quarter-wave plate. Light which behaves differently for different azimuths of the analysing Nicol we will term *heterotropic*. Linearly polarized light has properties completely determined by means of a plane containing the ray, and will thus be named *monohomal*. Two such perpendicular planes are in any case sufficient to define the character of the light, so that light for which a single plane is insufficient may be termed *dihomal*. Experiment shows that the superposition of two monohomal beams of light (with planes which do not coincide) produces dihomal heterotropes and also homotropes. Circularly and elliptically polarized light may, on account of its characteristic behaviour in the quarter-wave plate and Fresnel rhomb, be called *peripolar*, and *right* or *left peripolar* according to whether the plane of polarization of the resulting monohomal light is rotated in a clockwise or counter-clockwise direction with respect to the direction of the component of greater retardation. Monohomal light is accordingly *aperipolar*. In this way the abstract properties may be referred to under a nomenclature which, while convenient, does not introduce hypothetical elements.

As we have already seen, no new type of polarization is produced by the combination of linearly, circularly, and elliptically polarized light ; this is true also for the combination of any of these types with *indifferent* light. We will indicate these combinations by simple symbols, which also bring to mind their characteristic properties. The generally unequal intensities of the two perpendicularly polarized monohomal components may be denoted by I, I′, I″, etc., and the two symbols referring to a particular pair of components may be written together and separated by a sloping line, with also a suffix attached to one of the symbols to indicate their relative phase difference or incoherence. When each type of polarization is combined with every other in turn, the following seven types of polarization are obtained :—

1. Linearly polarized $1 = I/O$.
2. Circularly polarized $1 = I/I_{\lambda/4}$.
3. Elliptically polarized $1 = I/I'_{\lambda/4}$.
4. Indifferent $1 = I/I_{incoh.}$
5. Partially linearly polarized $1 = I/O + I'/I'_{incoh.}$
6. Partially circularly polarized $1 = I/I_{\lambda/4} + I'/I'_{incoh.}$
7. Partially elliptically polarized $1 = I/I'_{\lambda/4} + I''/I''_{incoh.}$

The symbol $I/I'_x + I''/I''_x$ suffices to designate all cases, if special values are given to I, I′, I″, and x. If our conceptions of the facts of polarization have been correct, there ought to be no conception which does not conform to the actual facts, and conversely no facts which do not agree with the conceptions. We may easily convince ourselves that there are no discrepancies of this kind. The analysis of the nature of the polarization of a given illumination may be performed according to the following table :—

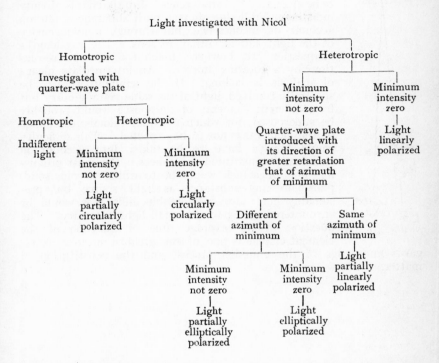

A further analysis of the direction of rotation in the circular and elliptical polarizations and the determination of the ratio of the axes for the latter have not been included in the table.

Each type of polarization may be produced independently by the following method. Light from the source L (Fig. 238) is transmitted almost normally by the unsilvered glass plate P, which also reflects at the same angle light from a more powerful source L' after the intensity has been cut down as desired by the Nicols N_1, N_2. The plane of polarization of N_2 is arranged so as to be parallel to the plane of reflection of P. Both transmitted and reflected beams traverse a quarter-wave plate, and by turning N_1, orienting the quarter-wave plate, and decreasing or cutting off the light from L or L', all the possible types may be represented.

The change of type of polarization which must be assumed to occur in indifferent light is intimately related to change of phase in each type of polarization in particular. Thus the coherence question

FIG. 238.

again arises. If the question whether and by what means is indifferent light resolvable into polarized constituents is considered, the position is as follows. The lengths over which the rays retain essentially the same polarization are, in the case of sunlight and light from lamps, decidedly too long for their lengths to be evaluated by interference. Interference is already indistinguishable for shorter path differences, not on account of incoherence, but through inhomogeneity of the light and for other reasons. The ray-lengths in question are, however, much too short for resolution by a rotating mirror. An intermediate means of analysis is lacking. If the sunlight were to be spectrally resolved, light of the same refrangibility but from different elements of the source would probably be superposed, for which an equal velocity of change of the elements is not to be expected. This difficulty would always have to be taken into account in chemically constituted substances. The most promising line of attack would be to utilize a cold, solid, phosphorescing substance as light source, but presumably here also considerable difficulties would be encountered owing to the small light intensity. The question of the average time of duration of the element change is one of the greatest interest as regards knowledge of the emission process and the constitution of matter.

CHAPTER XIII

THE EXPLANATION OF RECTILINEAR RAYS, REFLECTION, AND REFRACTION BY THE PROPAGATION OF WAVES

In Huygens' "Traité de la lumière" * appears the first attempt to correlate and render consistent the different properties of light which had from time to time been discovered, and to explain some by others, so as to reduce the number of necessary fundamental properties and the number of fundamental concepts indispensable for a correct comprehension of the underlying processes. The principal fruits of Huygens' labours lay in his demonstration of the possibility of deriving all the essential features of rectilinear propagation, reflection, and simple and double refraction from the *rate of propagation* of light. Let us follow briefly Huygens' line of reasoning.

The fact that light is developed during the process of combustion made it appear probable to him that we are here concerned with a motion. The magnitude of the velocity of spreading out, and the way in which one beam of light is able to pass unaffected through another dispelled the idea of matter shot away after the manner of an arrow. It was far more probable that we have to think of a spreading out of impulses transferred from particle to particle as in the case of *sound*. Descartes' experiment, to endeavour to show that the rate of spreading out of light was *instantaneous*, Huygens showed to be inconclusive, and he drew attention to Römer's actual determination of the finite velocity of light. According to Huygens, this is 600,000 times (really almost 1,000,000 times) that of sound in air. Important differences, however, exist in the behaviour of light and sound. Whilst the sound motion proceeds from bodies as a whole, the light motion comes from the individual points of the luminous body. Also the medium in which light is propagated cannot be the air, since light passes through a Torricellian vacuum, which is impermeable to sound. It was more likely to be a medium which can readily permeate all matter, consisting also of elastic particles able to impart their impulse one to another. Their elasticity, according to Huygens, was afforded by their being composed of still smaller elastic particles, and so on, a conception which appeared quite plausible to Huygens. He illustrated the transference of impulse by a row of contiguous elastic spheres, for which a velocity imparted to the first is transferred in a

* Huygens, " Traité de la lumière," à Leide (1690).

short, but finite, time to the last, all the intermediate spheres remaining at rest. Such impulses may traverse the series in opposite directions simultaneously, and cross one another.

The conception of a regular sequence of equidistant waves sent out by the source of luminosity was alien to Huygens; in fact he explicitly refuted the idea of a periodicity analogous to that of sound waves (loc. cit., p. 15). His conception of light waves was rather of an irregular succession of isolated pulses, whose effects only become noticeable when several of the weak individual impulses coming from different centres add up or unite to form a stronger wave (loc. cit., p. 17). Impulses such as these are imparted not only in one direction along a straight line, but to all the particles in contact with the pulsating one. Thus in general the spreading out occurs simultaneously on all sides spherically.

These conceptions give a method of derivation of the *optically effective* waves from the " elementary waves "; this has been designated the *Huygens' principle*.

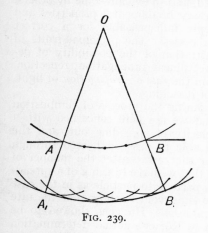

FIG. 239.

Huygens quite recognized the fertility of this principle, attributing his successful application of it to the similar but less successful efforts of Hooke and Pardies, but at the same time he was fully aware of its weaknesses. " Et tout cecy ne doit pas sembler estre recherché avec trop de soin, ni de subtilité; puisque l'on verra dans la suite, que toutes les propriétez de la lumière, et tout ce qui appartient à sa reflexion et à sa refraction, s'explique principalement par ce moyen " (loc. cit., p. 18).

Huygens next illustrates and applies his principle by deducing that the propagation of light is necessarily rectilinear. Suppose that light spreads out from the source O (Fig. 239) in the form of a spherical wave, and that when the radius of the latter has reached a certain value part of the wave is cut off by a screen which only allows the portion AB to pass. Huygens then regards the points of the spherical surface AB arrived at by the impulses exactly as if they were the original excitation centres of subsidiary spherical waves. This means to say that he draws no distinction as to whether a particle which receives and transmits an impulse is the *first* to have received it, or whether it has been communicated through the agency of a series of others. Imagining spherical waves of radii $AA_1 = BB_1$ to be constructed about every point of the portion of spherical surface AB as centre, these spheres will, after the time necessary for propagation from A to A_1 has elapsed, be tangential to the enveloping portion of the spherical surface A_1B_1, at which they will arrive simultaneously and in greatest density under conditions for *reinforcement*. In the space outside OAA_1 and OBB_1 the waves will arrive in succession through *scattering* and consequently be ineffective. This still holds if O is very distant, AB indefinitely small, and OA parallel to OB. In this way the light from a distant source, on passing through a small aperture, fills a cylinder whose base is given by the aperture. It is evident that Huygens regarded diffraction effects as absent or negligible. If, however, it is assumed that *actual* light is propagated rectilinearly, each ray must, according to Huygens' theory, become continually weaker as it passes on its way owing to loss of impulses laterally, a factor which is of greater importance the more confined the wave-surface. This circumstance also was disregarded by Huygens.

Let us interrupt the résumé of Huygens' work for a moment and consider how he probably arrived at these ideas. In their essentials they evidently have a two-fold origin, his natural experience and his particular line of thought. It would be quite natural for the son of a seafaring people and the inhabitant of a town intersected by canals

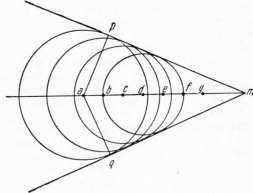

Fig. 240.

to make observations upon water waves. As a boy, no doubt, he would have thrown pebbles into water and observed the interaction of ripples generated simultaneously or successively at two different points. He could not fail to have observed the wedge-shaped waves produced by moving a stick rapidly through water in one direction, or the waves from the bow of a moving boat, and must have recognized that practically the *same* effect is produced by dropping several pebbles into the water in succession at intervals along a straight line. These observations contain the nucleus of his most important discoveries. The resultant wave *pmq* (Fig. 240) is the envelope of the elementary waves generated successively in $a, b, c \ldots$ If u is the velocity of m, v that of the elementary waves, and a the angle amp, then $v/u = \sin a$. If the wave velocity happened to be different on either side of am, as in Fig. 241 for example, with v above and v' below, then we have $v/u = \sin a$ and $v'/u = \sin \beta$ and consequently $\sin a/\sin \beta = v/v'$. The generation of elementary waves at $a, b, c, \ldots$ may, however, be considered as produced by the incidence upon *am* of a wave *as* of velocity *v* in a direction such that *as* makes an angle — α with *am* at *a*. Then, regarding Fig. 241 as the intersection of the interface of two media by a plane of incidence containing incident, reflected, and refracted waves, and imagining the latter to be *cylindrical* instead of

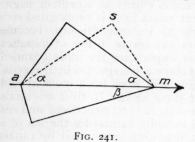

circular, we have the essential features of Huygens' explanation of reflection and refraction (loc. cit., pp. 21-36). With reference to total reflection Huygens remarks (loc. cit., p. 37) that, if $\beta > a$ and $\sin a \lessgtr \mu$, the elementary waves of the resultant refracted wave either reinforce one another in the direction of the interface, in the case of the equality, or, in the other case, are totally unable to reinforce one another, since

FIG. 241.

the smaller waves are *contained inside* the larger. Here was the first, though perhaps imperfect, physical explanation of total reflection. Next follows a proof of Fermat's principle of least time for the case of refraction (loc. cit., pp. 39-41).

Huygens does not explain by means of his principle the case of the propagation of a completely enclosed spherical wave; in fact his method, instead of forming a useful simplification, renders the matter more complicated. If, however, we are considering a portion of a wave which has a perfectly arbitrary boundary or curvature, its approximate manner of progression may be determined by regarding each point of the wave as a starting-point of elementary waves. The method here applied consists in endeavouring to estimate the more complicated cases by a combination of simple known ones. The process is allied to the method, used by Daniel Bernoúlli, Fourier, and others in mathematical physics, of constructing the general solution of a problem from particular solutions. It is a laxity to regard a point of a wave as the centre of another wave. If this were the case, each point of a wave would necessarily radiate waves in all directions, that is, backwards as well as forwards. Huygens' principle would then lose all its applicability and significance. Each point of a wave behaves in fact as if it were *very near to the centre* of excitation. We shall return to this question later.

The *second* line of thought which Huygens here employed was the result of his observations and investigations on the impact of elastic bodies, to which he refers * (loc. cit., p. 14). The *complete* transference of impact velocity which occurs between a series of contiguous spheres of equal mass appeared particularly significant to him. He imagined the ether to be composed of such equal massive spheres. Supposing heavier spheres to be at the bottom, lighter spheres on striking them from above would rebound; this afforded an inconvenient way of representing a partial reflection (loc. cit., p. 20). Reflection

---

* Huygens, " De motu corporum ex percussione." " Opera posthuma " (1703).

from a denser medium accordingly presented no difficulties (loc. cit., pp. 21-26), but that from a rarer medium appeared a complete enigma (loc. cit., p. 39).   The reason for this was that Huygens' impact investigations concerned isolated bodies, whose velocity is readily transferred by a *pushing* but not by a *pulling*.   The motion of a sphere towards, and a collision with, a sphere of smaller mass was not regarded by Huygens as reflection, whereas Young later considered both cases as reflection and was able to elucidate the phase change occurring in reflection from denser or rarer media.   Since Huygens thus considered only impulses of *one* particular type, that is, impacts tending to increase the density, and a uni-directional propagation, the generality of his investigation is limited, but is fully qualified nevertheless to elucidate the principal phenomena of light propagation.

Huygens' ideas on transparency and the propagation of refracted light in transparent media are interesting.   He regarded material media as consisting possibly of a sponge-like structure of contiguous particles, through which the substance of the magnetic and gravitation vortices (the ether) were able to stream freely and which were held together by some external pressure.   He considered this pressure justifiable, since water which had been boiled remained suspended in an inverted glass tube even under the bell of an air-pump.   Of the origin of the pressure he says nothing.*   One idea of Huygens was that light was propagated solely in the portions occupied by the matter in such a conglomerate.   He considered it more probable, however, that the ether could pass easily through the pores of bodies (Torricelli, Boyle), for which reason the resistance to inertia of evacuated vessels depended only on the mass of the walls!   In the sponge-like structure, since all matter has the same gravitational acceleration, the size of the pores was to Huygens an indication of unequal specific mass. Water weighs only 1/14 as much as an equal volume of mercury, but even the particles of the latter could not be densely packed, since gold is still heavier.   Thus to Huygens all atoms were of equal specific density and probably also of identical form.   With the permeability hypothesis light was transported in transparent substances either by the ether parts or by these and the material parts simultaneously, always, however, with a smaller velocity in the denser substances. Huygens explained opacity by damping occurring on encountering soft inelastic portions (loc. cit., pp. 26-32).

In homogeneous media the light waves spread out uniformly in all directions (spherically).   If, however, a wave spreads out from a particular point in the atmospheric air, which decreases in density with the height, the *wave-surfaces* obtained by joining the points reached simultaneously by the wave after short successive intervals of time are no longer spherical.   Two wave-surfaces separated in time by a definite short interval have a separation in space which increases with their height in the atmosphere.   The rays which spread out from the luminous centre are curved, but run everywhere perpendicular to the elements of the wave-surfaces which they intersect.

* On no account can an ether *permeable* to matter exert a pressure able to hold together the structure of the substance.

This is the origin of terrestrial and astronomical refraction. To explain these effects by the theory of elementary waves, Huygens considers an example. Suppose that an element of the wave-surface ABC (Fig. 242) is vertical, i.e. the immediately preceding ray elements aA, bB, cC are horizontal. If, now, the elementary waves in the lower atmospheric layers advance more slowly, and the region of densest intersection of the elementary waves is regarded as the new wave-surface, then this surface is $A_1B_1C_1$, and the corresponding ray elements are AA_1, BB_1, CC_1, which by the construction are rendered perpendicular to the wave-surface, when all the differences are small (loc. cit., pp. 42-48).

It must have been of importance to Huygens to test the efficacy of his theory with reference to the double refraction phenomena discovered by Bartolinus which had appeared till then to throw open to ridicule all the established optical facts and theories. He therefore studied the calcite phenomena very carefully. The calcite rhombohendron is bounded by parallelograms, whose angles are given by

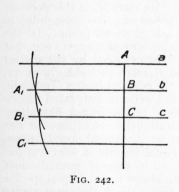

FIG. 242.

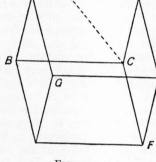

FIG. 243.

Huygens as 101° 52' and 78° 8'. It has *two* opposite corners which are formed by *three* obtuse angles, while the remainder are formed each by two acute and one obtuse angle. If the obtuse angle ACB (Fig. 243) of the parallelogram face at the blunt corner C is bisected by the line CE, and a plane is imagined to pass through CE perpendicular to the parallelogram face, the plane also contains the edge CF formed by the two other bounding surfaces. The plane thus determined, and any plane parallel to it, Huygens terms a *principal section* (" section principale," loc. cit., p. 52). An incident ray is in general divided into two rays on entering the calcite, one of which, the ordinary ray, conforms to the ordinary Descartes' law of refraction, while the other extraordinary ray is not limited in this way. As long as the plane of incidence coincides with a principal section HH (Fig. 244), *both* of the refracted rays remain in this same plane. While a ray S incident normally and an oblique ray R are always refracted as ordinary rays O respectively without and with deviation, the extraordinary refraction exhibits the peculiarity that a ray incident normally in the principal section gives an extraordinary ray e which is deviated by 6° 40′ towards the blunt corner C.   A ray R, incident in the principal section at 73° 20′ with the rhombohedron surface, that is *almost* parallel to the third edge of the blunt corner, gives an undeviated extraordinary ray e.   The edge referred to makes an angle of 70° 57′ with the surface of the rhombohedron and is therefore by no means *exactly* parallel to the ray, a fact to which Huygens drew Bartholinus' attention, the latter being inclined to ascribe this parallelism to an essential property of the phenomena (loc. cit., pp. 53, 57).   Huygens studied both refractions quantitatively by an appropriate modification of Kepler's method (cf. loc. cit., pp. 45 and 47).   The sine law always held for the ordinary ray, the refractive index being about 5/3 for calcite and about 3/2 for rock-crystal ; for the extraordinary refraction the sine ratio was not constant.   The deviation for extraordinary refraction was, however, for calcite always less than for the ordinary, attaining the same value as the latter for a particular orientation. The following may be mentioned as of interest.   If the extraordinary

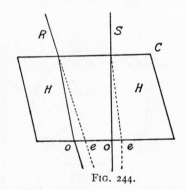

Fig. 244.

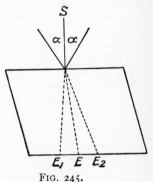

Fig. 245.

constituent of a ray incident normally in the principal section passes through a point E (Fig. 245), it will, when equally inclined at an angle α on either side of the normal, touch points E_1 and E_2 such that $EE_1 = EE_2$ (loc. cit., p. 57).

To extend his theory to include double refraction, Huygens tried the hypothesis of two different waves, one, the *ordinary*, being propagated in the ether of the crystal, and the other, corresponding to extraordinary refraction, propagated both in the ether *and* in the material parts of the crystal. Since the ordinary refraction was satisfactorily explained by spherical waves, Huygens suspected that the characteristics of the extraordinary refraction might be explicable by *spheroidal* (ellipsoidal) waves. This hypothesis recommended itself to him through observation of the crystalline structure of calcite and rock-crystal, which exhibited a different disposition of its microscopic parts, that is, density in different directions. Prisms of rock-crystal indicated that they were doubly refracting, though to a less marked degree than calcite, which explained why quartz lenses could not be used for telescopes.

His very first attempt to apply the refraction construction to spheroidal elementary waves showed a favourable result. It was at once apparent that the refracted ray for normal incidence was deviated if the axes of the ellipsoidal waves were assumed to be oblique with respect to the surface of separation. It was now necessary to fix the shape of the ellipsoid and the orientation of its axes in the crystal (loc. cit., pp. 58-60). Picturing the appearance of the blunt corner of a calcite rhomb (Fig. 246) and imagining the three principal sections respectively normal to each of the three faces, these intersect in a line, called by Huygens the axis of the corner, subtending equal angles with each of the three edges to the corner. If, now, the direction of the axis of the wave spheroid of rotation of which Huygens first thought did not coincide with that of the axis of the corner, *each* of the three principal sections would not indicate the *same* optical characteristics. The inclination of the axis of the corner to each of the faces of the corner amounts to 45° 20'. The orientation of the spheroid being known, the fact that for normal incidence the extraordinary ray is

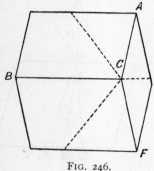

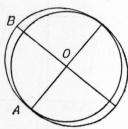

FIG. 246.   FIG. 247.

deviated in the principal section from the ordinary ray by 6° 40' towards the blunt corner is sufficient to establish the shape of the spheroid. By calculations based on his data, Huygens found the following to be in agreement with the facts. If OA (Fig. 247) is the axial direction of the calcite and the ordinary wave spreading out from the point O of the crystal is represented by a sphere of radius OA, the surrounding oblate spheroid of rotation AB with axis of rotation OA represents the corresponding extraordinary wave emerging simultaneously from O. The ratio of OA to OB is as 8 to 9 (more exactly as 93410 to 105032), while the ratio of OA to the corresponding path in air is 3/5 (loc. cit., pp. 54, 63, 68).

With this idea Huygens was, in fact, able to elucidate all the new optical phenomena arising with calcite. The following may be cited as an example. Placing a calcite rhomb on a leaf of printed matter, the letters are seen on two separate levels, the ordinary image as the higher, and the extraordinary as the lower, on account of the weaker refraction. Viewing the images with two eyes, their separation appears four times as great when the eyes lie in a line perpendicular

to the principal section as when in a line parallel to it.   A description
and quantitative explanation of this are given (loc. cit., pp. 77-82).
Finally Huygens indicates the effects which are to be expected when
arbitrarily oriented prepared sections are used.   The most noteworthy is the single image obtained on looking through the crystal
in the direction of the axis ; for this purpose the crystal is ground off
perpendicular to its axis at its blunt corners.   At the end of the
chapter are to be found the observations on polarization, reflections
on the structure of crystals referred to on pages 187 and 260, and
as appendix the necessary calculations.

Huygens' method of construction may be described, omitting
unnecessary complications, as follows.   The plane of incidence is
considered to lie in the plane of the paper (Fig. 248) ; MN represents
its intersection with the calcite-air surface, SO a ray incident externally upon the calcite.   Let SO be produced to S', and a sphere of

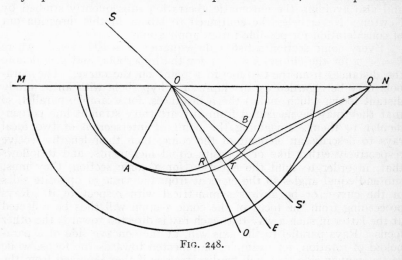

FIG. 248.

any convenient radius be described about O as centre.   At its intersection with SOS' let a tangent plane be constructed intersecting
MN in Q.   If now a sphere of 3/5 the radius of the former is described
about O, its point of contact R with the tangential plane passing
through Q gives the ordinary ray OR.   Let OA be the direction of
the axis of the calcite.   A spheroid is now described about the smaller
sphere such that its axis of rotation OA (the minor axis) = OR is 8/9
the length of the major axis.   The point of contact T of the tangent
plane through Q to the spheroid now gives the extraordinary ray OT.
The tangent planes are simultaneously tangential to all the other
elementary waves set up by the incident wave.   It is easily seen that
the construction is only confined to one plane so long as the axis is
symmetrical with respect to the plane of incidence, that is either
coincident with it or *perpendicular* to it.   For any other orientation
the extraordinary ray is *inclined* to the plane of incidence, in which

case methods of descriptive or analytical geometry are desirable for solution of the problem.

Having established the theory of reflection and refraction, Huygens proceeded to ascertain the form of the reflecting and refracting surfaces which would bring together light emerging from a point source into a real or virtual point image. Kepler (" Paralipomena ad Vitelionem ") had already made special reference to the optical properties of the foci of conic sections, and Descartes * had conceived the idea of using in optical instruments surfaces of rotation whose meridian sections were conic sections instead of the usual spherical reflecting and refracting surfaces. The latter describes this project at length in his " Dioptrics " and also in his " Géométrie." Huygens saw that the idea would not be applicable without first surmounting the practical difficulties of manufacturing such surfaces on account of irregularities in form, which replace spherical aberration difficulties, and also avoiding the chromatic aberration subsequently studied by Newton. Nevertheless he continued to labour in this direction out of consideration for possible future applications.

Every conic section satisfies the equation $u + kv = const.$, where $k = + 1$ for the ellipse, $k = - 1$ for the hyperbola, and u, v denote the distances from the two foci to a point on the curve. The parabola may be regarded as an ellipse or a hyperbola with an infinitely distant focus, which makes the u distances, for example, parallel, so that they may be measured from any arbitrary straight line perpendicular to them. Imagining the point of intersection of two focal rays to describe an element of the conic, then their lengths receive respectively either like or opposite equal increments, and it follows that, in order to fulfil the equation for a conic section, they must subtend equal angles to the element from the same or opposite sides of the curve, or be always symmetrical with respect to it. Rays proceeding from the focus of the conic section will thus be reflected at the latter in such a way that each ray is directed towards the other focus. Rays parallel to the axis will, at the concave side of a paraboloid of rotation, for example, be reflected towards the focus, while at the convex side they will be dispersed as if they emerged from the focus. Rays emergent from the focus will be reflected back parallel to the axis.

According to Huygens' theory, for an image of a luminous point to be produced, it is not sufficient only for the rays to meet in one point, but the rays from the first point, or their respective elementary waves, must arrive at the second point *simultaneously*. Here is an important advance beyond the Kepler-Descartes view. It is at once obvious that for the two foci the Huygens' condition is fulfilled (e.g. a reflecting ellipse). Applying Huygens' theory to the case of a hyperbola, it is apparent that light radiating from one of its foci and reflected by one of its branches behaves as if each ray or elementary wave had emerged *simultaneously* from the other focus.

* Descartes, " Discours de la méthode ; plus la Dioptrique, les Météores, et la Géométrie," Leyde (1637).

If, however, the luminous point A is situated in *one* medium, and its image B in a second, the interface of the two media must be arranged in such a way that the elementary waves traverse the path between A and B in *equal* times. Thus, if u, v are the distances in air, c, c_1 the velocities in the first and second media, the equation which applies will be $u/c + v/c_1 = const.$, or $u + c/c_1 \cdot v = const.$, that is $u + \mu v = const.$ where μ is the refractive index passing from the first to the second medium.

To construct an interface with this property, let A (Fig. 249) be the luminous point, B its image, and D the intersection of the line joining A, B with the interface. Supposing that the refractive index from A to B is 3/2, a point H is taken such that DH = 3/2 DB, HM is drawn equal to DB, and DM is joined. If now an arc of radius AF > AD is drawn with A as centre, and a second arc of radius 2/3 FH and centre B, their intersections give two points of the meridian curve of the required surface. The radius of the second arc may be conveniently obtained by drawing FN parallel to DM, HN being the required length.

The curves $u + \mu v = const.$, the " Cartesian ovals," were first dis-

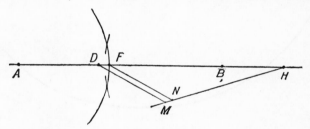

FIG. 249.

cussed by the gifted founder of analytical geometry, Descartes, in the second book of his " Géométrie." Conic sections may be regarded as special cases of the series. Ovals corresponding to the particular value $u + 2v = const.$ are shown in Figs. 250 and 251 ; these may also be drawn mechanically without difficulty by fastening a thread to a pin at A, passing it first round the pencil at S, then round the second pin B, and back to the pencil, to which the end is secured. The ovals may either enclose *both* the points A and B or only one of the points (B), according as the constant value of $u + 2v$ is chosen so that D lies outside or inside the line AB. Obviously only in the latter case would the results be applicable dioptrically for a medium of refractive index 2. It is possible, however, for both A and B to be situated in the air if the bounding curve of the second medium is completed by a circular arc MN drawn about B, a device often employed by Descartes in his dioptrical investigations.

For a refractive index $\mu = 3/2$, for example, the thread would have to pass twice from A to S, and three times from S to B, which, without special arrangements, would involve too much friction for a good mechanical execution of the construction. In such cases the construction must be performed point by point, or by calculation. The former may be accelerated somewhat by the method illustrated in

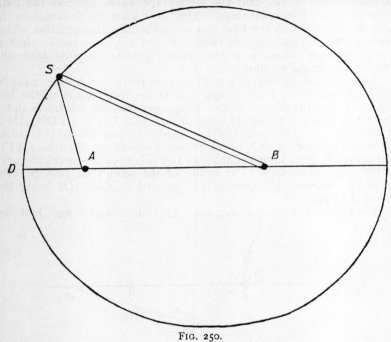

FIG. 250.

Fig. 252. The two points A, B are marked off on the straight line SS. On either side of A the lines AM are drawn upwards equally inclined to SS at any convenient angle. Similarly from B the lines BN are

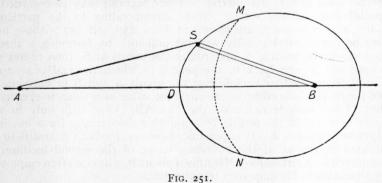

FIG. 251.

drawn downwards, but with an inclination to SS giving μ times the gradient of the lines AM. The sum of the ordinates for the two lines now corresponds to the sum $u + \mu v$. From the figure it is obvious that the sum denoted by the length I, for example, gives a curve completely enclosing B, while that denoted by II results in an enclosure of both A and B. BI and AI, or BII and AII are the first construction radii. To determine additional points, the paper is cut along SS and the parts are shifted relatively to each other in such a way that the chosen ordinate sum gives a somewhat larger value for the radius A and a smaller one for B. The pairs of points given by these values

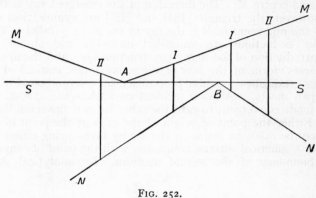

FIG. 252.

are then constructed and the process repeated. The constant sum must, of course, be measured off by a scale which may be fixed perpendicular to SS.

In his " Dioptrics " Descartes observes that under certain special conditions refracting media bounded by a surface of rotation whose meridian curve is an ordinary conic section are capable of concentrating light at a *single* point. Imagining a glass ellipsoid of revolution having for its meridian surface an ellipse with major axis a and

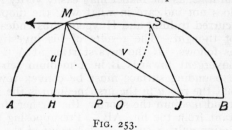

FIG. 253.

excentricity $e = 2/3$, a ray parallel to the major axis and tangential to the ellipse is refracted, if the refractive index is exactly $3/2$, towards the focus of the ellipse, while the normal at the point of tangency passes through the centre. The ray incident along the major axis also passes through the focus. That this is true for every ray incident parallel to the axis is clear from the following. In Fig. 253, A, B are the extremities of the major axis, H, J the foci, u, v two light rays passing through the point M of the ellipse, MP the normal at M which also bisects the angle between u and v. By a well-known geometrical theorem HP/PJ = u/v, and therefore PJ = $2a\ ev/(u+v)$, and by the equation of the ellipse ($u+v=2a$), PJ = $v\ .\ e$. Regarding v as a ray originating in the focus and emerging from glass of refractive index $1/e$, the direction of the ray in the air may be found from Snell's construction by drawing from J a line parallel to the normal PM and marking the point of intersection S with it of a circle of radius $v\ .\ e$. (= JP) and centre M. The direction of the emergent ray is then SM. Since, however, the triangles JSM and MPJ are symmetrical with respect to the mid-point of MJ, the ray in the air is parallel to the axis. Descartes' deductions are somewhat unwieldy and obscure, owing to the introduction of too many construction lines and the application of Descartes' form of the law of refractive index instead of Snell's. Descartes establishes a similar proposition for a hyperboloid of revolution of two sheets.   A beam incident parallel to the axis on the one sheet is made convergent toward the other focus if the refractive index is $1/e$. Either the point of origin of the rays or the point of convergence may be made to reside in the air by introducing either a plane surface or a spherical surface, concentric with the point of convergence, as the boundary of the second medium.   By analytical geometry

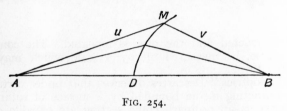

FIG. 254.

Huygens was able to show that these propositions also follow from the principle of *equal time*, as the reader may easily verify for himself.

Descartes does not indicate in what way the dioptric application of the ovals occurred to him, and Huygens thus endeavours to ascertain his line of thought.   The results of his investigation may be briefly stated as follows.   If the rays starting at A (Fig. 254) are to be rendered convergent towards B in a medium refracting towards the normal, its bounding surface must be convex towards A.   It is then obvious that the ray u in the first medium is the longer, and the ray v in the second medium the shorter, the farther the point of incidence M is distant from the line AB.   Presupposing a knowledge of the law of refraction only, a small displacement of the point M in the meridian curve serves to give a simple deduction involving infinitesimals. In Fig. 255 the meridian curve is indicated by MM and the normal by LL.   Displacing the ray uv over an element ds of the meridian curve, we find, for the corresponding increment of the ray lengths,

$$du = ds\ .\ \sin a \quad \text{and} \quad dv = -\ ds\ .\ \sin \beta = -\ ds\ \frac{\sin a}{\mu},$$

so that $du + \mu dv = 0$ or $u + \mu v = const.$, which is exactly the same relation as follows from the Huygens' principle of equal time.   The fact that Descartes and Huygens were not able to make use of the symbols of the differential calculus does not in any way affect the essentials of their deduction.

As Huygens ascertained, the consideration of rays and the application of the laws of reflection and refraction lead to results in accordance with the deductions from the theory of elementary waves. If thus a collection of rays diverges from a point and after any number of reflections and refractions converges towards another point, then all the individual rays of such a system may be regarded as traversing the path between the two points in *equal times* and, so long as we are dealing with a single medium, the paths are of *equal length*.   If the various rays are divided off from the starting-point forwards, or from the convergence point backwards, into elements of equal time or, where we are concerned with the same medium, into elements of equal length, each system of division points lies in a wave-surface at which the elementary waves arrive at the same instant of time. The rays are the normals to the elements of the wave-surface, but it

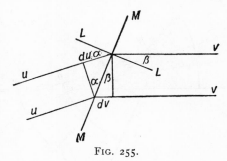

Fig. 255.

is only in the simplest cases that the normals intersect in a single point, only when a wave is divergent from or convergent to a single point. Even if a pencil of rays that is homocentric enters a spherical glass surface, the homocentricity is lost after this *single* refraction.   In Fig. 256 the plane of the paper is supposed to contain the centre of a glass sphere, the central ray being indicated by CC, and the ray making the greatest angle with this by RR.   The paths of other intermediate rays are also indicated, the whole being diagrammatical and exaggerated for the sake of clearness.   Following Huygens, an idea of the course of the wave-surfaces in this complex is obtainable by the following process, which justifies itself by what has been cited above.   Between the two extreme rays, whose point of intersection is at *a*, an arc of any convenient radius is marked off with a pair of compasses using *a* as centre.   With *b* as centre, the arc is now continued between the second and third rays, and the process is repeated until all the points of intersection *a*, *b*, *c*, *d*, *e*, ... have been used.   The juxtaposition of the arcs so constructed gives a section of the wave-surface by the plane of the figure.   The figure shows eight such intersections obtained by dividing off both in the forward and in the backward direction. The wave-surface itself is obtained by rotating the figure about CC. A remarkable shape of the section of the wave-surface arises when the construction is carried out between the points of intersection a, b, c, d, e . . . Commencing with an arc radius ab and centre a between the rays intersecting in a, the arc has to be continued from b with centre c between the two rays intersecting in c and the process repeated from the centres d, e . . . Thus, as the wave-surface from w_1 arrives at the points of intersection a, b, c, d, e . . . it is bent back on itself, and the wave originally concave to the right has an additional convex part which grows at the cost of the former, until when the series of points a, b, c, d, e, . . . has been passed it

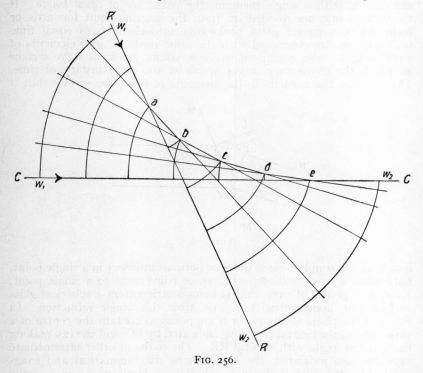

FIG. 256.

occupies the whole wave-surface. Imagining the wave-surface to be a sheet of some stretchable substance, as it proceeds on its way from w_1 it contracts, gradually becomes inverted, and expands again.

To be consistent with reality, a correction must be made to the above diagrammatical representation. In place of the single rays of Fig. 256 there is a continuous sequence of rays and instead of the points a, b, c, d, e . . . a continuous series of intersections, termed a *focal line*, which may also be regarded as the *envelope* of the system of rays, that is, as the curve to which all the rays are tangent. If a thread is stretched taut round the convex side of the focal line and its end attached to a pencil, on unwinding the thread the pencil describes a section of the wave-surface. The latter is thus an *involute* * of the focal line, or the focal line the *evolute* of the section of the wave-surface. To obtain a mental picture of the section of the wave-surface within the focal line region, a thin stiff rod may be imagined to roll round the focal line without slipping. Concentrating attention upon particular points of the rod, each point which comes into contact once with the focal line describes one of the reflex sections.

* As to the idea of evolutes and involutes, cf. Huygens, " Horologium oscillatorium. De motu pendulorum," Paris (1673.) Also cf. Newton, " Method of Fluxions," London (1736).

CHAPTER XIV

A FURTHER EXPLANATION OF THE BEHAVIOUR OF LIGHT BY MEANS OF PERIODICITY

DIFFRACTION

BEFORE entering upon the subject matter of this chapter, it would be well to glance at the development of acoustics. Although the investigation of the tones of vibrating strings was one of the earliest of the exact studies (Pythagoras), physical acoustics has nevertheless made very slow progress. The ideas of Aristotle concerning the excitation and propagation of sound were still very confused, although he expressed somewhat more definite views on the echo and on resonance (cf. " De anima," Vol. II, p. 8). On the other hand Vitruvius, the military engineer of Cæsar and Augustus, appropriately compares the propagation of sound with the progress of water waves and brings forward the spatial spreading out of the former as a point of discrimination from water waves (" De architectura "). The astronomer Cl. Ptolemy (second century, A.D.) has left a manuscript known by the name of " Harmonicum Libri III," which was published with a Latin translation in 1682 by John Wallis. Physical acoustics, which forms the subject of the first book, is very mediocre ; mention is made of the fact that the more stretched and the harder substance emits the higher note, bronze a higher one than lead, and shorter strings and pipes higher notes than longer ones (Cap. 3). In Cap. 4 continuous and discontinuous variations of pitch are described (the howl of the wolf as of the former type), pleasant and unpleasant combinations of sound are dealt with, and the analogous effects with colours mentioned. Cap. 8 contains remarks to the effect that the length of a pipe and the straining load of a string are useless for the exact determination of their harmonic properties, the monochord with displaceable bridge alone being suitable for this purpose ; this bears evidence of Ptolemy's experimental skill. However incomplete our knowledge of the physical acoustics of antiquity may be, it is scarcely probable that this period could have had much to hand down to us. If we pass on to the Renaissance period, we find evidence in Francis Bacon (1561-1626) of unprejudiced opinions and methods of observation. In his " Historia Soni et Auditus " he expresses the view that sound does not consist of a bodily impact of the air, since it does not move a flame, a small feather, or a fine thread. The duration of the sound from a bell that had been struck originated in its *trembling*, with the suppression of which the sound also ceases at once. The insight of his contemporary Galileo (1564-1642) was still more comprehensive. He observed a vibrating and sound-emitting tool in use on a lathe and noticed the doubled number of indentations produced in the same length of material as soon as its note struck the octave ; he was acquainted with resonance and illustrated it by the manner of setting a heavy bell into motion, and noticed the lines into which the dust collects upon the sound-box of a violin, and so on. His son Vincenzio (1606-1649) had learnt that a four-fold increase of the load upon a string doubles its frequency of vibration. The " Harmonicorum Liber " (1636) of Mersenne (1588-1648) already contains a summary of the most important laws of physical acoustics, and there is there set forth the influence of the length, thickness, and load of a string upon its frequency of vibration. Mersenne determines the frequency of vibration by increasing the length of the string under constant load until the vibrations could be counted directly. He knew that the same string would give several tones bearing a simple relation to one another. In his " Ballistica " he gives the first of the more refined determinations of the velocity of sound in air. During Newton's lifetime Sauveur (1655-1716) made his fine observations on beats (1700), on the evaluation of the frequency of a fixed note by this means (1700), and by another method (1713). The harmonic tones of a vibrating string had been demonstrated prior to Sauveur by John Wallis by the rider method. Shortly afterwards Sorge (1744) and Tartini (1754) discovered combination tones.

The most important advance in the wave theory and physical acoustics at about this time was due to Newton, who set forth his discoveries in this direction in the first edition of his " Principia," 1687 (pp. 354-372). He points out that diffraction is a necessary accompaniment of each type of wave (water wave or sound wave), shows how to compute the velocity of propagation of either type from the properties of the medium, and deduces theoretically the velocity of sound waves from the pressure and density of the fluid elastic medium. Newton's formula in the last case was incomplete it is true, and received its last refinements at the hands of Laplace 130 years later, nevertheless it formed the basis of all the later theories. While on the one hand Euler, Lagrange, Daniel Bernoulli, D'Alembert and Poisson, down to the beginning of the nineteenth century, concerned themselves principally with the extension of theoretical acoustics and the wave theory, experimenters such as Chladni and Thomas Young developed the same by their experimental researches.

Colour has often been compared with musical notes, for example by Ptolemy, Descartes, and Newton. Grimaldi thought he was entitled to assume that an efflux of light was periodic in its properties and even to give expression to the principle that light added to light might produce darkness. This principle is still valid although it no longer follows as a result of Grimaldi's experiments. The whole of Huygens' optics is based upon the analogy of light with water waves and sound. The periodicity of light exhibited itself unmistakably in Hooke's experiments and in Newton's in particular. Though Huygens did not live to become acquainted with Sauveur's experiments on beats, both Hooke and Newton did. Nevertheless Hooke merely introduced the periodicity of waves into the optical theory in a quite extraneous manner, while on the whole Huygens and Newton left it out of consideration altogether, although the fundamental acoustical principles were known to all three, and to Newton in particular, who, as the conspicuous promoter of this branch of natural philosophy, must have had them completely at his command. Newton, however, was completely dominated by the opinion that, except under special circumstances, light did not pass round corners as according to his wave theory it should be able to do; also it may have been that the wave theory was made distasteful to him by his conflict with Hooke. After emphasizing in the first edition of the " Principia " the diffraction of *all* waves, and demonstrating the alternating flow of the portion of an incompressible medium displaced by a vibrating body into the space left behind it, he makes the following emphatic statement (p. 360) : " Hallucinantur igitur qui credunt agitationem partium flammae ad pressionem per Medium ambiens secundum lineas rectas propagandam conducere. Debebit ejusmodi pressio non ab agitatione sola partium flammae sed a totius dilatatione derivari." Thus the way from reality to the most logical apprehension of it is not always straight and short, but often circuitous, and only when the goal has been attained are the chance psychological circumstances recognizable which have effected the diversion or prevented an unobstructed view. Such were probably the circumstances which brought to maturity Newton's astronomical inferences from Huygens' mechanical discoveries, while in return Huygens founded the wave theory of light, apparently so very nearly embarked upon by Newton, but without either of the two being able to understand the other.

The wave theory of light cannot be regarded as psychologically impossible in the Huygens-Newton period, since the essential and necessary acoustical and optical elements were already available and only required combination. But if we consider the contentiousness which then enshrouded quite simple, clear, and to us almost self-evident things, it may easily be supposed that the investigators of this period had not yet acquired the necessary impartiality with regard to unfamiliar, or even their own new, discoveries to make successful application of them with their faculty for combinative construction. But, to continue, de Mairan (1737) had the singular idea that each tone must correspond to a special air particle for every tone to be propagated simultaneously undisturbed. In his prize dissertation on light, the younger Joh. Bernoulli confessed openly even in 1736 that Newton's propositions concerning the velocity of sound were incomprehensible to him. The state of affairs was, of course, quite different at the beginning of the nineteenth century, a hundred years after Huygens and Newton had established their theories, when Thomas Young took the field and began to experiment in acoustics and optics.

As the result of his study of the eye and his Göttingen doctorate dissertation on the human voice, Thomas Young, a member of the medical profession, was led to take up the study of optics and acoustics, and recognized the numerous instances of similarity between light and sound. His thought was incited by the observation of beats, the separation of a vibrating string into equal aliquot parts, and the bending of sound round obstacles.* After an extensive comparison of optical and acoustical phenomena, together with a careful investigation of Newton's objections to the vibration theory, with a reduction of them to their proper perspective, he came to the conclusion that the comprehension of *all* the known optical phenomena was facilitated by the wave hypothesis, and that some of them were explicable *solely* by this hypothesis.† Soon he was able to submit some original optical experiments which his views had led him to undertake, and various other experiments which his theory showed to be completely explicable.‡ With the skilful repetition of Grimaldi's experiment on the diffraction of light by a wire, the *inner* fringes showed themselves to be produced by light from both edges of the wire deflected *into* the shadow, since they vanished when the light from one of the sides was screened off. Young, in a cautious philosophical and general manner, lays down the interference principle somewhat in this manner : § *As in the case of sound (a musical note), so also in a (coloured) beam of light there follows a succession at regular intervals of alternately opposite properties (states) which are mutually able to destroy (neutralize) each other.* With this careful expression of the principle, we are no longer concerned with a hypothesis but with a fact fully confirmed by experimental analysis. The form of the interference experiment, which involves two neighbouring slits illuminated by another *single* slit, is first given by Young in his " Lectures " published in 1807, Lecture 23, Plate 20, Fig. 267, and Lecture 39, Plate 30, Fig. 442. ‖ The experiment is also referred to in Young's letter of 19th October, 1819, to Fresnel.¶ Many of Young's later experiments relating to this subject are again discussed in 1817 in his article " Chromatics " in the " Encyclopædia Britannica." It cannot be denied that by means of Young's experiments, accomplished with unusually clear philosophical insight and no mean experimental skill, and also without any great financial outlay, the science of optics experienced a very considerable advance. The prospective research student might observe from this that an important and apparently impenetrable truth is often really only very lightly obscured, and is readily disclosed when the seeker makes an attack in the right direction. In spite of his great work, Young was not to rejoice in the fruits of his labours immediately, for a scientific reactionary, who felt himself called to uphold Newton's theory even to an iota, commenced an unparalleled attack upon him and the

---

* Young, " Outlines of Experiments and Inquiries respecting Sound and Light," *Phil. Trans. Roy. Soc.* (1800).

† Young, " On the Theory of Light and Colours," *Phil. Trans. Roy. Soc.* (1802).

‡ Young, " An Account of Some New Cases of the Production of Colours not hitherto Described," *Phil. Trans. Roy. Soc.* (1802).

§ Young, " Experiments and Calculations Relative to Physical Optics," Bakerian Lecture, *Phil. Trans. Roy. Soc.* (1804).

‖ Young, " A Course of Lectures on Natural Philosophy and Mechanical Arts " (1807).

¶ Young, " Miscellaneous Works," edited by G. Peacock (1855), Vol. 1, p. 393.

Royal Society as well. Young's reputation was actually marred by it for many years, and recovered only after the labours of Fresnel had been made public. What must have been the feelings of this critic (probably Henry Brougham) when, in 1827, the Rumford medal was consigned to the dying Fresnel, and Young in the same year was elected a foreign member of the National Institute of France?

The combination of Newton's theory, in which any type of wave is presumed to spread out uniformly in all directions, with the law of interference as laid down by Young, when utilized to supplement Huygens' theory, at once gives a greater insight into the behaviour of light. Then not only rectilinear propagation, occurring in the ordinary way, may be understood, but also the departure from it under special conditions, namely *diffraction*. The effects produced vary greatly according to the dimensions of the boundary of the screen which limits the wave, or of the reflecting or refracting surfaces, and with the relation of the wave-length to those dimensions. In Fig. 257, *ab* represents an aperture in a screen and thus also the portion of the wave-surface

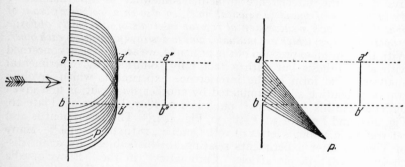

FIG. 257.

passing the aperture. Huygens' isolated pulses are only propagated to an appreciable extent in the space *aba'b'*, and come together in the region external to this only in succession, and ineffectively, by being scattered. If it is assumed, however, that in points along *ab* there originate simultaneously waves which spread out uniformly in all directions, their coincidence at the point P external to *aba'b'* will occur differently according as the path difference between P and the different points of *ab* consists of a *large* or *small* number of wave-lengths. If the maximum path difference *a*P − *b*P contains a large number of wave-lengths, the waves arrive at P with every possible relative phase-difference (Fig. 257), so that they either completely or almost completely annul one another. The effect is thus the same as in the case considered by Huygens. On the other hand, if *a*P − *b*P contains only a few wave-lengths, or only a fraction of one, the waves which meet at P as in Fig. 257 may show an appreciable resultant illumination, and so produce a diffraction effect. The greater the number of wave-lengths contained in the length *ab*, the less distinct are the diffraction effects, which, on the contrary, appear more marked as the number of wave-lengths in *ab* decreases. If *ab* contains only a fraction of a wave-length, this is the condition for a complete diffusion throughout the space behind the screen. This is the reason why the sound which enters a room through an aperture in the window shutter can be heard, disregarding reflection from the walls, at every part of the room, while in the ordinary way the diffraction of light is only visible on admitting the light through a narrow slit. The shortest sound waves are always a few centimetres in length, while the wave-length of light of appreciable visibility is from 0·0004 — 0·0007 mm.

By observing the properties of the periodicity and the magnitudes of the periods, both Young and Fresnel, more especially the latter, effected a considerable progress in optics. The former assumed that a reflection occurred at the edge of the diffracting object with the production of interference between the reflected and the direct ray, while Fresnel soon dropped the assumption of a reflection and was able to explain the diffraction effects and regular reflection and refraction satisfactorily merely from the periodicity and the uniform spreading out of light in all directions. If only a narrow triangular region of a plane reflecting or refracting surface is left uncovered (Fig. 258), it is easy to prove, as Fresnel did, that the light will be regularly reflected or refracted at the end ab and be scattered at c by diffraction in both cases, since at ab many, and at c only a few, wave-lengths are contained in the dimensions of the effective surface. When a reflecting or refracting surface is not perfectly polished, it contains tiny projections and hollows which are not vanishingly small compared with the wave-length and thus

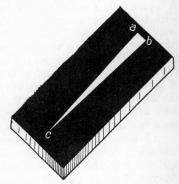

FIG. 258.

produce path-differences which bring about a partial extinction of the reflected or refracted light. The roughnesses are more effective by perpendicular than by oblique or glancing incidence, and produce a greater effect with the shorter violet wave-lengths than with the longer red ones. For glancing incidence rough surfaces give the best images, and as the roughness is increased the gradually disappearing images assume a red coloration. All these facts are easily verifiable by experiment, and their explanation from the standpoint adopted by Fresnel does not involve any difficulty.*

Although Fresnel had indicated quite clearly the importance of the magnitude of the wave-length, this factor was forgotten a few decades after the publication of his works. Otherwise it would not have been stated in practically all the relevant publications that sound behaves with respect to propagation, reflection, and refraction in exactly the same way as light, and it would have been impossible to find experimental support for this assertion by means of experiments

* Fresnel, " Œuvres," Vol. 1, p. 227.

with acoustical mirrors and lenses,* which only operate under special conditions and are otherwise illusory. Aperiodic sound waves and simple percussion waves, such as the sound waves from sparks and projectile waves, always spread out uniformly in all directions.† If a portion of such a wave is cut off by a screen, diffraction on a large scale occurs,‡ originating chiefly at the boundary of the wave at the edge of the obstacle. In fact, the sound bends round corners ; if regular reflection and refraction are to be obtained with such waves, closed wave-surfaces must be utilized, by constructing reflecting and refracting surfaces with the aid of Huygens' equations

$$u + v = \text{const.} \quad \text{and} \quad u + \mu v = \text{const.}$$

Good results are obtainable with musical notes or other sounds only if they are of a sufficiently high pitch, for example with the ticking of a clock, the notes of shrill whistles, or of the König rods, so that the dimensions of the mirrors and lenses comprise many wave-lengths.§ A high-pitched note or noise behaves quite differently from a low one with respect to a small reflecting or shadow-forming object, such as a book cover. The former, for example the rushing sound of a gas flame or a small waterfall, may be strengthened or weakened, i.e. reflected into or screened off from the ear, by a book held in front of the latter. The telegraph poles, as they appear to fly past the window of a railway train, momentarily increase by reflection the intensity of the high-pitched noises of the train. Low-pitched sounds, however, into which the whole head is plunged simultaneously, so to speak, are quite unresponsive to such means.

All this follows as a matter of course from Fresnel's theory, but acoustical investigators were apparently ignorant of the advances in optics. But also those who worked with optical instruments failed to observe that all optical images are diffraction images. Abbe ‖ and Helmholtz ¶ had again to point out this limitation of the optical power on account of diffraction and the finite magnitude of the wave-length of light.

We will now consider a few diffraction experiments. The simplest is the Grimaldi experiment already mentioned. Nowadays, in order to secure a greater intensity of illumination, sunlight entering through a narrow vertical slit is allowed to fall on a wire of not too great a thickness, parallel to the slit and situated at a distance of 1 to 2 metres from it, and its shadow is intercepted upon a sheet of white paper or,

* Sondhauss, A. König.

† A. Toepler, " Beobachtungen nach einer neuen optischen Methode," Bonn (1864), and *Pogg. Ann.*, Vol. 127 (1866).

‡ Mach, " Über den Verlauf der Funkenwellen in der Ebene und im Raume," *Sitzb. d. Wiener Akad.*, Vol. 77 (1878), also 1877 and 1879 ; cf. also the literature on projectiles, etc., pp. 113 and 238 of the text.

§ Mach and Fischer, " Die Reflexion und Brechung des Schalles," *Sitzb. d. Wiener Akad.* (1876) ; *Pogg. Ann.*, Vol. 149.

‖ Abbe, " Beiträge zur Theorie des Mikroskops und der mikroskopischen Wahrnehmung," *Arch. f. mikrosk. Anatomie* (1874).

¶ Helmholtz, " Die theoretische Grenze für die Leistungsfähigkeit der Mikroskope," *Pogg. Ann. Jubelband* (1874), pp. 557-584.

when it is desired to view the effects from behind, upon a piece of ground glass. The shadow is seen bordered by three coloured fringes decreasing in width in the outward direction (the outer fringes) and the shadow itself is intersected parallel to its length by an uneven number of bright, coloured, fringes (the inner fringes). A screen, consisting one-half of red, and the other half of blue, ground glass separated in a sharp line arranged horizontally, shows the fringes in the red light to be broader than those in the blue. Very bright effects are obtained if the screen is replaced by a lens of about 25 to 30 cm. focal length and the eye is placed at the image of the slit. The whole of the lens surface then appears bright and exhibits clearly the coloured fringes. If the lens is covered by a screen provided with a slit placed so as to intersect the fringes at right angles, and a direct-vision prism is held in front of the eye with its dispersion vertical, the fringes now appear as spectra converging towards the violet. Instead of a slit illuminated by sunlight a thin piece of platinum-iridium wire stretched by a small weight and placed so as to glow in a Bunsen burner may be satisfactorily used.

When Young and Fresnel examined this Grimaldi diffraction effect in detail, observing the diffraction pattern on a screen or with a magnifying lens at various distances from the diffracting body, they at first arrived at concordant views of the phenomena, which Fresnel expressed diagrammatically with the aid of Fig. 259. He assumed the direct light coming from S and that deflected at A to produce the hyperbolic *outer* fringes of foci A and S, and that deflected at A and B the inner hyperbolical fringes of foci A and B.* He could not retain the assumption of a deviation by reflection, since the polished back of a razor blade did not produce any stronger diffraction fringes than its edge. Slits of equal width either between two edges or two cylinders gave identical diffraction patterns, so that the hypothesis of deflecting atmospheres had to be dropped. The first minimum of the outer fringes appeared, moreover, where according to the theory the first maximum should be found, which was satisfactorily explicable by a change of phase of half a vibration on reflection, as long as reflection could be regarded as occurring at all. Fresnel finally found that the measured distance of the fringes from the edge of the geometrical shadow did not exactly correspond with the theoretical value, but that both were in the ratio $1·873 : 2$. Accurate measurements indicated a departure from the theory amounting to more than $\frac{1}{6}$ mm.

In the experiments with the diffracting screen of Fig. 129, Fresnel found that the diffraction pattern from the lower part of the screen, which was produced by *four* edges, was not more diffuse than that from the upper part, as would be expected, but on the contrary more distinct.

According to Young's theory, if light passes through a slit (Fig. 260), both its edges should have produced interference fringes similar to those for the Fresnel mirror, only with the light entering through the slit superposed. Instead, it was found that the separation of the innermost minima was about double that of two consecutive dark

* Fresnel, " Œuvres complètes," Vol. 1, p. 95.

fringes situated at the outside. The simplest and best way of exhibiting this Fresnel found to be to place a lens over the slit so as to form an image of the light source upon the screen used for observing the diffraction pattern ; but the effect is visible even without the lens and with the screen placed at a correspondingly greater distance. On gradually reducing the width of the slit, there occurs a visible spreading out of the *whole* of the light passing through the slit ; not only are the rays

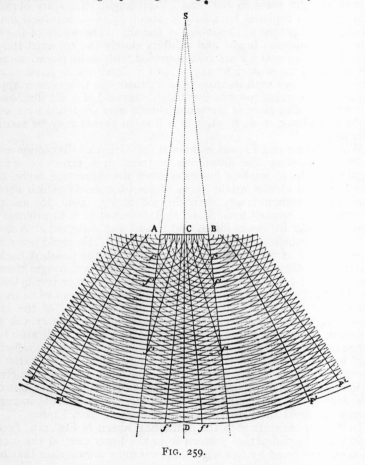

Fig. 259.

from the edge displaced, but the whole beam broadens out, including the light from the middle portions of the slit. In this way Fresnel came to the conclusion that not only the light which strikes the edges of the obstacles, but the *whole* of the light must be regarded as spreading out in all directions and producing the diffraction effects through mutual interference. The new standpoint explains at once both why Young's theory is apparently satisfactory as a first approximation,

and why it fails as an exact theory.   Though the rays coming from S
and striking the points A, B of the edges are not *the only effective rays*,
the rays from S passing in *the neighbourhood of the boundary of the
wave A, B* are the *most effective*, and consequently the diffraction
fringes retain their *hyperbolic* form.

Fresnel thus commences with Huygens' conception of the expand-
ing elementary waves, but brings into consideration their periodicity
and possibility of interference.   By a combination of these two standpoints in the " corrected Huygens' principle " he was able to link
together in an obvious way a large number of data.   His method
of attack, however, introduces certain difficulties, as will shortly
appear.   If L (Fig. 261) represents a point source of light and P a
point illuminated, the latter must receive exactly the same illumina-

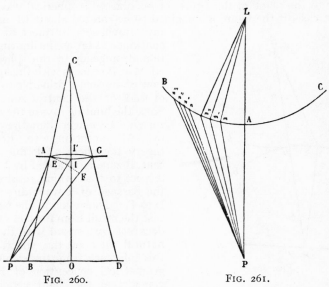

FIG. 260.   FIG. 261.

tion whether the light is imagined as passing directly from L to P, or
is stopped at some intermediate position BAC, and is regarded as
proceeding from thence to P in elementary waves interfering at P.
This latter view Fresnel found to involve unavoidable mathematical
difficulties.   Under identical conditions the elementary waves reaching
P from a surface element of the principal wave are proportional to
the elements of the wave-surface, but are weaker the more obliquely
they pass with reference to the normal of the surface element.   But
what is to be the influence of the obliquity ?   In order to ameliorate
this difficulty, Fresnel proceeded as follows.   In Fig. 261 let the lines
Pm, Pm', Pm'', Pm''' be drawn exterior to LAP, in such a way that
$Pm = PA + \lambda/2$, $Pm' = Pm + \lambda/2$, and so on.   In this way elements
are divided off along AB having the elementary rays of two consecutive elements in full opposition and therefore annulling one another.

Since the elements become continually shorter with increasing obliquity of the rays Pm, Pm', Pm'', etc., the intensity transported to P by the elementary waves can be expressed in the form of a series $a - a' + a'' - a''' + \ldots$ with terms numerically decreasing in magnitude and alternating in sign. Fresnel assumed that the sum lay between the limits a and $a - a'$, and reduced approximately to $a/2$. The central elements are thus the ones principally effective, these sending approximately normal and almost parallel rays to P, while the oblique rays mutually compensate one another so that the dependence of the intensity on the inclination to the normal may be left out of consideration. It is also obvious that similar considerations will apply whether the elements are regarded as portions of a narrow linear belt of wave, portions of a cylindrical wave with axis perpendicular to the plane of the figure, or portions of a spherical wave. In the last case, if the figure is imagined to be rotated about LP and the

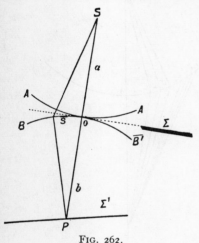

FIG. 262.

rays drawn so as to meet at P are continued as far as the limiting position of tangency to the sphere, the effect at P reduces with the application of Fresnel's principle to a half of that of the central zone at A. Since the limiting rays of the central zone are $\lambda/2$ longer than the central ray AP, according to Fresnel's theory the effect at P due to the central zone is retarded by $\lambda/4$ with respect to that which results from the passage of a wave direct from L to P. Thus even in the simplest case the result from Fresnel's theory does *not* correspond with the most natural view of the effect. But this inference from the elementary geometrical conception of Fresnel zones, that the light penetrating into the shadow of the diffracting body is retarded by $\lambda/4$ with respect to the ray grazing the edge, and that the light reaching the illuminated region is accelerated with respect to it by the same amount, is in good agreement with actual fact. (Cf. Figs. 259 and 260.)

In order to present his principle in a form useful for computation purposes, Fresnel proceeded as follows. A line is drawn from the point source S (Fig. 262) to P, one of the points illuminated. Suppose the continuation of the plane of the diffracting object intersects SP in O. Confining our thoughts in the first instance to the plane of the figure, the reference plane, let the distance of an element ds of the wave surface AA' of radius a from the point O be s, measured in the plane of the screen, with which the arcs of radii a and b practically coincide in all regions contributing appreciably to the effect. If the vibration at P due to an element ds at O of the direct wave is represented by $ds \cdot \sin 2\pi t/T$, then an element distant s from O, for which the rays have a path longer by u, affords a contribution

$$ds \cdot \sin 2\pi(t/\mathrm{T} - u/\lambda),$$

or

$$ds \cdot \cos 2\pi u/\lambda \cdot \sin 2\pi t/\mathrm{T} - ds \cdot \sin 2\pi u/\lambda \cdot \cos 2\pi t/\mathrm{T}.$$

Since for the increment in path u exactly the same conditions obtain as for the path between the two lenses of the Newton lens combination of radii of curvature a and b, its value is

$$u = \frac{s^2}{2a} + \frac{s^2}{2b} = \frac{a + b}{2ab}s^2.$$

Introducing this into the above expression, the latter becomes

$$(ds \cdot \cos \pi \frac{a + b}{ab\lambda} s^2) \sin 2\pi \frac{t}{\mathrm{T}} - (ds \cdot \sin \pi \frac{a + b}{ab\lambda} s^2) \cos 2\pi \frac{t}{\mathrm{T}}.$$

Considering all the elementary rays, the coefficients in the brackets become

$$\int ds \cdot \cos \pi \frac{a + b}{ab\lambda} s^2 \text{ and } \int ds \cdot \sin \pi \frac{a + b}{ab\lambda} \quad .$$

The intensity at P is

$$\left[\int ds \cdot \cos \pi \frac{a + b}{ab\lambda} s^2 \right]^2 + \left[\int ds \cdot \sin \pi \frac{a + b}{ab\lambda} s^2 \right]^2$$

and the amplitude is given by the square root of this expression.

Now imagine the arcs AA', BB' corresponding to the radii a and b, and the line Ps to turn about the axis SOP without altering the positions of the screens denoted by $\varSigma$ and $\varSigma'$, and let the plane of $\varSigma$ contain the axes of a rectangular co-ordinate system XY, with O as origin and Y parallel to the edge of the screen. With a little consideration it will be seen that the integral expressions are now transformed to

$$\iint dx \cdot dy \cdot \cos \pi \frac{a + b}{ab\lambda} (x^2 + y^2) \text{ and } \iint dx \cdot dy \cdot \sin \pi \frac{a + b}{ab\lambda}(x^2 + y^2).$$

These may be expanded respectively by the formulæ for cos (A + B) and sin (A + B), which effects a separation of the variables. Since the variables x and y under the integral sign are indistinguishable from one another, the expressions

$$\int dx \cdot \cos \pi \frac{a + b}{ab\lambda} x^2 \text{ and } \int dx \cdot \sin \pi \frac{a + b}{ab\lambda} x^2$$

need only be considered in the calculations. If, now, we put

$$x \sqrt{\pi \frac{a + b}{ab\lambda}} = v \sqrt{\frac{\pi}{2}},$$

the last expressions become

$$\int dv \cdot \cos \frac{\pi}{2} v^2 \text{ and } \int dv \cdot \sin \frac{\pi}{2} v^2,$$

with a multiplying factor of $\sqrt{\dfrac{ab\lambda}{2(a + b)}}$. The value of these integrals between the limits o and $\pm \infty$ is $\frac{1}{2}$ or between the limits $- \infty$ and $+ \infty$ is I. When the integration is performed between other limits, this must be done with the aid of numerical tables. Lastly, the consideration may be introduced that the expression for the intensity at P has yet to be multiplied by the factor $1/a^2b^2$, since the light from S is assumed to spread out first into a sphere of radius a, from the elements of which it then spreads out into a sphere of radius b.

If the method of calculation is applied first to an unobstructed spreading out of the light, by introducing the limits $- \infty$ and $+ \infty$, and bearing in mind that the very oblique elementary rays are ineffective, the expression $\lambda^2/(a + b)^2$ is found for the intensity at P. The phase difference with respect to the direct ray amounts in this case to $\pi/2$, i.e. a quarter vibration.

Fresnel considers in detail the case of an opaque screen bounded by a straight edge, with the edge assumed vertical, say, and the screen obscuring the right-hand half of the field. Let the X axis be horizontal and the Y axis vertical. The integration limits then change with the position of the point under consideration ; for P (Fig. 263) the integration with respect to x is to be performed between the limits $x = 0$ and $x = + \infty$, for P' from $x = - x_1$ to $x = + \infty$, for P'' from $x = + x_2$ to $x = + \infty$, while y is to be integrated from $- \infty$ to $+ \infty$.

FIG. 263.

The results of Fresnel's method of computation for this case are to be found in a numerical table or by a graphical construction, and they agree with experiment to within the limits of the unavoidable errors.* With a homogeneous illumination there appear outside the shadow alternate maxima and minima of brightness which continually decrease in amplitude and separation the farther the distance out from the edge of the shadow. The minima are never zero even close in to the edge, and approach the value of the full illumination at the outside. From the edge of the shadow inwards there are no maxima and minima, but the intensity of illumination gradually approaches zero. With white light three coloured maxima alone are visible, but their saturation, as in the Fresnel mirror experiment, indicates nothing as to the ratio of the intensities. Some of these results may be foreseen without making the calculations by constructing a rough approximation to the formulæ. This is particularly the case for the fringes outside the shadow. If values of v are taken as abscissæ and $\cos v$ or $\sin v$ as ordinates, undulating curves of a constant wave-length are obtained. On the other hand, in the case of $\cos v^2$ or $\sin v^2$, the wave-lengths decrease with increasing v. In the integral expressions the amplitudes must, therefore, also decrease with increasing v.†

* Fresnel, " Œuvres complètes," Vol. I, pp. 382 and 383.
† For a more explicit discussion cf. Billet, " Traité d'optique," and Verdet-Exner.

Fresnel investigated similarly the diffraction produced by a narrow slit between the two straight edges of two screens, and also that produced in the shadow of a very narrow screen.*

Poisson, a member of the commission of the French Academy which judged Fresnel's successful prize-dissertation, noticed the immediate applicability of Fresnel's formulæ to cases where the effective portion of the wave-surface became a surface of rotation about the ray SP as axis. He made the at first sight surprising deduction that the mid-point of the shadow of a small circular screen must be illuminated with exactly the same brightness as if the screen were absent. This result was at once confirmed experimentally by Arago with a screen of 2 mm. diameter, and also deduced by Fresnel by a quite elementary method.† To a person well acquainted with the Grimaldi-Young effects Poisson's result would be scarcely surprising, for he would expect that when Grimaldi's straight wire was exchanged for a small circular screen, a ring-system with a bright centre and odd number of rings would arise in place of the symmetrical bright inner fringes; the result would be dubious only in its quantitative aspects.

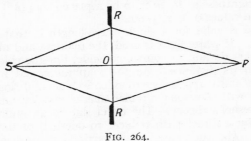

FIG. 264.

If the ray SP (Fig. 264) from a source S passes through the mid-point of an aperture in a screen and is normal to the latter, and s is the distance of a point of the aperture from O, the intensity of illumination at P is, considering the whole of the wave which passes through the aperture,

$$\frac{1}{a^2b^2}\left[\int 2\pi . s . ds . \cos \pi \frac{a+b}{ab\lambda}s^2\right]^2 + \frac{1}{a^2b^2}\left[\int 2\pi . s . ds . \sin \pi \frac{a+b}{ab\lambda}s^2\right]^2.$$

Since the differential of the argument of the cosine or sine is, apart from a constant factor, $s . ds$, the integration gives simple sine or cosine formulæ once more. When the radius of the aperture is limited to that of the first Huygens' zone, the expression is to be integrated from $s = 0$ to $s^2\frac{a+b}{2ab} = \frac{\lambda}{2}$, and for the intensity at P, $\frac{4\lambda^2}{(a+b)^2}$ is obtained. The retardation with respect to the direct undiffracted wave is, as before, $\pi/2$.

According to Fresnel's more elementary theory, circles are imagined

* Fresnel, " Œuvres complètes," Vol. 1, pp. 355, etc.
† Arago, " Mémoires sur la diffraction," p. 460 ; *Pogg. Ann.*, Vol. 30, p. 235.

drawn in the plane of the screen with O as centre and with radii in the sequence, $\sqrt{1}$, $\sqrt{2}$, $\sqrt{3}$, $\sqrt{4}$, thus with their areas proportional to 1, 2, 3, 4 and marking off rings of *equal* area. The largest of the circles R is imagined to form the boundary of the aperture (Fig. 266). First let there be an even number of circles and the path difference of the limiting ray SRP an even number of wave-lengths with respect to the central ray SOP. In this case, as we pass inwards, there is a succession of rings of equal area sending out light alternating in effect, the corresponding rays from two adjacent rings arriving at P relatively retarded by half a wave-length, with the production of darkness at this point. On the other hand, if SRP − SOP contains an odd number of half wave-lengths, brightness is obtained at P since there is one zone left uncompensated. If the intensity of the undisturbed wave at P is denoted by 1, the intensity of illumination varies from 0 to 4 according to whether the first or second condition obtains. Both cases may be produced at will for any given value of b and OR = r by solving the equation $\dfrac{r^2(a + b)}{ab} = 2n \cdot \lambda$ for a, say, giving $a = \dfrac{r^2b}{2n\lambda b - r^2}$ for darkness. For brightness at P, $2n$ is to be replaced by $(2n + 1)$; in either case n has the values 0, 1, 2, 3, etc.

The above is valid for a single wave-length λ, that is, for homogeneous light. If white light is used, the maxima and minima for the different colours do not, of course, coincide, but the colour at a point P varies with its distance from the diaphragm and from the light source. P naturally appears surrounded by coloured rings.

The effect with Poisson's circular disk is also accounted for quite simply by Fresnel's theory. The effect due to an undisturbed wave arising at P by a direct path reduces to one-half of that of the first central zone. The successive zones partially neutralize one another and the outermost zones become successively more ineffective on account of the obliquity of the rays which are sent out. The only difference between Poisson's disk and the former case is that the construction of zones with path differences of the corresponding rays of $\lambda/2$ begins at the edge of the disk and is continued outwards. If the disk is small, owing to the consequent smallness of the obliquity of the rays near its edge the first zone adjacent to the disk is now quite as effective as if it were the central zone which is screened off.

If at some point O of the ray SP between a light source S and an illuminated point P a plane glass plate is imagined set up perpendicular to the ray, and upon it constructed the Fresnel $\lambda/2$ zones for the points S and P, then it will be readily seen that the illumination at P will continually increase with the number of *either* odd or even zones made opaque. If SO = ∞, for a complete coincidence of phase it is found that PO = $f_1 = 2r^2/\lambda$, where r denotes the radius of the first (central) zone. The zone plate manufactured in this way thus behaves like a lens of focal length f_1. In fact, Soret * found that a kind of telescope might be constructed by replacing both objective and eyepiece by appropriate zone plates. Such zone plates exhibit

* Soret, *Pogg. Ann.* (1875).

additional foci at distances given by $f_3 = 2r^2/3\lambda$, $f_5 = 2r^2/5\lambda$, etc., in which $\frac{1}{3}$, $\frac{1}{5}$, etc., of the rays are effectively concentrated, as may be deduced from elementary considerations. Such considerations also indicate that these zone plates will not only perform the duties of condensing lenses, but also of dispersive lenses, since there are also *virtual* foci, situated at the same distances on the same side of the plate as the source.

Lord Rayleigh observed that the intensity at the focus of a zone plate could be increased four-fold if, instead of blocking out either the even or odd zones, these were allowed to contribute towards the effect with a further retardation of $\lambda/2$; this may be effected in several ways according to the methods of R. W. Wood.

Subsequently to Fresnel, considerable progress with the investigation of diffraction phenomena was made by Fraunhofer.* He succeeded in producing phenomena of considerable brightness in a particularly simple form easily accessible to theory and measurement. Fraunhofer directed a telescope towards a slit which served to admit the light, placed a second diffracting slit over the objective parallel to the first, and then observed the diffraction pattern with the aid of the eyepiece. A lens had been placed over the diffracting slit once by Fresnel and the diffraction effects observed in its image plane with the aid of a magnifying lens. In Fraunhofer's case the telescope objective thus replaces Fresnel's first lens, and the eyepiece his magnifying lens. The diffraction effects gain considerably in brightness by this means, since the observations are made at a region where the light is concentrated again by the objective. Fresnel used a point source as illuminant ; if to increase the intensity a linear source, i.e. a slit, is desired, in Fresnel's method care must be taken to have the diffracting edges accurately parallel to the slit, on account of the incoherence of the light from different points of the slit ; but with Fraunhofer's method this is superfluous since in this case the different points of the slit are reproduced side by side in the image of the diffraction effects.

A clearer view will be obtained with the consideration of a few simple experiments. If a luminous point source is viewed through a telescope, and a screen provided with a narrow slit is placed over the objective, with the slit vertical, a feather-like diffraction pattern is seen with the feather-ribs vertical, situated with the maximum brightness at the position of the previous image and with symmetrical maxima and minima on either side. If the slit is displaced without changing its direction, the form and position of the diffraction pattern remain the same, since all points of the objective give the same images ; but if the slit is turned in its own plane, the feather-like diffraction pattern rotates with it in the same direction, for the feather-ribs are always parallel to the length of the slit.

If, in Fig. 265, L indicates the orientation of a slit by which light enters through a window shutter, S that of the objective slit, and l that of the inverted image of L, it is at once obvious from the previous

* Fraunhofer, " Neue Modifikation des Lichtes durch die gegenseitige Einwirkung und Beugung der Strahlen, und Gesetze derselben," *Denkschriften der k. Akad. d. Wiss. zu München* (1821 and 1822), Vol. 8, pp. 1-76.

experiment that the diffraction patterns surrounding l will be those

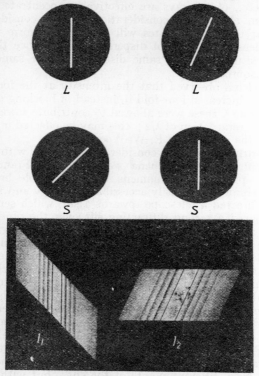

Fig. 265.

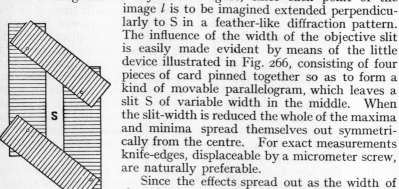

indicated diagrammatically in the figure, since each point of the image l is to be imagined extended perpendicularly to S in a feather-like diffraction pattern. The influence of the width of the objective slit is easily made evident by means of the little device illustrated in Fig. 266, consisting of four pieces of card pinned together so as to form a kind of movable parallelogram, which leaves a slit S of variable width in the middle. When the slit-width is reduced the whole of the maxima and minima spread themselves out symmetrically from the centre. For exact measurements knife-edges, displaceable by a micrometer screw, are naturally preferable.

Since the effects spread out as the width of the objective slit is decreased, but lose in intensity, without a displacement of the slit across the lens affecting the scale and form of the phenomenon, it is natural to think of placing a number of equal and parallel

Fig. 266.

PLATE X

JOSEPH FRAUNHOFER

slits in front of the objective, in order, in the case of very narrow slits, to retain a high intensity of illumination. Fraunhofer thus confessed himself astonished to observe, on using two equal parallel slits placed side by side, instead of merely a strengthened effect, one which was interspersed with new minima. To become experimentally familiar with the various factors operative, a piece of blackened card bent thrice, as shown in section in Fig. 267, and provided with two equal slits s_1, s_2 parallel to the bends, may be satisfactorily employed. If one of the objective slits s_1, s_2 is covered, the effects already described are obtained, but if light from the same entrance slit passes through both these slits, then an effect is obtained which differs from the former only in the appearance of new minima. If the card is pressed symmetrically inwards or pulled out over the objective, so that s_1, s_2 approach each other or move apart, the fundamental phenomenon and also its breadth remain unchanged, but the new minima can be seen to move apart or together over the former. Each slit by itself thus gives the *same* diffraction pattern at the *same* relative position ; since, however, these

FIG. 267.

patterns are superposed, the light coming from the same source through the slits s_1, s_2 with a relative path difference produces a *new* interference. The latter interference is essentially similar to the Fresnel mirror fringes, s_1, s_2 being considered as the two coherent light sources. If the telescope has a sufficiently long focal length, s_1, s_2 may be made so narrow that the white middle field of the image of one of the slits is broad enough to contain in a length corresponding to the distance between s_1, s_2, 10-15 secondary interference fringes. Provided that these fringes are sufficiently broad their colours also exhibit quite plainly the character of the Fresnel interference fringes, an effect which is absent in very narrow fringe systems for physiological-optical reasons. If a Jamin's compensator is placed with one plate in front of s_1 and the other in front of s_2, a rotation of the plates produces a displacement of these interference fringes, while the maxima and minima arising from one slit remain stationary.

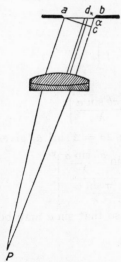

FIG. 268.

Although Fraunhofer specified the laws which followed from his experiments, he did not develop any theory. This was the work of Schwerd,* but may be easily recognized as a specialization of Fresnel's

* F. M. Schwerd, " Die Beugungserscheinungen aus den Fundamentalgesetzen der Undulationstheorie analytisch entwickelt und in Bildern dargestellt," Mannheim (1835).

theory applied to the Fraunhofer case. Let us consider first a vertical slit placed in front of the objective of a telescope which, when illuminated by an infinitely distant vertical linear source, produces a diffraction pattern in the focal plane of the objective. Rays from the infinitely distant source, incident perpendicularly upon the plane of the slit (Fig. 268), will arrive at all points of ab, its intersection with the plane of the figure, in the same phase. If a parallel beam coming obliquely from ab is imagined to strike the objective, this would arrive at a point in the focal plane in the same phase throughout if the plane ac perpendicular to the beam, subtending an angle a with ab were the wave-surface. But, actually, each ray arrives at P in a different phase, and the elementary pencil of rays which reaches P from an element dx of the slit may be represented by

$$k\,dx \, \sin\left(\phi + \frac{2\pi x \sin a}{\lambda}\right)$$

or the total effect by

$$\sin\phi \, . \, k \int dx \, . \, \cos\frac{2\pi x \sin a}{\lambda} + \cos\phi \, . \, k \int dx \, . \, \sin\frac{2\pi x \sin a}{\lambda}.$$

Denoting the integral expressions taken between the limits o and b, where b is the breadth of the slit, by A and B,

$$A = \frac{k\lambda}{2\pi \sin a} \sin\frac{2\pi b \sin a}{\lambda},$$

$$B = -\frac{k\lambda}{2\pi \sin a}\left[\cos\frac{2\pi b \sin a}{\lambda} - \mathrm{I}\right],$$

and the intensity I is accordingly

$$A^2 + B^2 = \left(\frac{k\lambda}{2\pi \sin a}\right)^2 . \, 2\left[\mathrm{I} - \cos\frac{2\pi b \sin a}{\lambda}\right],$$

which, when transformed by the formula $\mathrm{I} - \cos 2a = 2\sin^2 a$, gives

$$I = \left(\frac{k\lambda}{2\pi \sin a}\right)^2 . \, 4\left[\sin\frac{\pi b \sin a}{\lambda}\right]^2 = k^2\left[\frac{\sin\dfrac{\pi b \sin a}{\lambda}}{\dfrac{\pi \sin a}{\lambda}}\right].$$

If we are only concerned with small deflections so that $\sin a$ may be replaced by a, then

$$I = k^2 b^2\left[\frac{\sin\dfrac{\pi b a}{\lambda}}{\dfrac{\pi b a}{\lambda}}\right]^2.$$

From this formula, and also from its graphical representation, we may directly show that the diffraction effect consists of bright fields separated by absolutely dark vertical bands, such that the central bright field is twice as bright as the remaining outer ones; their intensity falls off rapidly from the centre outwards.

Supposing we now have two parallel, equal narrow slits situated side by side with *m*, say, as the distance between their similarly situated left-hand edges, for the interference between the light from both slits coming at an angle α with the slit normal on the telescope axis we have the expression

$$i \cdot \sin \phi + i \cdot \sin\left[\phi + \frac{2\pi m \sin \alpha}{\lambda}\right]$$

giving an intensity

$$2i^2\left[1 + \cos \frac{2\pi m \sin \alpha}{\lambda}\right] = 4i^2 \cos^2\left[\frac{\pi m \sin \alpha}{\lambda}\right],$$

where $i = \sqrt{I}$. The addition of a second slit thus merely introduces in I a factor $4 \cos^2 \frac{\pi m \sin \alpha}{\lambda}$, which makes the intensity vary between 4I and zero. When *one* of the factors is zero, the total intensity is also zero. The minima introduced by the new factor are all equidistant and are dependent only upon *m*. If $m = 2b$, the new minima are half the distance apart of those for a *single* slit of width *b*.

The next natural step to take is to try the effect of placing 3, 4, 5 . . . or any number of parallel slits equally spaced side by side, by doing which Fraunhofer arrived at the grating, a very important apparatus, whose diffraction spectra have proved singularly adapted to the measurement of wave-lengths. Fraunhofer only gives us the results of his experiments ; the theory, based on Fresnel's principles, was developed by Schwerd. If there are *n* equal and parallel slits of breadth *b*, any two successive slits being separated by a distance *d*, it is found, by applying Schwerd's argument in a way similar to that for the case of one or two slits, that

$$I = b^2 \left[\frac{\sin \frac{\pi b \sin \alpha}{\lambda}}{\frac{\pi b \sin \alpha}{\lambda}}\right]^2 \left[\frac{\sin \frac{\pi n(b + d) \sin \alpha}{\lambda}}{\sin \frac{\pi (b + d) \sin \alpha}{\lambda}}\right]^2.$$

We will not discuss this formula further, but pass on to a simple method of illustrating the properties of grating spectra.

If an elementary pencil of rays comes from a particular slit (Fig. 269) at an angle α with the slit normals and is then incident upon the telescope objective, then, following Schwerd, the whole pencil is divided into subsidiary pencils, commencing at the edge of the slit, such that the last ray of *one* of these pencils represents a path difference of $\lambda/2$ between the plane through the edge of the slit perpendicular to the rays and the plane of the slit. The rays from o and

FIG. 269.

1, for example, have the path difference $\lambda/2$, those from o and 2, $2\lambda/2$, from o and 3, $3\lambda/2$, etc. Thus obviously the first subsidiary pencil is annulled by the second, the third by the fourth, and so on. If the slit comprises an *even* number of these half wave-length elements, they completely annul one another, but on the other hand, if it contains either an *odd* number of elements or not an exact even number, then there is a *residual* effect from a single half wave-length element or from a portion of one.   Remembering that the exact manner of division into elements changes with the obliquity of the pencil of rays, it is at once possible to estimate, without any special calculations, the positions of the principal maxima and minima of the diffraction patterns for the cases previously considered.   The main properties of grating spectra may also be obtained in this way.   If, in Fig. 269, 0, 1, 2, 3, . . . represent narrow slits, for which the deviations of the diffracted light may be quite large without an extinction of the light from each slit by itself occurring, then a reinforcement results for an obliquity such that the path difference is λ for the light from the slits 0 and 1, i.e. also λ for 1 and 2, 2 and 3, and so on.   A path difference of 2λ, 3λ, 4λ, . . . for the light from two successive slits is likewise the condition for reinforcement.   This will be further illustrated below.

According to Fresnel, vibrations of equal period and like direction may be compounded graphically by representing the amplitudes of the components by straight lines proportional to their magnitude drawn from a fixed point and mutually inclined at an angle which is the same fraction of the complete rotation (360°) as the jump in phase between the components is of the complete vibration.   The diagonal of the parallelogram constructed in this way represents the amplitude of the resultant and the angles subtended by the components the phase differences with respect to them.   If, instead of the construction analogous to the parallelogram of forces, that similar to the force polygon is employed, then each successive amplitude is constructed as a vector with direction corresponding to its phase at the extremity of the previous vector.   The line joining the starting-point and end-point of the polygon gives the resultant amplitude and phase.   If the polygon is closed, the resultant vibration is zero.   Cornu's spiral depends on the polygon construction and, when adapted to the Fresnel treatment of diffraction phenomena, may be utilized with advantage for the graphical solution of the problems.   Schwerd made numerous applications of the above-mentioned parallelogram construction and its corresponding analytical form.

The manner of using the Fresnel-Schwerd principle in suitable cases to compound an infinite number of rays may be indicated.   If we imagine a long vertical slit placed in front of the telescope objective, the elementary rays coming perpendicularly from the slit and meeting, with zero phase difference, at the focus must produce there an amplitude kb, where k is determined by the intensity of the source and b by the slit width.   Rays coming at an angle a with the slit normal and telescope axis, however, occupy in Fresnel's construction a fan-shaped region (an " amplitude fan ") of angle $\omega = (2\pi b \sin a)/\lambda$. The amplitude which corresponds to an element of the fan is thus $kb \cdot d\omega/\omega$.   Let the amplitude fan be divided by the line of symmetry, and the amplitudes at an element $d\beta$ making an angle β with the line of symmetry be projected upon the latter.   This gives for the semi-angle the sum

$$\frac{kb}{\omega} \int_{0}^{\omega/2} \cos \beta \, . \, d\beta = \frac{kb}{\omega} \sin \frac{\omega}{2},$$

and, since for every element $d\beta$ a symmetrical one exists, for the whole angle we have

$$\frac{2kb}{\omega} \cdot \sin\frac{\omega}{2} = kb \, \frac{\sin\dfrac{\omega}{2}}{\dfrac{\omega}{2}}.$$

Squaring and introducing the value of ω, for the intensity we obtain the previous value

$$I = k^2 b^2 \left[\frac{\sin\dfrac{\omega}{2}}{\dfrac{\omega}{2}}\right]^2 = k^2 b^2 \left[\frac{\sin\dfrac{\pi b \sin a}{\lambda}}{\dfrac{\pi b \sin a}{\lambda}}\right]^2.$$

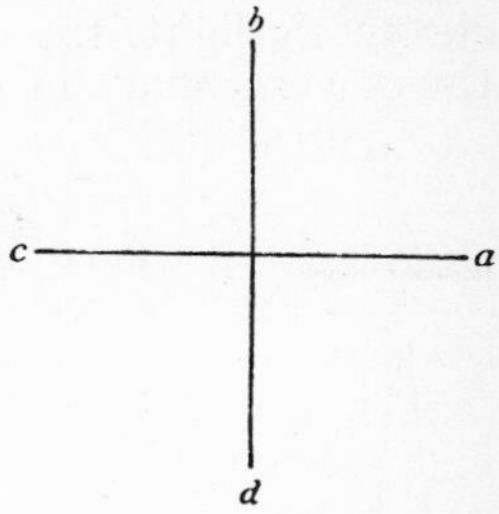

FIG. 269 a.

The fan principle also gives a very good illustration of the essential properties of more complicated diffraction effects, for example, that with two slits of width b separated by the same distance. From the fan construction it is at once obvious that for $b \sin a = \lambda/4, 3\lambda/4, \ldots$ $(2n \pm 1)\lambda/4$ new minima appear. For $b \sin a = \lambda/4$ the fan is easily prepared ; ab (Fig. 269a) is the fan for the first slit, bc the missing fan corresponding to the space between the slits, cd the fan for the second slit, which annuls the effect of the first. For $b \sin a = 3\lambda/4$, $abcd$ is the fan for the first slit, $dabc$ the missing fan for the space between the slits, and $cdab$ that of the second slit. Here ab and cd are uniformly covered twice, and bc and da once, so that the resultant is again zero.

Now let the same principle be employed to explain grating spectra. At the focus all the elementary rays are in the condition of full reinforcement and we thus have an image of the light source. For a point P to one side of the focus, however, the amplitude fan covers an angle $\omega = (2\pi B \sin a)/\lambda$, where B represents the whole width of the grating, only with the obvious distinction that the elementary rays corresponding to the grating bars are absent. The opaque portion bears the same ratio to the transparent portion as the slit width a to the distance between the slits b. If the number of the narrow slits is considerable, no difference is observable in the image at the focus, apart from a decrease in brightness, from that which would be seen through a slit of width B ; the diffraction fringes are in that case narrow, that is, an almost perfectly sharp image of the source is seen at the focus. This would be an end of the matter if it were not for the fact that for $(a + b) \sin a = \lambda$ each of the fan elements f due to a single slit is spread out over a larger region F with which all the other fan elements exactly coincide and produce a reinforcement. When this condition holds, the p fan elements of the whole grating give a resultant pR, where R is the resultant of a single fan. If, however, there is any departure in either direction from exact conformity with the relation $(a + b) \sin a = \lambda$, the coincident resultants R themselves shift out into a fan, whereby the final resultant must necessarily decrease in magnitude. These fans may be regarded as the original amplitude fans, and we thus arrive at the conclusion that simply a (less intense) diffraction image of the light source is to be seen at that point also for which $(a + b) \sin \alpha = \lambda$, the image corresponding to a slit of width B, which is thus for large values of B a sharp image once more.

The same holds for $(a + b) \sin \alpha = n\lambda$ where n is an integer. Monochromatic light, the employment of which has been tacitly assumed, thus gives a sharp image for $\sin \alpha = n\lambda/(a + b)$ in which $n = 0, 1, 2, 3,$ . . . Naturally, with white light, grating spectra are produced which result from a superposition of the monochromatic slit images.

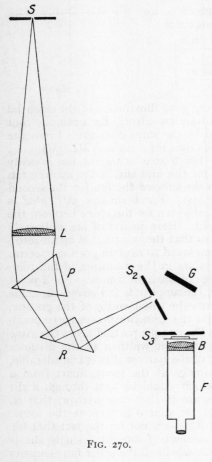

For an experimental confirmation of the effects described I make use of the following arrangement. Sunlight enters through a slit S (Fig. 270) in a window shutter, strikes the achromatic lens L, a dispersing prism P, and a reflecting prism R, and forms a pure spectrum on a silvered plane glass plate G in front of which stands the dull black screen S_2 provided with a slit. Practically monochromatic light from G falls on the diffraction grating B whose effective breadth is limited by a third slit S_3. If S_1, S_2, S_3 are sufficiently narrow, there appears in the telescope F a system of approximately equidistant monochromatic diffraction patterns, each of which corresponds to the diffraction effect for one grating slit. On increasing or decreasing the width of S_3, that is, the width of the grating, the fringes of one of the diffraction patterns become correspondingly narrower or wider: If R is turned, which does not disturb the minimum deviation and the sharpness of the spectrum on G, the equidistant diffraction patterns crowd together if the illumination of G is changed from red to violet.

Fig. 270.

When S_3 is sufficiently wide, diffraction is no longer visible and a series of sharp equidistant monochromatic slit images of S_2 is seen.

It must be remarked that the use of sunlight and spectral resolution is essential for the success of the experiment. Coloured glasses are not sufficiently monochromatic and sodium light is too feeble for a good demonstration. On the other hand a glowing platinum-iridium wire stretched taut in a Bunsen flame serves the purpose of reproducing many polychromatic diffraction effects better than a slit illuminated by daylight or the light from a lamp.

If monochromatic violet light from a narrow slit is incident upon a finely-ruled wide grating covering the objective, a series of fine parallel violet lines is visible in the eyepiece. These lines move outwards away from the central line, which remains fixed at the focus, and the colours also change, as the illumination is gradually varied to red. With white light the colour effects are seen *simultaneously* instead of in succession as in the last experiment, i.e. the central line at the focus, where all the colours are superposed, appears white, and symmetrically on either side is a series of spectra which have their violet ends turned towards the centre and their red ends outwards. With finely-ruled gratings the spectra are so pure that the Fraunhofer lines are distinguishable. The symmetrical colour deviations produced by the diffraction, measured by the sine of the angle of deviation, or for small deviations by the angle itself, are proportional to the wave-lengths. In this case the longer wave-lengths are thus the more strongly deviated ; this is the reverse of what occurs in ordinary prismatic refraction.

When employing grating spectra it must be borne in mind that the successive spectra are in general superposed. If we assume 39 : 68 as the ratio of the wave-lengths of the still fairly visible extreme violet to the red of similar visibility, the deviations 1, 2, 3, 4, $\cdots$ of the violet may be set proportional to 39, 78, 117, 156, . . . and those of the red proportional to 68, 136, 204, 272, . . . From this we see that, though the spectrum next the centre V_1R_1 (39-68) is free, the next outer one V_2R_2 (78-136) is already partially covered by the third V_3R_3 (117-204), and this holds to a greater extent still for the third and fourth and so on. To separate such spectra, following the procedure of Fraunhofer, they are observed through a prism with its dispersional direction arranged perpendicular to the deflections due to diffraction.

It must also be remembered that many spectra may even be absent altogether. If, suppose, for a certain deviation $a \sin a = m\lambda$ and $(a + b) \sin a = n\lambda$, then it follows that $m = an/(a + b)$, where a represents the slit widths and b their distance apart. If n has some integral value, but at the same time m is also an integer, then the spectrum of the nth order and also all spectra of an order which is a multiple of n disappear, since the rays from each individual slit of the grating annul one another separately.

Gratings combine to a certain extent the advantages of narrow and wide slits, large deviations and sharp images. The troublesome secondary maxima and minima are reduced to a state of invisibility by the multiplicity of the interference from numerous slits.

The most important application of grating spectra is to the determination of the wave-length of light. For this purpose a narrow slit is fixed at the focus of an achromatic objective so as to behave as if placed at an infinite distance, and the objective sends out parallel light which impinges normally on a finely-ruled grating. After transmission by the grating the light falls on a telescope focussed for infinity. If first the central image of the illuminated slit is observed through the telescope, and the telescope is then turned by means of the divided circle so that a Fraunhofer line of the mth order spectrum is opposite the cross-wires, then

$$\frac{a+b}{m} \cdot \sin a = \lambda,$$

where a is the angle through which the telescope was turned and λ the wave-length of the given Fraunhofer line.

From experiments with gratings finely ruled on glass, using the angle for the first order spectrum with light incident normally, the following values were obtained for the wave-lengths of the Fraunhofer lines indicated (Fraunhofer, *Gilbert's Ann.*, Vol. 74, p. 359) :—

C	.	.	.	.	0·00002422 Paris inch
D	.	.	.	.	0·00002175 ,,
E	.	.	.	.	0·00001945 ,,
F	.	.	.	.	0·00001794 ,,
G	.	.	.	.	0·00001587 ,,
H	.	.	.	.	0·00001464 ,,

If a spectrum is viewed with one eye, and the half of the pupil towards the violet side is covered by a suitably thin glass or mica plate, Talbot observed that it became intersected perpendicular to the direction of dispersion by dark bands. The bands *disappear* when the plate is changed over to the red side of the spectrum. This asymmetry caused Brewster to conjecture a special, as yet unknown, polarity of light, the existence of which became manifest in this phenomenon. But if it be remembered that there are two effects of a one-sided nature occurring together, dispersion and retardation in the plate, a sufficient explanation is afforded by co-operative or oppositional combination of these two factors ; this also appears from Airy's investigation. Talbot at once recognized that the dark spectral bands occur in those colours for which the two halves of the beam, recombined at a point of the retina, have received, owing to the plate, a relative retardation of an odd number of half wave-lengths.

For a further explanation some extremely simple experiments will suffice. The vertical slit of the collimator tube S (Fig. 271) is viewed through the telescope B, both being focussed for infinity. The slit may be shortened at will by pushing across it the card P from which a triangular portion has been cut away. The tube B is provided with the cap K with its central portion removed and in front of it is the screen II about the central line of which the vertical slit Σ may be displaced and thus varied in width symmetrically. Σ is the diffracting obstacle. The ordinary diffraction pattern is visible on looking into the telescope, namely, a central band double the width of the remaining ones which surround it on either side. If the slit of S is shortened by means of P until it is practically a point, and a direct-vision prism D is placed over the eyepiece with dispersion vertical and violet below, the monochromatic diffraction patterns are seen one above the other (Fig. 208b). The minima $a, b, c, d, e, \ldots$ converge below towards the violet. If the width of the slit Σ is reduced to one-half, the fringes are now all twice as wide and the minima, $b, d, f, \ldots$

only are visible (Fig. 208a). The former minima represented by dotted lines in Fig. 208a may thus be considered as the result of interference between light from *two contiguous* slits of width $\Sigma/2$. If the Jamin's compensator is introduced so that the line of division between the glass G_r (Fig. 271) to the right of the observer and G_l to the left divides the slit in two, we have Talbot's case. The dotted minima are displaced to the *right* if the greater retardation occurs on the right-hand side, whereas the minima corresponding to each separate half of the slit, denoted by the full lines, remain fixed. If the ocular prism is turned in a clockwise direction with respect to the observer, the minima indicated by full lines are turned so as to lie obliquely downwards to the left, while with a properly estimated rotation the dotted minima appear vertical. For an angle a between the direction of dispersion and the vertical, the effective component to the left is $\sin a$ if the complete dispersion of the prism is denoted by 1. If now the dotted minima are vertical, they also remain visible if the slit of S is made as long as one chooses. It is now perfectly obvious that these minima, namely the Talbot bands, *cannot* remain visible if D is turned in a counter-clockwise direction, which causes an increase of the obliquity of these bands.

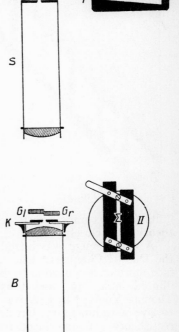

FIG. 271.

Only the brightest region of the diffraction pattern between the minima *bb* is sufficiently strong to manifest itself effectively in the spectrally resolved pattern. We may thus simplify the previous figure (Fig. 208) to Fig. 272, in which RH and VH represent respectively the horizontal and vertical dispersion components, *bb* the central minima of each half-slit, and the dotted lines (Fig. 208a) the minima resulting from the path difference between the two half-slits. It is at once obvious that (1) with any considerable horizontal dispersion the minima *bb* in the image of a vertical slit must be obliterated, (2) with our present arrangement, if the right-hand side rays from Σ are retarded most, the violet must lie to the left for the Talbot bands to remain visible in the slit spectrum, (3) with a decrease in width of Σ, and with increased retardation, the dispersion must be increased for the visibility of the Talbot bands to be retained. The Talbot bands find many applications, for which reason they have been described here.

Here we will mention a phenomenon observed accidentally by Newton and only afterwards recognized as a diffraction effect. Newton allowed sunlight to fall on a concave glass mirror, amalgam coated on its convex side, through an aperture in a paper screen placed with the aperture at the centre of curvature of the mirror. Where the regularly reflected light returned to the screen, the aperture was seen surrounded by faint coloured rings. If the mirror image of the aperture lay to the side of the aperture, both appeared connected by a white circle in which the aperture and its image were diametrically opposite one another. Inside and outside the white circle concentric coloured rings were apparent. Newton recognized that the effect was caused by the incomplete reflection or scattering from *both* the reflecting mirror surfaces. He repeated with these rings all the experiments which he had carried out with the coloured rings of his lens combination and also thought he had explained the two totally different effects by the same principle, the hypothesis of

FIG. 272.

" fits." It is unnecessary here to examine the inadequacy of this theory more closely.

A new element was introduced into these experiments in 1775 by the Duc de Chaulnes,* who intentionally made the front mirror surface more or less opaque by breathing upon it or by smearing it with diluted milk, etc., and thus obtained a very brilliant coloration.

Thomas Young † in 1802 was the first to give a rudimentary, but nearly correct theory. Young considered the ray from O (Fig. 273) incident perpendicularly on the front semi-opaque glass surface at A as split up into two portions. The one passes through the semi-opaque surface to the amalgam surface at B, where it is reflected back to A and there scattered ; for example, it may be sent out along AE.

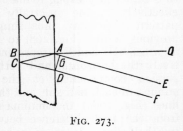

FIG. 273.

The other portion of the ray OA is scattered directly from A, along AC for example, where CAB is associated as angle of refraction with OAE as angle of incidence ; in C a regular reflection along CD then occurs and emergence in the usual manner along DF parallel

* Duc de Chaulnes, *Mem. Acad.*, Paris (1755).
† Young, " On the Theory of Light and Colours," *Phil. Trans. Roy. Soc.* ; and article on " Chromatics," *Encycl. Brit.*

to AE. For the two nearly parallel and only slightly separated portions of the ray only the order of scattering and regular refraction and
reflection is changed.   The two portions with common origin have, up
to DG perpendicular to AE, a small path difference which *increases*,
as a simple calculation or construction of the optical paths indicates,
with increasing angle of emergence with respect to OA.   If the figure
is imagined rotated about OA as axis, it is obvious that at the point O
of the distant screen, where the nearly parallel constituents meet,
interference rings must be produced surrounding O, with white as
the lowest order at O and with higher order colours to the outside.

The more complete theory of this phenomenon was established in
1851 by Stokes.   At a friend's suggestion he endeavoured to produce
the coloured rings by sending the light through two parallel planes
which had been rendered semi-opaque.   From the negative results
Stokes concluded that it was necessary for the light to pass to and
fro through the *same* set of particles.   This was considered to be due

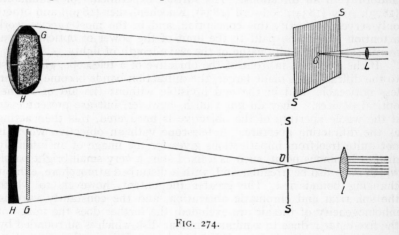

FIG. 274.

to the fact that, although the particles in the layer were small, they
were still large compared with the wave-length of light.   Owing to
the irregular arrangement of the particles, regular interference could
only occur if the light was affected twice by the same particle in
exactly the same manner.   By using polarized light, whose character
was found to be unaffected, Stokes finally recognized that *diffraction*
and not scattering was operative in the Newton phenomenon.

The effect observed by Newton is rendered very large and the
colours obtained saturated in the following manner.   Sunlight from
a condensing lens L (Fig. 274), divergent after passing the focus O,
which is at the centre of curvature of a concave telescope mirror H
silvered on its front face and of 3-4 metre radius, is incident upon
the latter and if possible fills the whole of its aperture (about 20 cm.).
The image from L and the mirror image are coincident at O.   A
screen S provided with an aperture is now placed in the plane of O
so that the light is able to pass.   Immediately a fairly plane glass

plate G lightly dusted with lycopodium is placed in front of the mirror the rings are seen extending upon the screen to a radius of from 10 to 20 cm. Moving the plate closer to the mirror increases, and moving it farther away decreases, the size of the rings. If between L and O a dispersing prism and a total reflecting prism are interposed, then by turning the latter the monochromatic illumination of H may be varied and the rings made to grow larger or smaller. The effect is seen with considerable intensity, since all parts of the mirror H contribute towards almost identical rings with centre O.

Thomas Young had already conceived, in 1802, that diffraction plays an important part in the formation of images by optical instruments. Fresnel's modification of Huygens' principle (1818) caused the development of a conviction that all optical images are merely diffraction maxima and thus, just as all light phenomena, the result of the interference of a light-mechanism which spreads itself out uniformly in all directions. The further experiments of Fraunhofer (1823), Airy (1834), Schwerd (1835), Knochenhauer (1839), and others only served to fortify this conception, and in the most precise work attention had to be paid to the limit of the power of optical instruments set by the finite value of the wave-length of light.

If the aperture, in front of the objective of a telescope, giving rise to the diffraction is made larger, the diffraction bands become smaller, less noticeable, and in the end invisible without the aid of further optical devices. They do not vanish, however, but are present even if the whole aperture of the objective is uncovered, this then acting as the diffracting aperture. A telescope with an objective which is not quite free from imperfections gives for the image of an infinitely distant luminous point, such as a fixed star, a very small bright patch which may also be irregular and, with a disturbed atmosphere, exhibit changing boundaries. The greater the extent, however, to which the spherical and chromatic aberration, and the constantly varying inhomogeneity of the air are excluded, the further does the image of the fixed star reduce to a minute circular disk which is surrounded by several alternately dark and bright rings. This is the diffraction image of a point, whose form and size are determined by the full aperture of the objective. The amount of this diffraction image seen depends on the brightness of the star and the magnification of the eyepiece. The image referred to is most perfect when a Foucault's silvered parabolic concave mirror is used as objective, as this does away most completely with the aberrations.

To explain the manner of formation of the diffraction image, first let the whole aperture of the objective be imagined square and divided up by vertical and horizontal lines. In Fig. 275 let $ab = A$ denote a horizontal section through the aperture. The rays from the fixed star are incident perpendicularly upon this aperture and the objective, omitted from the figure, makes them converge to the focus P at which they arrive all in the same phase. The elementary rays inclined at an angle a with the axis of the objective are made to converge to a point Q to one side of P, and are there completely extinguished if $A \sin a = \lambda$. These extinctions occur to the right and left of P also for A sin $a = m\lambda$. Since the square aperture acts in the same way vertically as horizontally, such extinctions or minima must also occur above and below P. The diffraction image of a star is thus a small bright square, which represents a portion of a circle whose vertical diameter is intersected by horizontal minima and horizontal diameter by vertical minima, the clearness of which falls off very rapidly from the centre. Feebler spectra also occur along the diagonal directions, but these are not explicable in such a simple manner.

Now consider an objective with circular aperture. Although the problem is now much more complicated, it is obvious that when once the position of extinction for elementary rays subtending an angle a to the axis is found, this minimum may, by symmetry, be applied to a circle about P. The diffraction image is, therefore, in this case a small circular disk, surrounded by rings of a brightness rapidly decreasing outwards.

For a circular aperture Airy performed the necessary integration for the determination of the minima by means of a convergent series.

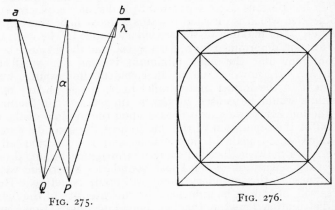

FIG. 275. FIG. 276.

Schwerd attained the same end by mechanical quadrature, a division of the circle into 180 trapezia. For the first minimum bordering on the central disk it was found that sin $a = 0{\cdot}610\ \lambda/r$ where r is the radius of the aperture. A good approximation may be obtained quite briefly. Taking, instead of the circular aperture, two square ones (Fig. 276), one of side $2r$ circumscribing the circle, and the other of side $\sqrt{2}r$ inscribing the circle, the above elementary deduction may be applied to both cases. For the first minimum in the one case sin $a = \lambda/2r$, and for the second sin $a = \lambda/\sqrt{2}r$, the mean of which is sin $a = 0{\cdot}635\lambda$ which, in fact, only differs slightly from the value found by the more laborious method.

The diffraction images of the fixed stars were first observed by William Herschel,* then further investigated under different conditions by Arago, and used by Foucault as a measure of the optical

* J. F. W. Herschel, " On Light."

resolving powers of telescopes. Since only very small angles are dealt with, we may write more simply $a = 0.610\lambda/r$. Assuming, in round numbers, $\lambda = 5 \times 10^{-4}$ mm. and $r = 50$ mm. as measure of the radius of the central diffraction disk, we have $a = 61 \times 10^{-7}$. If two luminous points are separated by double this angular measure, the central diffraction disks exactly touch. Points with a smaller angular separation than this can thus, for an aperture of 10 cm. diameter, no longer be distinguished as separate. In this case $2a = 122 \times 10^{-7}$, or according to Foucault, the reciprocal value $1/2a$ denotes the optical resolving power. The least separation of optical points for which the images are noticeably separate is thus, for the instrument we have been considering, 2·5 secs. in angular measure. It is evident that the resolving power is independent of the focal distances, and is determined only by the aperture.

Although in the above way the limit of *direct* telescopic observation is attained, it does not exclude the possibility of further investigation by optical methods. Consider with A. Michelson two narrow slits, with their homologous edges separated by a distance e, placed in front of an objective which is directed towards a linear light source parallel to the slits. The maxima of the secondary bands in the central field of view are now determined by $e . \sin a = m\lambda$, and the distance between one maximum and the next minimum is thus for small angles $a = 1/2 . \lambda/e$. If, now, a second independent line source were to appear next to the former and parallel to it, the secondary maxima and minima would be caused to vanish altogether when the maxima due to the one source were superposed upon the minima of the other. With double the separation of the line sources the secondary maxima and minima would again become visible, and so on periodically. If the interspace between the line sources is imagined bright also, with an increasing separation of the linear boundaries a periodic variation in distinctness of the secondary bands will occur as before. The distinctness will, of course, be influenced by the intensity of the light and by its distribution between the two bounding lines. Now, suppose that we have been looking at an unknown distant line object, for which from the resolution of the telescope it was impossible to say whether the object was single, double, or merely a narrow band. Then it is only necessary to view the object through an objective provided with two slits with their distance apart e variable by a micrometer screw, to be able, under favourable conditions, to distinguish between these possibilities. Similar cases occur, for example, when only the diffraction disk of a fixed star or of a planet's satellite remains visible. The disk appears intersected at once by secondary minima when the star is viewed through two slits with appropriate separation. By a micrometrical variation of the distance e apart, Michelson's method affords a means of distinguishing whether one is looking at a single or at a double star, of determining the distance apart of the two stars, or the diameter of the satellite. Of course, if b is the width of one slit and e the separation of the homologous edges, the slits can at the most only be made to approach one another to the distance $e = b$, which sets a limit to the measurements. To carry the investigation further, Michelson made the light from the source under investigation pass *via* three mirrors S, S′, S″ (Fig. 277), of which S and S′ are mutually perpendicular and can be separated to any desired distance, and *via* the plane parallel plates P, P′ likewise parallel to the mirrors, into the *same* telescope aperture R. This aperture can be varied at will, and the angular separation of the two beams be made as small as desired by rotating the plate P, so as to give the secondary bands any desired width.

Microscope images, obtained under different conditions, may be considered in a similar way. We shall not discuss them here, as very detailed accounts are to be found elsewhere.

The great importance of diffraction or interference maxima and minima in all optical data will, by now, be fairly obvious. Where a telescope or microscope is used to measure angles or length, they are not essentially different from interference refractometers, and may, as the foregoing examples show, readily assume the form of the latter.

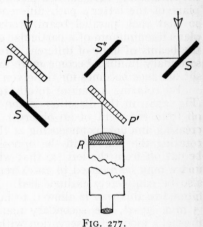

FIG. 277.

Let us now discuss with the aid of a historical example the influence of the dimensions of the light source upon the diffraction or interference image. Grimaldi allowed the sunlight to enter through two narrow adjacent openings in the window shutter and thought he observed that certain parts of the region illuminated by both sources appeared darker than if illuminated by one opening alone. From this he concluded that light when added to light may produce darkness. It may be safely assumed from his diagram that here he had really not observed interference at all. In this matter he was deceived by a contrast effect and through it was led to formulate a correct and important law upon the basis of an incorrect observation. A slight quantitative modification of the experiment, however, is sufficient to render the interference plainly visible. If in the silvering of a glass plate covering the opening in the window shutter a very fine line is scratched with a dividing machine, the familiar diffraction pattern of a single slit is produced by the sunlight on a screen. With a sufficiently strong diffraction effect through a very narrow slit the finite angle subtended by the solar disk (·5°) will no longer be a source of disturbance. For a screen distance of 70 cm. the central white field of view exhibiting diffraction was about 4 cm. wide. If, instead of a single line, two identical parallel ones are ruled with a separation of 1/32 mm., the diffraction pattern remains the same, only with two distinct secondary minima visible in the white central field. For a slit separation of 1/16 mm., 5 dark bands may be counted in the central field, for 1/8 mm., 11, and for 1/4 mm., 23. The greater the distance apart of the slits, the more numerous, but more indistinct, are the fringes. For a slit distance of 1/2 mm., secondary minima would no longer be visible without further modification of the apparatus.

The explanation of this that is usually given is that with an increase in separation of the slits the sunlight entering the apparatus ceases to be coherent, which, however, is not fully compatible with the facts. It is quite obvious that the slit separation would be without influence upon the quality of the effect if the sun were an infinitely distant point-like fixed star. In that case every one of the rays of the parallel beam incident upon the slits would be coherent. But with the finite surface subtended by the sun, each point gives a parallel beam of a different direction, and the constituents of its perpendicular wave-surface passing through the two slits have in the plane of the latter a path difference dependent upon their direction, so that each parallel beam produces on the screen or in the focal plane its minimum of a particular order in a different direction. Since the beams of light of different directions are mutually *incoherent*, the secondary minima become more and more indistinct, the greater the slit distance becomes for the given visual angle subtended by the sun.

By rotating a pair of totally-reflecting prisms, combined as in R (Fig. 278), in the direction of the arrow the sun's image may be cut off from the sight of an observer looking through the prisms, in increasing amounts commencing at the right-hand limb.* Similarly, by rotating the pair R' in the opposite direction, the sun's image may be cut off from the left, so that with the combination of the two the image may be reduced to an extremely narrow red band of light, and also be completely extinguished. If the practically parallel sunlight filtered in this way is allowed to fall on a vertical pair of narrow slits ·5 mm. apart, the secondary maxima and minima are seen, using Fresnel's mode of observation with the magnifying lens, as alternate red and black bands. When the filtering is less sharp, yellow appears in the red bands. A complete survey of the nature of the effect may be obtained by placing in front of Fresnel's lens a horizontal slit intersecting the vertical diffraction bands perpendicularly, and resolving the effect by a direct-vision prism with its dispersion direction vertical. Under these conditions a complete interference pattern would converge like a fan towards the violet. With a broad band of sunlight, at first, however, only a smooth continuous spectrum is seen. Decreasing the width of the band, the interference fringes separate out first in the violet, and the separation advances towards the red, while at the same time the spectrum is extinguished in succession from the violet end onwards. The luminous band of sunlight comprised between the limits of total reflection is, in fact, not chromatically equivalent throughout. Only the longest wave-lengths pass through the *whole* breadth of the band, while the shorter wave-lengths

---

* E. and L. Mach, " Versuche über Totalreflexion und deren Anwendung," *Sitzb. d. Wiener Akad.*, Vol. 113 (Oct., 1904) ; previously with G. v. Osnobischin, *Anz. d. Akad.* (1875) ; with B. Brauner, *ibid.*, Vol. 19 (1877).

draw back towards the central line of the luminous region. When the limits of total reflection are thus brought together, the shortest wavelengths disappear first, while the extreme and most feeble red remains till the last. This is also the reason why this filtration experiment cannot be extended to a slit separation of more than ·5 mm.

If it is desired to increase the slit separation still more, a sufficient light intensity must be provided, which in the above case necessitates arranging for homogeneity of colour, which is obtained by achromatizing the limits of the total reflection. It is possible for a ray of white light to be incident upon a crown glass prism of angle 45° (Fig. 279) in such a way that the whole of the coloured emergent beam is totally reflected at once from the combined reflection prisms R.

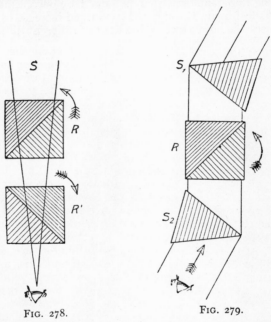

FIG. 278.   FIG. 279.

If the light afterwards passes through a crown glass prism S_2 turned through 180° with respect to S_1, on looking in the direction of the arrow towards the sun, the latter is seen to be traversed by a black limit of total reflection, which passes from left to right across the sun as the whole combination is turned in a counter-clockwise direction. A second prism combination $S_1'R'S_2'$, the mirror image of the former with respect to a vertical plane through the direction of the incident light, renders it possible to cut off the sun's image at a black limit, in succession from right to left, and therefore to reduce the visible image of the sun to a narrow white band. The direct sunlight is allowed to pass through a heliostat, and through the prisms S_1, R, S_2, S_1', R', S_2', after which it falls upon the objective of a telescope of focal length 2-3 metres. After making a slight adjustment of the positions of the prisms, a white line of sunlight is obtained in focus. If, now, a screen provided with a pair of narrow slits about 3 mm. apart is placed in front of the objective, some very fine and distinct specimens of the secondary minima are seen in the central white field ; these vanish when one of the slits is covered, and are displaced when the Jamin's compensator is rotated in front of the slits. There is no doubt that, with the appropriate arrangement, the two may be separated to any distance without the interference ceasing to be visible. Only *apparently* incoherent light, then, is obtained with widely separated slits. One might feel inclined to try to effect the sifting out of the parallel coherent components for the two slits by setting up a series of screens provided with congruent slits, but it would soon be apparent that what is gained by decreasing the width of the slits is lost again through the associated increase in diffraction, which increases the admixture of the light of different directions.

APPENDIX

" Mémoires de Physique et de Chimie de la Société D'Arcueil."   Tome
Second, pp. 254-267.   Paris, 1809

SUR UN PROPRIÉTÉ DES FORCES RÉPULSIVES QUI AGISSENT SUR LA LUMIÈRE

PAR M. MALUS

DANS mon dernier Mémoire (p. 143) [1] j'ai annoncé que la lumière réfléchie à la surface des corps diaphanes, acquiert de nouvelles propriétés qui la distinguent essentiellement de celle qui émane directement des corps lumineux.

J'ai continué depuis mes recherches sur le même sujet, et en soumettant au calcul le résultat de mes expériences, je suis parvenu à des conséquences remarquables qui jettent un nouveau jour sur le mode d'action que les corps exercent sur la lumière.

J'avois observé que lorsque la lumière est réfléchie sous un certain angle par la surface d'un corps diaphane, elle acquiert les propriétés des rayons qui ont été soumis à l'action de la double réfraction ; en partant de cette remarque, je suis parvenu avec de simples substances diaphanes, à modifier des rayons de lumière, de manière à ce qu'ils échappent entièrement à la réflexion partielle qu'on observe ordinairement à la surface de ces corps.   Je fais traverser un nombre quelconque de ces substances, par un rayon solaire, sans qu'aucune de ses molécules soit réfléchie, ce qui donne un moyen de mesurer avec exactitude la quantité de lumière que ces corps absorbent ; problème que la réflexion partielle rendoit impossible à résoudre.

La lumière qui a éprouvé cette modification se comporte d'une manière analogue avec les corps opaques polis.

Sous des angles déterminés, elle cesse de se réfléchir et se trouve totalement absorbée, tandis qu'en deça et au-delà de ces angles elle est réfléchie en partie à la surface de ces corps.

Lorsqu'on fait tomber un rayon solair sur une glace polie et non étamée, ce rayon est réfléchi en partie à la première et à la seconde surface, et son intensité augmente avec l'angle d'incidence compté de la perpendiculaire ; c'est-à-dire qu'elle est d'autant plus grande que le rayon est plus incliné sur la face réfléchissante.

Mais si la lumière directe est soumise à cette loi d'intensité, celle qui a déja été réfléchie suit une loi toute différente lorsqu'elle est de nouveau réfléchie par une seconde glace.   Dans certaines directions, au lieu d'augmenter d'intensité avec l'angle d'incidence, elle diminue,

[1] P. 312 of this Appendix.

au contraire, et après avoir atteint un certain *minimum*, elle commence à augmenter suivant la même loi que la lumière directe. Ces *minima* sont relatifs, soit à l'inclinaison du rayon sur les surfaces réfléchissantes, soit à l'angle que ces surfaces forment entre elles, en sorte que la lumière réfléchie par la seconde glace est fonction de ces trois angles. Cette fonction a un *minimum* absolu, c'est-à-dire, pour lequel l'intensité de la lumière réfléchie par la seconde glace est absolument nulle. Le calcul m'a conduit directement aux circonstances qui donnent ce *minimum*, et je l'ai vérifié par une expérience très-simple que je vais décrire.

Si on prend deux glaces inclinées l'une à l'autre de 70° 22' ; si ensuite on conçoit entre ces deux glaces une ligne qui fasse avec l'une et l'autre un angle de 35° 25', tout rayon réfléchi par une des glaces parallèlement à cette ligne, ne sera pas réfléchi de nouveau par la seconde ; il ne pénétrera sans qu'aucune de ses molécules éprouve l'action des forces répulsives qui produisent la réflexion partielle. En deça et au-delà des angles que j'ai indiqués, le phénomène cessera d'avoir lieu, et plus on s'éloignera de ces limites dans un sens ou dans l'autre, plus la quantité de lumière réfléchie augmentera.

Cette faculté de pénétrer entièrement les corps diaphanes que la lumière a acquise par une première réflexion, elle la perd ou la conserve dans diverses circonstances que j'ai étudiées, ce qui m'a conduit à la loi suivant laquelle s'opère ce singulier phénomène.

Si on fait tourner une seconde glace autour du premier rayon réfléchi *a* en faisant constamment, avec lui, un angle de 35° 25', et si dans un plan perpendiculaire à ce rayon on conçoit deux lignes l'une *b* parallèle à la première glace, et l'autre *c* parallèle à la seconde, la quantité de lumière réfléchie par celle-ci est proportionelle au carré du cosinus de l'angle compris entre les lignes *b c*, elle est à son *maximum* quand ces lignes sont parallèles, et nulle lorsqu'elles sont perpendiculaires. En sorte que les limites du phénomène se rapportent à trois axes rectangulaires *a b c* dont l'un est parallèle à la direction du rayon, l'autre à la première surface réfléchissante, et enfin le troisième perpendiculaire aux deux premiers.

Substituons à la seconde glace un miroir métallique, et nommons *a' b' c'* les axes rectangulaires du second rayon analogues aux axes *a b c* du premier. Si on reçoit ce rayon sur une glace polie non étamée, et qui fasse avec lui un angle de 35° 25', on remarque les phénomènes suivans qui sont indépendans de l'angle d'incidence sur le miroir métallique. Si *b'* est parallèle à *b*, c'est-à-dire si le miroir métallique est parallèle à l'axe *b*, le rayon qu'il réfléchit conserve ses propriétés par rapport à une glace située parallelement à l'axe *c'* : il la pénètre en entier : si *b'* est parallèle à *c*, le rayon réfléchi conserve ses propriétés pour une glace parallèle à l'axe *b'*.

Dans les positions intermédiaires la quantité de lumière qui aura conservé sa propriété pour une glace parallèle à l'axe *b'*, est proportionelle au carré du sinus de l'angle compris entre les axes *b'*, *b*, et celle qui a conservé sa propriété par rapport à une glace parallèle à l'axe *c'*, est proportionelle au carré du cosinus du même angle.

Lorsque le miroir métallique fait un angle égal avec les axes *b c*, *b'* fait avec chacun d'eux un angle de 45°, alors la lumière se comporte de la même manière sur une glace parallèle à l'axe b' ou à l'axe c', elle semble, dans ce cas, avoir repris tous les caractères de la lumière directe.

Si on dissèque le rayon réfléchi par le miroir métallique à l'aide d'un cristal de spath calcaire en disposant sa section principale parallèlement au plan de réflexion, le rapport des intensités du rayon réfracté extraordinaire et du rayon ordinaire, est égal au carré de la tangente de l'angle compris entre les deux axes $b\ b'$.

Si on fait subir à la lumière plusieurs réflexions sur des miroirs métalliques, avant de la soumettre à l'action d'un second corps diaphane, les phénomènes sont analogues à ceux que je viens d'exposer. Si l'axe b' du second rayon est parallèle à l'axe b ou c du premier, si l'axe b'' du troisième est parallèle à l'axe b' ou c' du second et ainsi de suite, la propriété proposée de la lumière ne sera nullement altérée ; si ces axes sont inclinés les uns aux autres elle se divisera relativement aux deux miroirs consécutifs suivant la loi que j'ai indiquée.

Si on fait tourner autour de l'axe c du premier rayon réfléchi, la surface d'un corps opaque poli tel que du marbre noir, on voit la lumière réfléchie diminuer jusqu'à une certaine limite où elle est nulle, et au-delà de laquelle elle commence à augmenter.

Tous les phénomènes ordinaires de l'optique peuvent s'expliquer soit dans l'hypothèse d'Huyghens qui les suppose produits par les vibrations d'un fluide éthéré, soit d'après l'opinion de Newton qui les suppose produits par l'action des corps sur les molécules lumineuses considérées elles-mêmes comme appartenant à une substance soumise aux forces attractives et répulsives qui servent à expliquer les autres phénomènes de la physique. Les lois relatives à la marche des rayons dans la double réfraction peuvent encore s'expliquer dans l'une ou l'autre hypothèse. Mais les observations que je viens de décrire prouvant que les phénomènes de réflexion sont différens pour un même angle d'incidence, ce qui ne peut avoir lieu dans l'hypothèse d'Huyghens ; il faut nécessairement en conclure non-seulement que la lumière est une substance soumise aux forces qui animent les autres corps, mais encore que la forme et la disposition de ses molécules ont une grande influence sur les phénomènes.

Si on transporte aux molécules lumineuses les trois axes rectangulaires $a\ b\ c$ auxquels se rapportent les phénomènes que j'ai décrits, et si on suppose que l'axe a étant toujours dans la direction du rayon ; les axes b ou c deviennent par l'influence des *forces répulsives* perpendiculaires à la direction de ces forces ; alors tout les phénomènes de la réflexion totale, de la réflexion partielle, et les circonstances les plus extraordinaires de la double réfraction, deviennent une conséquence les unes des autres et se déduisent de cette loi unique, savoir ; que

Si on considère dans la translation des molécules lumineuses leur mouvement autour de leurs trois axes principaux a, b, c, la quantité des molécules dont l'axe b ou c deviendra perpendiculaire à la direction des forces répulsives, sera toujours proportionelle au carré du sinus de l'axe que ces lignes auront à décrire autour de l'axe a, pour prendre cette direction et reciproquement, la quantité des molécules dont les axes b ou c se rapprocheront le plus possible de la direction des forces répulsives, sera proportionelle au carré du cosinus de l'axe que ces lignes auront à décrire dans leur rotation autour de l'axe a pour parvenir dans le plan qui passe par cet axe et la direction des forces.

Dans le cas de la double réfraction, et lorsqu'on considère les phénomènes que presentent deux cristaux contigues on peut traduire cette loi de la manière suivante.

Si on conçoit un plan passant par le rayon ordinaire et l'axe du premier cristal, et un second plan passant par le rayon extraordinaire et l'axe du second cristal, la quantité de lumière provenant de la réfraction ordinaire du premier corps, et réfractée ordinairement par le second cristal, est proportionelle au carré du cosinus de l'angle compris entre les deux plans proposés, et la quantité de lumière réfractée extraordinairement proportionelle au carré du sinus du même angle. Si c'est le rayon extraordinaire du premier cristal sur lequel on opère, on obtient un résultat analogue en changeant le mot ordinaire en extraordinaire, et reciproquement.

Quant à la réflexion, si on considère, par exemple, un rayon réfléchi par une première glace en faisant avec elle un angle de $35°\,25'$, et tombant sous le même angle sur une seconde glace ; l'angle compris entre les deux surfaces étant d'ailleurs arbitraire : il faut concevoir par ce rayon réfléchi un plan perpendiculaire à la première glace, et un autre perpendiculaire à la seconde ; la quantité de lumière réfléchie par celle-ci sera proportionelle au carré du cosinus de l'angle compris entre les deux plans proposés.

Je me bornerai à quelques exemples de l'application de cette loi.

Lorsqu'un rayon est réfléchi par la surface d'une glace sous un angle de $54°\,35'$, on reconnoît que toutes ses molécules sont disposées de la même manière, puisqu'en présentant perpendiculairement à ce rayon un prisme de cristal de carbonate calcaire dont l'axe est dans le plan de réflexion, toutes ses molécules sont réfractées en un seul rayon ordinaire, aucune d'elles n'est réfractée extraordinairement. Dans ce cas, les axes analogues de ces molécules sont tous parallèles entre eux, puisqu'elles se comportent toutes de la même manière. Nommons b, l'axe de ces molécules qui se trouvent perpendiculaires au plan de réflexion. Toutes les molécules dont l'axe c étoit perpendiculaire à ce plan ont pénétré le corps diaphane. Donc, si on présente aux molécules réfléchies et sous le même angle une seconde glace, parallèle à leur axe c, elles se trouveront dans le cas de celles qui n'ont pas pu être réfléchies par la première, le rayon pénétrera donc en entier cette seconde glace. L'expérience confirme, en effet, que dans cette circonstance toutes les molécules échappent aux forces de réflexion.

Lorsqu'on place l'un sur l'autre deux rhomboïdes de spath calcaire, de manière à ce que leurs sections principales soient parallèles, un rayon solaire parallèle à ces sections principales ne produit que deux rayons émergens : celui qui provient de la réfraction ordinaire ou extraordinaire du premier cristal, est réfracté par le second en un seul rayon ordinaire ou extraordinaire. En effet, on conçoit dans ce cas, que soit que les axes des cristaux soient parallèles, soit qu'ils soient placés en sens contraire, tout rayon sorti du premier cristal parallèle ment à sa section principale, n'est pas divisé par le second, car son mouvement a lieu autour de l'axe b ou de l'axe c, et nous avons vu par les phénomènes de la réflexion, que toutes les fois que le mouvement a lieu autour de ces axes, le rayon n'est pas altéré ; toutes les molécules conservent leurs mêmes axes parallèles. La rotation autour de l'axe a étant la seule qui change la position respective des axes des molécules d'un même rayon.

Lorsque le rayon incident fait un angle quelconque avec les sections principales, les rayons qui proviennent de la double réfraction du premier cristal sont divisés en deux par le second, en sorte qu'on obtient alors quatre rayons émergens. Il y a cependant dans cette circonstance deux cas différens où les phénomènes sont très-distincts. Celui où les axes des cristaux sont parallèles, et celui où ils sont situés en sens contraire. Lorsque les axes sont parallèles il faut employer une lumière très vive, et éloigner sensiblement le plan d'incidence de celui des sections principales, pour parvenir à appercevoir les rayons réfractés, ordinairement par un cristal et extraordinairement par l'autre. En effet, d'après la théorie, le *maximum* d'intensité de ces deux rayons n'est pas la trentième partie de celle du rayon qui provient de la réfraction ordinaire des deux cristaux ; ce qui avoit fait penser aux physiciens qui ont écrit sur cette matière, que lorsque les sections principales et les axes sont parallèles, la lumière se comporte de la même manière que dans la section principale, quelle que soit la direction du rayon incident : cependant en employant une lumière vive, et les circonstances convenables, l'observation répond parfaitement à la théorie. Le phénomène est beaucoup plus sensible, lorsque les axes sont situés en sens contraire.

La réfraction extraordinaire est produite par une force répulsive, dont l'action est proportionelle au carré du sinus de l'angle compris entre l'axe du cristal et l'axe principal a de la molécule lumineuse. Toutes les molécules dont l'axe b est perpendiculaire à cette force sont réfractées ordinairement, te toutes celles dont l'axe c lui est perpendiculaire sont réfractées extraordinairement. Les molécules réfractées ordinairement qui échappent à la force répulsive, sont dans le cas de celles qui échappent à la réflexion dans la première classe de faits que j'ai rapportés.

Les phénomènes de la double réflexion à la seconde surface des cristaux diaphanes, sont analogues à ceux de la réfraction dans deux cristaux dont les sections principales sont parallèles et leurs axes situés en sens contraire ; en y joignant cette propriété commune à tous les corps diaphanes, que lorsque la face réfléchissante est parallèle à l'axe c des molécules lumineuses, la réflexion est nulle sous un angle déterminé.

Ainsi, sans la connoissance de cette propriété singulière des corps diaphanes, la partie la plus extraordinaire des phénomènes de la double réfraction seroit restée inexplicable.

Je n'entrerai pas dans de plus longs détails sur l'application de la théorie que j'ai exposée ; je me contenterai de dire qu'elle ramène à une même source une foule de faits qui sembloient n'avoir entre eux aucune analogie, et dont le défaut de liaison rendoit la mesure presque impraticable.

Je ne prétends pas indiquer la cause de cette propriété générale des forces répulsives qui agissent sur la lumière, je donne seulement les moyens de lier entre eux les phénomènes, de les prévoir par le calcul et de les mesurer avec exactitude ; de même en rapportant les formes des molécules lumineuses à trois angles rectangulaires, comme le seroient ceux d'un octaèdre, je ne préjuge rien sur la forme réelle de ces molécules, mais je présente ce résultat comme une conséquence du calcul auquel m'a conduit l'analyse des phénomènes que j'ai observés.

" Mémoires de Physique et de Chimie de la Société D'Arcueil." Tome Second, pp. 143-158.   Paris, 1809

SUR UNE PROPRIÉTÉ DE LA LUMIÈRE RÉFLÉCHIE

PAR M. MALUS

Lorsqu'un rayon solaire est réfléchi ou réfracté, il conserve en général ses propriétés physiques ; et, soumis à de nouvelles épreuves, il se comporte comme s'il émanoit directement du corps lumineux : le prisme, en dispersant les rayons colorés, ne fait que changer leur direction respective, sans altérer leur nature. Il y a cependant des circonstances où l'influence de certains corps imprime aux rayons qu'ils réfléchissent, ou qu'ils réfractent, des caractères et des propriétés qu'ils transportent avec eux, et qui les distinguent essentiellement de la lumière directe.

La propiété de la lumière que je vais décrire est une modification de ce genre. Elle avoit déjà été apperçue dans une circonstance particulière de la duplication des images, offerte par le spath calcaire ; mais le phénomène qui en résultoit étant attribué aux propriétés de ce cristal, on ne soupçonnoit pas qu'il pût être produit non-seulement par tous les corps cristallisés qui donnent une double réfraction, mais encore par toutes les autres substances diaphanes solides ou liquides et même par les corps opaques.

Si on reçoit un rayon de lumière perpendiculairement à la face d'un rhomboïde de spath calcaire, ce rayon se divise en deux faisceaux, l'un qui se prolonge dans la direction du rayon incident, et l'autre qui fait avec celui-ci un angle de quelques degrés. Le plan qui passe par ces deux rayons jouit de plusieurs propriétés particulières, et on le nomme plan de la section principale. Il est toujours parallèle à l'axe des molécules intégrantes du cristal et perpendiculaire à la face réfringente naturelle ou artificielle. Lorsque le rayon incident est incliné à la face réfringente il se divise également en deux faisceaux, l'un qui est réfracté suivant la loi ordinaire, et l'autre suivant une loi extra-ordinaire qui dépend des angles que le rayon incident forme avec la surface réfringente et la section principale. Lorsque la face d'émergence est parallèle à la face d'incidence, les deux rayons émergens sont parallèles au rayon incident, parce que chaque rayon éprouve aux deux faces opposées le même genre de réfraction.

Si actuellement on reçoit sur un second rhomboïde dont là section principale soit parallèle à celle du premier, les deux rayons qui ont déjà traversé celui-ci, ils ne seront plus divisés en deux faisceaux comme l'eussent été des rayons de lumière directe. Le faisceaux provenant de la réfraction ordinaire du premier cristal sera réfracté par le second suivant la loi de la réfraction ordinaire, comme si celui-ci avoit perdu la faculté de doubler les images. De même le faisceau provenant de la réfraction extraordinaire du premier cristal sera réfracté par le second suivant la loi de la réfraction extraordinaire.

Si le premier cristal restant immobile on fait tourner le second de manière que la face d'incidence reste parallèle à elle-même, chacun des deux rayons provenant de la réfraction du premier cristal commence à se diviser en deux faisceaux ; en sorte, par exemple, qu'une partie du rayon provenant de la réfraction ordinaire, commence à se réfracter extraordinairement, ce qui produit quatre images. Enfin, après un quart de révolution le faisceau provenant de la réfraction ordinaire du premier cristal est en entier réfracté extraordinairement par le second ; et réciproquement, le faisceau provenant de la réfraction extraordinaire du premier cristal est en entier réfracté par le second suivant la loi ordinaire, ce qui réduit de nouveau à deux le nombre des images. Ce phénomène est indépendant des angles d'incidence, puisque dans le mouvement du second cristal les faces réfringentes des deux rhomboïdes conservent entre elles la même inclinaison.

Ainsi le caractère qui distingue la lumière directe de celle qui a été soumise à l'action d'un premier cristal, c'est que l'une a constamment la faculté d'être divisée en deux faisceaux, tandis que dans l'autre cette faculté dépend de l'angle compris entre le plan d'incidence et celui de la section principale.

Cette faculté de changer le caractère de la lumière et de lui imprimer une nouvelle propriété qu'elle transporte avec elle, n'est pas particulière au spath d'Islande ; je l'ai retrouvée dans toutes les substances connues qui doublent les images, et ce qu'il y a de remarquable dans ce phénomène c'est qu'il n'est pas nécessaire pour le produire d'employer deux cristaux d'une même espèce. Ainsi le second cristal, par exemple, pourroit être de carbonate de plomb ou de sulfate de barite : le premier pourroit être un cristal de soufre et le second un cristal de roche. Toutes ces substances se comportent entre elles de la même manière que deux rhomboïdes de spath calcaire. En général cette disposition de la lumière à se réfracter en deux faisceaux ou en un seul, ne dépend que de la position respective de l'axe des molécules intégrantes des cristaux qu'on emploie, quels que soient d'ailleurs leurs principes chimiques et les faces naturelles ou artificielles sur lesquelles s'opère la réfraction. Ce résultat prouve que la modification que la lumière reçoit de ces différens corps est parfaitement identique.

Pour rendre plus sensibles les phénomènes que je viens de décrire, on peut regarder la flamme d'une bougie à travers deux prismes de matières différentes donnant la double réfraction et posés l'un sur l'autre. On aura en général quatre images de la flamme ; mais si on fait tourner lentement un des prismes, autour du rayon visuel comme axe, les quatre images se réduiront à deux, toutes les fois que les sections principales des faces contiguës seront parallèles ou rectangulaires.

Les deux images qui disparoissent ne se confondent pas avec les deux autres, on les voit s'éteindre peu-à-peu tandis que les autres augmentent d'intensité.   Lorsque les deux sections principales sont parallèles, une des images est formée par des rayons réfractés ordinairement par les deux prismes, et la seconde par des rayons réfractés extraordinairement Lorsque les deux sections principales sont rectangulaires, une des images est formée par des rayons réfractés ordinairement par le premier cristal, et extraordinairement par le second, et l'autre image par des rayons réfractés extraordinairement par le premier cristal et ordinairement par le second.

Non seulement tous les cristaux qui doublent les images peuvent donner à la lumière cette faculté d'être réfractée en deux faisceaux ou en un seul, suivant la position du cristal réfringent, mais tous les corps diaphanes solides ou liquides, et les corps opaques eux-mêmes, peuvent imprimer aux molécules lumineuses cette singulière disposition qui sembloit être un des effets de la double réfraction.

Lorsqu'un faisceau de lumière traverse une substance diaphane, une partie des rayons est réfléchie par la surface réfringente, et une autre partie par la surface d'émergence.   La cause de cette réflexion partielle qui a jusqu'ici échappé aux recherches des physiciens, semble avoir, dans plusieurs circonstances, quelque analogie avec les forces qui produisent la double réfraction.

Par exemple, la lumière réfléchie par la surface de l'eau sous un angle de 52° 45′ avec la verticale, a tous les caractères d'un des faisceaux produits par la double réfraction d'un cristal de spath calcaire dont la section principale seroit parallèle ou perpendiculaire au plan qui passe par le rayon incident et le rayon réfléchie que nous nommerons plan de réflexion.

Si on reçoit ce rayon réfléchi sur un cristal quelconque, ayant la propriété de doubler les images, et dont la section principale soit parallèle au plan de réflexion, il ne sera pas divisé en deux faisceaux comme l'eût été un rayon de lumière directe, mais il sera réfracté tout entier suivant la loi ordinaire, comme si ce cristal avoit perdu la faculté de doubler les images.   Si, au contraire, la section principale du cristal est perpendiculaire au plan de réflexion, le rayon réfléchi sera réfracté tout entier suivant la loi extraordinaire.   Dans les positions intermédiaires il sera divisé en deux faisceaux suivant la même loi et dans la même proportion que s'il avoit acquis son nouveau caractère par l'influence de la double réfraction.   Le rayon réfléchic par la surface du liquide a donc, dans cette circonstance, tous les caractères d'un rayon ordinaire formé par un cristal dont la section principale seroit perpendiculaire au plan de réflexion.

Pour analyser complètement ce phénomène j'ai disposé verticalement la section principale d'un cristal, et après avoir divisé un rayon lumineux, à l'aide de la double réfraction, j'ai reçu les deux faisceaux qui en provenoient sur la surface de l'eau et sous l'angle de 52° 45′. Le rayon ordinaire, en se réfractant, a abandonné à la réflexion partielle une partie de ses molécules comme l'eût fait un faisceau de lumière directe, mais le rayon extraordinaire a pénétré en entier le liquide ; aucune de ses molécules n'a échappé à la réfraction.   Au contraire, quand la section principale du cristal étoit perpendiculaire au plan d'incidence, le rayon extraordinaire produisoit seul une réflexion partielle et le rayon ordinaire étoit réfracté en entier.

L'angle sous lequel la lumière éprouve cette modification en se réfléchissant à la surface des corps diaphanes, est variable pour chacun d'eux, il est, en général, plus grand pour les corps qui réfractent d'avantage la lumière.   Au-delà et en deca de cet angle une partie du rayon est plus ou moins modifiée, et d'une manière analogue à ce qui se passe entre deux cristaux dont les sections principales cessent d'être parallèles ou rectangulaires.

Lorsqu'on veut simplement prendre connoissance de ce phénomène sans le mesurer avec exactitude, il faut placer en avant d'une bougie ou le corps diaphane ou le vase contenant le liquide qu'on veut soumettre à l'expérience.   On examine à travers un prisme de cristal l'image de la flamme réfléchie à la surface du corps ou du liquide, on voit généralement deux images ; mais en tournant le cristal autour du rayon visuel comme axe, on s'apperçoit qu'une des images s'affoiblit à mesure que l'autre augmente d'intensité.   Au-delà d'une certaine limite, l'image qui s'étoit affoiblie recommence à augmenter d'intensité aux dépens de la seconde.   Il faut saisir à-peu-près le point où l'intensité de lumière est au *minimum*, et rapprocher ou éloigner de la bougie le corps réfléchissant, jusqu' à ce que l'angle d'incidence soit tel qu'une des deux images disparoisse totalement ; cette distance déterminée, si on continue à faire tourner lentement le cristal, on s'appercevra qu'une des deux images s'éteindra alternativement à chaque quart de révolution.

Le phénomène que nous avons remarqué dans les rayons qui se réfléchissent sous un certain angle à la surface d'un corps diaphane, a lieu aussi sous un autre angle dans les faisceaux réfléchis intérieurement par la surface d'émergence, et le sinus du premier angle est au sinus du second, dans le même rapport que les sinus d'incidence et de réfraction ; ainsi, en supposant la face d'incidence et la face d'émergence parallèles et l'angle d'incidence tel que le rayon réfléchi à la première surface présente le phénomène que nous avons décrit, le rayon réfléchi à la seconde surface sera modifié de la même manière. Si le rayon incident est tel que toutes ses molécules échappent à la réflexion partielle en traversant la face d'entrée, elles y échapperont de même en traversant la face de sortie.   Cette nouvelle propriété de la lumière offre un moyen de mesurer d'une manière précise la quantité de rayons absorbés à la surface des corps diaphanes, problême que la réflexion partielle rendoit presque impossible à résoudre.

Lorsqu'un corps, qui donne la double réfraction, réfléchit la lumière à sa première surface, il se comporte comme une substance diaphane ordinaire.   La lumière réfléchie sous un certain angle d'incidence acquiert la propriété que j'ai décrite ; et cet angle est indépendant de la position de la section principale qui n'influe que sur la double réfraction, ou sur les réflexions qui ont lieu dans l'intérieur du cristal.

En effet, les rayons qui se réfléchissent intérieurement à la seconde surface, présentent des phénomènes particuliers qui dépendent à la fois des forces réfringentes, et des propriétés de la lumière réfléchie que j'ai déjà exposées.

Lorsqu'un faisceau lumineux a été divisé en deux rayons à la première surface d'un rhomboïde de spath calcaire ; ces deux rayons sortent par la seconde face en deux faisceaux parallèles au rayon incident, parce que chacun d'eux éprouve, à cette face, le même genre de réfraction qu'à la première. Il n'en est pas de même de la lumière réfléchie. Quoique le rayon réfracté ordinairement à la première face, soit réfracté ordinairement à la seconde, il est néanmoins réfléchi à cette surface en deux faisceaux, l'un ordinaire, l'autre extraordinaire. De même le rayon réfracté extraordinairement se réfléchit en deux autres ; en sorte qu'il y a quatre rayons réfléchis, tandis qu'il n'y en a que deux émergens. Ces quatre rayons revenant à la première face du cristal en sortent par quatre faisceaux parallèles, qui font, avec cette surface, mais en sens contraire, le même angle que le rayon incident, et qui sont parallèles au plan d'incidence. Pour lier ce genre de réflexion à celui de la double réfraction, il faut concevoir, par les deux points d'émergence de la seconde face, deux rayons incidens, faisant, avec cette surface, mais en sens contraire, le même angle que les rayons émergens. Ces deux rayons, par leur réfraction à travers le cristal, produiront quatre faisceaux qui suivront exactement la route des rayons réfléchis. Ainsi, la loi de la double réfraction étant connue, celle de la double réflexion peut s'en déduire facilement.

Nous allons passer actuellement au genre de phénomène qui fait l'objet de ce Mémoire, et qui est relatif non à la loi suivant laquelle se dirigent les rayons, mais à la quantité et aux propriétés de la lumière qu'ils contienent.

Supposons l'angle d'incidence constant et le cristal posé horizontalement. Si on fait tourner le rhomboïde autour de la verticale de manière à rapprocher sa section principale du rayon incident, on voit diminuer peu-à-peu l'intensité du rayon ordinaire réfléchi extraordinairement, et du rayon extraordinaire réfléchi ordinairement. Enfin, lorsque le plan de la section principale passe par le rayon incident, ces deux rayons réfléchis disparoissent totalement, et il ne reste que le rayon ordinaire réfléchi ordinairement, et le rayon extraordinaire réfléchi extraordinairement. Ce dernier a néanmoins une intensité beaucoup moindre que le premier.

Si actuellement le rayon incident continuant à être compris dans la section principale, on augmente ou on diminue l'angle d'incidence, jusqu'à ce qu'il soit égal à 56° 30', alors le dernier rayon réfléchi disparoît totalement, et il ne reste que celui qui a été réfracté ordinairement et réfléchi ordinairement. Au-delà et en deça de cet angle, le rayon extraordinaire réfléchi extraordinairement, reparoît avec d'autant plus d'intensité qu'on s'éloigne davantage de cette limite. L'angle d'incidence dont je viens de parler est celui sous lequel un rayon réfléchi à la première surface, auroit acquis la propriété de se diviser en deux faisceaux ou en un seul, comme cela à lieu à la surface de tout autre corps diaphane. Le phénomène précédent se lie facilement à l'expérience dans laquelle nous avons pris l'eau pour exemple ; car si on fait tomber sur la surface du rhomboïde et sous l'angle d'environ 56° 30', un rayon disposé à ne se réfracter qu'en un seul faisceau extraordinaire, ce rayon ne produit pas de réflexion partielle à la première surface, ce qui semble expliquer pourquoi il n'en produit pas à la seconde."

Cependant, il n'en est pas de même lorsque le plan d'incidence fait un angle sensible avec la section principale. Si on fait tomber dans ce plan et sous l'angle d'environ 56° 30', le rayon dont nous venons de parler, il se comporte à la première surface comme dans les cas précédent ; il la traverse sans se réfléchir, mais à la seconde surface il est réfléchi en deux faisceaux qui parviennent à leur *maximum* d'intensité lorsque le plan d'incidence est perpendiculaire à la section principale.

On sent que la lumière réfléchie à la seconde face ne se comporte pas ici comme dans le cas précédent, parce que dans la première expérience le rayon incident réfracté et réfléchi est toujours dans un même plan, au lieu que dans le dernier cas la force répulsive qui produit la réfraction extraordinaire, détourne la lumière du plan d'incidence, en sorte qu'elle cesse d'être dans les mêmes circonstances par rapport aux forces qui agissent sur elle.

Si on examine la lumière qui provient de la réflexion partielle des corps opaques, tels que le marbre noir, le bois d'ébène, etc., on trouve également un angle pour lequel cette lumière jouit des propriétés de celle qui a traversé un cristal de spath d'Islande. Les substances métalliques polies sont les seules qui ne semblent pas susceptibles de fournir ce phénomène, mais si elles n'impriment pas aux rayons lumineux cette disposition particulière, elles ne l'altèrent pas lorsque la lumière l'a déjà acquise par l'influence d'un autre corps.

Cette propriété se conserve aussi dans les faisceaux qui traversent les corps qui réfractent simplement la lumière.

J'exposerai dans la seconde partie de ce Mémoire les circonstances, où à l'aide de la réflexion, sur les miroirs métalliques, on peut changer la disposition mutuelle des molécules d'un même rayon ordinaire ou extraordinaire, de manière que les unes se réfractent toujours ordinairement, tandis que les autres se réfractent extraordinairement. L'examen de ces diverses circonstances nous conduira à la loi de ces phénomènes, qui dépend d'une propriété générale des forces répulsives qui agissent sur la lumière.

NAME INDEX

SUBJECT INDEX

Catalogue of Dover
SCIENCE BOOKS

BOOKS THAT EXPLAIN SCIENCE

THE NATURE OF LIGHT AND COLOUR IN THE OPEN AIR, M. Minnaert. Why is falling snow sometimes black? What causes mirages, the fata morgana, multiple suns and moons in the sky; how are shadows formed? Prof. Minnaert of U. of Utrecht answers these and similar questions in optics, light, colour, for non-specialists. Particularly valuable to nature, science students, painters, photographers. "Can best be described in one word—fascinating!" Physics Today. Translated by H. M. Kremer-Priest, K. Jay. 202 illustrations, including 42 photos. xvi + 362pp. 5⅜ x 8.   T196 Paperbound **$1.95**

THE RESTLESS UNIVERSE, Max Born. New enlarged version of this remarkably readable account by a Nobel laureate. Moving from sub-atomic particles to universe, the author explains in very simple terms the latest theories of wave mechanics. Partial contents: air and its relatives, electrons and ions, waves and particles, electronic structure of the atom, nuclear physics. Nearly 1000 illustrations, including 7 animated sequences. 325pp. 6 x 9.   T412 Paperbound **$2.00**

MATTER AND LIGHT, THE NEW PHYSICS, L. de Broglie. Non-technical papers by a Nobel laureate explain electromagnetic theory, relativity, matter, light, radiation, wave mechanics, quantum physics, philosophy of science. Einstein, Planck, Bohr, others explained so easily that no mathematical training is needed for all but 2 of the 21 chapters. "Easy simplicity and lucidity . . . should make this source-book of modern physcis available to a wide public," Saturday Review. Unabridged. 300pp. 5⅜ x 8.   T35 Paperbound **$1.60**

THE COMMON SENSE OF THE EXACT SCIENCES, W. K. Clifford. Introduction by James Newman, edited by Karl Pearson. For 70 years this has been a guide to classical scientific, mathematical thought. Explains with unusual clarity basic concepts such as extension of meaning of symbols, characteristics of surface boundaries, properties of plane figures, vectors, Cartesian method of determining position, etc. Long preface by Bertrand Russell. Bibliography of Clifford. Corrected. 130 diagrams redrawn. 249pp. 5⅜ x 8.
T61 Paperbound **$1.60**

THE EVOLUTION OF SCIENTIFIC THOUGHT FROM NEWTON TO EINSTEIN, A. d'Abro. Einstein's special, general theories of relativity, with historical implications, analyzed in non-technical terms. Excellent accounts of contributions of Newton, Riemann, Weyl, Planck, Eddington, Maxwell, Lorentz, etc., are treated in terms of space, time, equations of electromagnetics, finiteness of universe, methodology of science. "Has become a standard work," Nature. 21 diagrams. 482pp. 5⅜ x 8.   T2 Paperbound **$2.00**

BRIDGES AND THEIR BUILDERS, D. Steinman, S. R. Watson. Engineers, historians, everyone ever fascinated by great spans will find this an endless source of information and interest. Dr. Steinman, recent recipient of Louis Levy Medal, is one of the great bridge architects, engineers of all time. His analysis of great bridges of history is both authoritative and easily followed. Greek, Roman, medieval, oriental bridges; modern works such as Brooklyn Bridge, Golden Gate Bridge, etc. described in terms of history, constructional principles, artistry, function. Most comprehensive, accurate semi-popular history of bridges in print in English. New, greatly revised, enlarged edition. 23 photographs, 26 line drawings. xvii + 401pp. 5⅜ x 8.   T431 Paperbound **$1.95**

CONCERNING THE NATURE OF THINGS, Sir William Bragg. Christmas lectures at Royal Society by Nobel laureate, dealing with atoms, gases, liquids, and various types of crystals. No scientific background is needed to understand this remarkably clear introduction to basic processes and aspects of modern science. "More interesting than any bestseller," London Morning Post. 32pp. of photos. 57 figures. xii + 232pp. 5⅜ x 8. **T31 Paperbound $1.35**

THE RISE OF THE NEW PHYSICS, A. d'Abro. Half million word exposition, formerly titled "The Decline of Mechanism," for readers not versed in higher mathematics. Only thorough explanation in everyday language of core of modern mathematical physical theory, treating both classical, modern views. Scientifically impeccable coverage of thought from Newtonian system through theories of Dirac, Heisenberg, Fermi's statistics. Combines history, exposition; broad but unified, detailed view, with constant comparison of classical, modern views. "A must for anyone doing serious study in the physical sciences," J. of the Franklin Inst. "Extraordinary faculty . . . to explain ideas and theories . . . in language of everyday life," Isis. Part I of set: philosophy of science, from practice of Newton, Maxwell, Poincaré, Einstein, etc. Modes of thought, experiment, causality, etc. Part II: 100 pp. on grammar, vocabulary of mathematics, discussions of functions, groups, series, Fourier series, etc. Remainder treats concrete, detailed coverage of both classical, quantum physics: analytic mechanics, Hamilton's principle, electromagnetic waves, thermodynamics, Brownian movement, special relativity, Bohr's atom, de Broglie's wave mechanics, Heisenberg's uncertainty, scores of other important topics. Covers discoveries, theories of d'Alembert, Born, Cantor, Debye, Euler, Foucault, Galois, Gauss, Hadamard, Kelvin, Kepler Laplace, Maxwell, Pauli, Rayleigh Volterra, Weyl, more than 180 others. 97 illustrations. ix + 982pp. 5⅜ x 8.
T3 Vol. 1 Paperbound $2.00
T4 Vol. II Paperbound $2.00

SPINNING TOPS AND GYROSCOPIC MOTION, John Perry. Well-known classic of science still unsurpassed for lucid, accurate, delightful exposition. How quasi-rigidity is induced in flexible, fluid bodies by rapid motions; why gyrostat falls, top rises; nature, effect of internal fluidity on rotating bodies; etc. Appendixes describe practical use of gyroscopes in ships, compasses, monorail transportation. 62 figures. 128pp. 5⅜ x 8.
T416 Paperbound $1.00

FOUNDATIONS OF PHYSICS, R. B. Lindsay, H. Margenau. Excellent bridge between semipopular and technical writings. Discussion of methods of physical description, construction of theory; valuable to physicist with elementary calculus. Gives meaning to data, tools of modern physics. Contents: symbolism, mathematical equations; space and time; foundations of mechanics; probability; physics, continua; electron theory; relativity; quantum mechanics; causality; etc. "Thorough and yet not overdetailed. Unreservedly recommended," Nature. Unabridged corrected edition. 35 illustrations. xi + 537pp. 5⅜ x 8. **S377 Paperbound $2.45**

FADS AND FALLACIES IN THE NAME OF SCIENCE, Martin Gardner. Formerly entitled "In the Name of Science," the standard account of various cults, quack systems, delusions which have masqueraded as science: hollow earth fanatics, orgone sex energy, dianetics, Atlantis, Forteanism, flying saucers, medical fallacies like zone therapy, etc. New chapter on Bridey Murphy, psionics, other recent manifestations. A fair reasoned appraisal of eccentric theory which provides excellent inoculation. "Should be read by everyone, scientist or non-scientist alike," R. T. Birge, Prof. Emeritus of Physics, Univ. of Calif; Former Pres., Amer. Physical Soc. x + 365pp. 5⅜ x 8. **T394 Paperbound $1.50**

ON MATHEMATICS AND MATHEMATICIANS, R. E. Moritz. A 10 year labor of love by discerning, discriminating Prof. Moritz, this collection conveys the full sense of mathematics and personalities of great mathematicians. Anecdotes, aphorisms, reminiscences, philosophies, definitions, speculations, biographical insights, etc. by great mathematicians, writers: Descartes, Mill, Locke, Kant, Coleridge, Whitehead, etc. Glimpses into lives of great mathematicians, from Archimedes to Euler, Gauss, Weierstrass. To mathematicians, a superb browsing-book. To laymen, exciting revelation of fullness of mathematics. Extensive cross index. 410pp. 5⅜ x 8. **T489 Paperbound $1.95**

GUIDE TO THE LITERATURE OF MATHEMATICS AND PHYSICS, N. G. Parke III. Over 5000 entries under approximately 120 major subject headings, of selected most important books, monographs, periodicals, articles in English, plus important works in German, French, Italian, Spanish, Russian (many recently available works). Covers every branch of physics, math, related engineering. Includes author, title, edition, publisher, place, date, number of volumes, number of pages. 40 page introduction on basic problems of research, study provides useful information on organization, use of libraries, psychology of learning, etc. Will save you hours of time. 2nd revised edition. Indices of authors, subjects. 464pp. 5⅜ x 8. **S447 Paperbound $2.49**

THE STRANGE STORY OF THE QUANTUM, An Account for the General Reader of the Growth of Ideas Underlying Our Present Atomic Knowledge, B. Hoffmann. Presents lucidly, expertly, with barest amount of mathematics, problems and theories which led to modern quantum physics. Begins with late 1800's when discrepancies were noticed; with illuminating analogies, examples, goes through concepts of Planck, Einstein, Pauli, Schroedinger, Dirac, Sommerfield, Feynman, etc. New postscript through 1958. "Of the books attempting an account of the history and contents of modern atomic physics which have come to my attention, this is the best," H. Margenau, Yale U., in Amer. J. of Physics. 2nd edition. 32 tables, illustrations. 275pp. 5⅜ x 8. **T518 Paperbound $1.45**

2

HISTORY OF SCIENCE
AND PHILOSOPHY OF SCIENCE

THE VALUE OF SCIENCE, Henri Poincaré. Many of most mature ideas of "last scientific universalist" for both beginning, advanced workers. Nature of scientific truth, whether order is innate in universe or imposed by man, logical thought vs. intuition (relating to Weierstrass, Lie, Riemann, etc), time and space (relativity, psychological time, simultaneity), Herz's concept of force, values within disciplines of Maxwell, Carnot, Mayer, Newton, Lorentz, etc. iii + 147pp. 5⅜ x 8.   S469 Paperbound **$1.35**

PHILOSOPHY AND THE PHYSICISTS, L. S. Stebbing. Philosophical aspects of modern science examined in terms of lively critical attack on ideas of Jeans, Eddington. Tasks of science, causality, determinism, probability, relation of world physics to that of everyday experience, philosophical significance of Planck-Bohr concept of discontinuous energy levels, inferences to be drawn from Uncertainty Principle, implications of "becoming" involved in 2nd law of thermodynamics, other problems posed by discarding of Laplacean determinism. 285pp. 5⅜ x 8.   T480 Paperbound **$1.65**

THE PRINCIPLES OF SCIENCE, A TREATISE ON LOGIC AND THE SCIENTIFIC METHOD, W. S. Jevons. Milestone in development of symbolic logic remains stimulating contribution to investigation of inferential validity in sciences. Treats inductive, deductive logic, theory of number, probability, limits of scientific method; significantly advances Boole's logic, contains detailed introduction to nature and methods of probability in physics, astronomy, everyday affairs, etc. In introduction, Ernest Nagel of Columbia U. says,"[Jevons] continues to be of interest as an attempt to articulate the logic of scientific inquiry." liii + 786pp. 5⅜ x 8.   S446 Paperbound **$2.98**

A HISTORY OF ASTRONOMY FROM THALES TO KEPLER, J. L. E. Dreyer. Only work in English to give complete history of cosmological views from prehistoric times to Kepler. Partial contents: Near Eastern astronomical systems, Early Greeks, Homocentric spheres of Euxodus, Epicycles, Ptolemaic system, Medieval cosmology, Copernicus, Kepler, much more. "Especially useful to teachers and students of the history of science . . . unsurpassed in its field," Isis. Formerly "A History of Planetary Systems from Thales to Kepler." Revised foreword by W. H. Stahl. xvii + 430pp. 5⅜ x 8.   S79 Paperbound **$1.98**

A CONCISE HISTORY OF MATHEMATICS, D. Struik. Lucid study of development of ideas, techniques, from Ancient Near East, Greece, Islamic science, Middle Ages, Renaissance, modern times. Important mathematicians described in detail. Treatment not anecdotal, but analytical development of ideas. Non-technical—no math training needed. "Rich in content, thoughtful in interpretations," U.S. Quarterly Booklist. 60 illustrations including Greek, Egyptian manuscripts, portraits of 31 mathematicians. 2nd edition. xix + 299pp. 5⅜ x 8.   S255 Paperbound **$1.75**

THE PHILOSOPHICAL WRITINGS OF PEIRCE, edited by Justus Buchler. A carefully balanced expositon of Peirce's complete system, written by Peirce himself. It covers such matters as scientific method, pure chance vs. law, symbolic logic, theory of signs, pragmatism, experiment, and other topics. "Excellent selection . . . gives more than adequate evidence of the range and greatness," Personalist. Formerly entitled "The Philosophy of Peirce." xvi + 368pp.   T217 Paperbound **$1.95**

SCIENCE AND METHOD, Henri Poincaré. Procedure of scientific discovery, methodology, experiment, idea-germination—processes by which discoveries come into being. Most significant and interesting aspects of development, application of ideas. Chapters cover selection of facts, chance, mathematical reasoning, mathematics and logic; Whitehead, Russell, Cantor, the new mechanics, etc. 288pp. 5⅜ x 8.   S222 Paperbound **$1.35**

SCIENCE AND HYPOTHESIS, Henri Poincaré. Creative psychology in science. How such concepts as number, magnitude, space, force, classical mechanics developed, how modern scientist uses them in his thought. Hypothesis in physics, theories of modern physics. Introduction by Sir James Larmor. "Few mathematicians have had the breadth of vision of Poincaré, and none is his superior in the gift of clear exposition," E. T. Bell. 272pp. 5⅜ x 8.   S221 Paperbound **$1.35**

ESSAYS IN EXPERIMENTAL LOGIC, John Dewey. Stimulating series of essays by one of most influential minds in American philosophy presents some of his most mature thoughts on wide range of subjects. Partial contents: Relationship between inquiry and experience; dependence of knowledge upon thought; character logic; judgments of practice, data, and meanings; stimuli of thought, etc. viii + 444pp. 5⅜ x 8.   T73 Paperbound **$1.95**

WHAT IS SCIENCE, Norman Campbell. Excellent introduction explains scientific method, role of mathematics, types of scientific laws. Contents: 2 aspects of science, science and nature, laws of chance, discovery of laws, explanation of laws, measurement and numerical laws, applications of science. 192pp. 5⅜ x 8.   S43 Paperbound **$1.25**

FROM EUCLID TO EDDINGTON: A STUDY OF THE CONCEPTIONS OF THE EXTERNAL WORLD, Sir Edmund Whittaker. Foremost British scientist traces development of theories of natural philosophy from western rediscovery of Euclid to Eddington, Einstein, Dirac, etc. 5 major divisions: Space, Time and Movement; Concepts of Classical Physics; Concepts of Quantum Mechanics; Eddington Universe. Contrasts inadequacy of classical physics to understand physical world with present day attempts of relativity, non-Euclidean geometry, space curvature, etc. 212pp. 5⅜ x 8. T491 Paperbound **$1.35**

THE ANALYSIS OF MATTER, Bertrand Russell. How do our senses accord with the new physics? This volume covers such topics as logical analysis of physics, prerelativity physics, causality, scientific inference, physics and perception, special and general relativity, Weyl's theory, tensors, invariants and their physical interpretation, periodicity and qualitative series. "The most thorough treatment of the subject that has yet been published," The Nation. Introduction by L. E. Denonn. 422pp. 5⅜ x 8. T231 Paperbound **$1.95**

LANGUAGE, TRUTH, AND LOGIC, A. Ayer. A clear introduction to the Vienna and Cambridge schools of Logical Positivism. Specific tests to evaluate validity of ideas, etc. Contents: function of philosophy, elimination of metaphysics, nature of analysis, a priori, truth and probability, etc. 10th printing. "I should like to have written it myself," Bertrand Russell. 160pp. 5⅜ x 8. T10 Paperbound **$1.25**

THE PSYCHOLOGY OF INVENTION IN THE MATHEMATICAL FIELD, J. Hadamard. Where do ideas come from? What role does the unconscious play? Are ideas best developed by mathematical reasoning, word reasoning, visualization? What are the methods used by Einstein, Poincaré, Galton, Riemann? How can these techniques be applied by others? One of the world's leading mathematicians discusses these and other questions. xiii + 145pp. 5⅜ x 8. T107 Paperbound **$1.25**

GUIDE TO PHILOSOPHY, C. E. M. Joad. By one of the ablest expositors of all time, this is not simply a history or a typological survey, but an examination of central problems in terms of answers afforded by the greatest thinkers: Plato, Aristotle, Scholastics, Leibniz, Kant, Whitehead, Russell, and many others. Especially valuable to persons in the physical sciences; over 100 pages devoted to Jeans, Eddington, and others, the philosophy of modern physics, scientific materialism, pragmatism, etc. Classified bibliography. 592pp. 5⅜ x 8. T50 Paperbound **$2.00**

SUBSTANCE AND FUNCTION, and EINSTEIN'S THEORY OF RELATIVITY, Ernst Cassirer. Two books bound as one. Cassirer establishes a philosophy of the exact sciences that takes into consideration new developments in mathematics, shows historical connections. Partial contents: Aristotelian logic, Mill's analysis, Helmholtz and Kronecker, Russell and cardinal numbers, Euclidean vs. non-Euclidean geometry, Einstein's relativity. Bibliography. Index. xxi + 464pp. 5⅜ x 8. T50 Paperbound **$2.00**

FOUNDATIONS OF GEOMETRY, Bertrand Russell. Nobel laureate analyzes basic problems in the overlap area between mathematics and philosophy: the nature of geometrical knowledge, the nature of geometry, and the applications of geometry to space. Covers history of non-Euclidean geometry, philosophic interpretations of geometry, especially Kant, projective and metrical geometry. Most interesting as the solution offered in 1897 by a great mind to a problem still current. New introduction by Prof. Morris Kline, N.Y. University. "Admirably clear, precise, and elegantly reasoned analysis," International Math. News. xii + 201pp. 5⅜ x 8. S233 Paperbound **$1.60**

THE NATURE OF PHYSICAL THEORY, P. W. Bridgman. How modern physics looks to a highly unorthodox physicist—a Nobel laureate. Pointing out many absurdities of science, demonstrating inadequacies of various physical theories, weighs and analyzes contributions of Einstein, Bohr, Heisenberg, many others. A non-technical consideration of correlation of science and reality. xi + 138pp. 5⅜ x 8. S33 Paperbound **$1.25**

EXPERIMENT AND THEORY IN PHYSICS, Max Born. A Nobel laureate examines the nature and value of the counterclaims of experiment and theory in physics. Synthetic versus analytical scientific advances are analyzed in works of Einstein, Bohr, Heisenberg, Planck, Eddington, Milne, others, by a fellow scientist. 44pp. 5⅜ x 8. S308 Paperbound **60¢**

A SHORT HISTORY OF ANATOMY AND PHYSIOLOGY FROM THE GREEKS TO HARVEY, Charles Singer. Corrected edition of "The Evolution of Anatomy." Classic traces anatomy, physiology from prescientific times through Greek, Roman periods, dark ages, Renaissance, to beginning of modern concepts. Centers on individuals, movements, that definitely advanced anatomical knowledge. Plato, Diocles, Erasistratus, Galen, da Vinci, etc. Special section on Vesalius. 20 plates. 270 extremely interesting illustrations of ancient, Medieval, enaissance, Oriental origin. xii + 209pp. 5⅜ x 8. T389 Paperbound **$1.75**

SPACE-TIME-MATTER, Hermann Weyl. "The standard treatise on the general theory of relativity," (Nature), by world renowned scientist. Deep, clear discussion of logical coherence of general theory, introducing all needed tools: Maxwell, analytical geometry, non-Euclidean geometry, tensor calculus, etc. Basis is classical space-time, before absorption of relativity. Contents: Euclidean space, mathematical form, metrical continuum, general theory, etc. 15 diagrams. xviii + 330pp. 5⅜ x 8. S267 Paperbound **$1.75**

4

DOVER SCIENCE BOOKS

MATTER AND MOTION, James Clerk Maxwell. Excellent exposition begins with simple particles, proceeds gradually to physical systems beyond complete analysis; motion, force, properties of centre of mass of material system; work, energy, gravitation, etc. Written with all Maxwell's original insights and clarity. Notes by E. Larmor. 17 diagrams. 178pp. 5⅜ x 8.   S188 Paperbound **$1.25**

PRINCIPLES OF MECHANICS, Heinrich Hertz. Last work by the great 19th century physicist is not only a classic, but of great interest in the logic of science. Creating a new system of mechanics based upon space, time, and mass, it returns to axiomatic analysis, understanding of the formal or structural aspects of science, taking into account logic, observation, a priori elements. Of great historical importance to Poincaré, Carnap, Einstein, Milne. A 20 page introduction by R. S. Cohen, Wesleyan University, analyzes the implications of Hertz's thought and the logic of science. 13 page introduction by Helmholtz. xlii + 274pp. 5⅜ x 8.   S316 Clothbound **$3.50**
                                                                        S317 Paperbound **$1.75**

FROM MAGIC TO SCIENCE, Charles Singer. A great historian examines aspects of science from Roman Empire through Renaissance. Includes perhaps best discussion of early herbals, penetrating physiological interpretation of "The Visions of Hildegarde of Bingen." Also examines Arabian, Galenic influences; Pythagoras' sphere, Paracelsus; reawakening of science under Leonardo da Vinci, Vesalius; Lorica of Gildas the Briton; etc. Frequent quotations with translations from contemporary manuscripts. Unabridged, corrected edition. 158 unusual illustrations from Classical, Medieval sources. xxvii + 365pp. 5⅜ x 8.
                                                                        T390 Paperbound **$2.00**

A HISTORY OF THE CALCULUS, AND ITS CONCEPTUAL DEVELOPMENT, Carl B. Boyer. Provides laymen, mathematicians a detailed history of the development of the calculus, from beginnings in antiquity to final elaboration as mathematical abstraction. Gives a sense of mathematics not as technique, but as habit of mind, in progression of ideas of Zeno, Plato, Pythagoras, Eudoxus, Arabic and Scholastic mathematicians, Newton, Leibniz, Taylor, Descartes, Euler, Lagrange, Cantor, Weierstrass, and others. This first comprehensive, critical history of the calculus was originally entitled "The Concepts of the Calculus." Foreword by R. Courant. 22 figures. 25 page bibliography. v + 364pp. 5⅜ x 8.
                                                                        S509 Paperbound **$2.00**

A DIDEROT PICTORIAL ENCYCLOPEDIA OF TRADES AND INDUSTRY, Manufacturing and the Technical Arts in Plates Selected from "L'Encyclopédie ou Dictionnaire Raisonné des Sciences, des Arts, et des Métiers" of Denis Diderot. Edited with text by C. Gillispie. First modern selection of plates from high-point of 18th century French engraving. Storehouse of technological information to historian of arts and science. Over 2,000 illustrations on 485 full page plates, most of them original size, show trades, industries of fascinating era in such great detail that modern reconstructions might be made of them. Plates teem with men, women, children performing thousands of operations; show sequence, general operations, closeups, details of machinery. Illustrates such important, interesting trades, industries as sowing, harvesting, beekeeping, tobacco processing, fishing, arts of war, mining, smelting, casting iron, extracting mercury, making gunpowder, cannons, bells, shoeing horses, tanning, papermaking, printing, dying, over 45 more categories. Professor Gillispie of Princeton supplies full commentary on all plates, identifies operations, tools, processes, etc. Material is presented in lively, lucid fashion. Of great interest to all studying history of science, technology. Heavy library cloth. 920pp. 9 x 12.
                                                                        T421 2 volume set **$18.50**

DE MAGNETE, William Gilbert. Classic work on magnetism, founded new science. Gilbert was first to use word "electricity," to recognize mass as distinct from weight, to discover effect of heat on magnetic bodies; invented an electroscope, differentiated between static electricity and magnetism, conceived of earth as magnet. This lively work, by first great experimental scientist, is not only a valuable historical landmark, but a delightfully easy to follow record of a searching, ingenious mind. Translated by P. F. Mottelay. 25 page biographical memoir. 90 figures. lix + 368pp. 5⅜ x 8.   S470 Paperbound **$2.00**

HISTORY OF MATHEMATICS, D. E. Smith. Most comprehensive, non-technical history of math in English. Discusses lives and works of over a thousand major, minor figures, with footnotes giving technical information outside book's scheme, and indicating disputed matters. Vol. I: A chronological examination, from primitive concepts through Egypt, Babylonia, Greece, the Orient, Rome, the Middle Ages, The Renaissance, and to 1900. Vol. II: The development of ideas in specific fields and problems, up through elementary calculus. "Marks an epoch . . . will modify the entire teaching of the history of science," George Sarton. 2 volumes, total of 510 illustrations, 1355pp. 5⅜ x 8. Set boxed in attractive container.   T429, 430 Paperbound, the set **$5.00**

THE PHILOSOPHY OF SPACE AND TIME, H. Reichenbach. An important landmark in development of empiricist conception of geometry, covering foundations of geometry, time theory, consequences of Einstein's relativity, including: relations between theory and observations; coordinate definitions; relations between topological and metrical properties of space; psychological problem of visual intuition of non-Euclidean structures; many more topics important to modern science and philosophy. Majority of ideas require only knowledge of intermediate math. "Still the best book in the field," Rudolf Carnap. Introduction by R. Carnap. 49 figures. xviii + 296pp. 5⅜ x 8.   S443 Paperbound **$2.00**

5

FOUNDATIONS OF SCIENCE: THE PHILOSOPHY OF THEORY AND EXPERIMENT, N. Campbell.
A critique of the most fundamental concepts of science, particularly physics. Examines why
certain propositions are accepted without question, demarcates science from philosophy,
etc. Part I analyzes presuppositions of scientific thought: existence of material world,
nature of laws, probability, etc; part 2 covers nature of experiment and applications of
mathematics: conditions for measurement, relations between numerical laws and theories,
error, etc. An appendix covers problems arising from relativity, force, motion, space,
time. A classic in its field. "A real grasp of what science is," Higher Educational Journal.
xiii + 565pp. 5⅝ x 8⅜.   S372 Paperbound **$2.95**

THE STUDY OF THE HISTORY OF MATHEMATICS and **THE STUDY OF THE HISTORY OF SCIENCE,
G. Sarton.** Excellent introductions, orientation, for beginning or mature worker. Describes
duty of mathematical historian, incessant efforts and genius of previous generations. Explains how today's discipline differs from previous methods. 200 item bibliography with
critical evaluations, best available biographies of modern mathematicians, best treatises
on historical methods is especially valuable. 10 illustrations. 2 volumes bound as one.
113pp. + 75pp. 5⅜ x 8.   T240 Paperbound **$1.25**

MATHEMATICAL PUZZLES

MATHEMATICAL PUZZLES OF SAM LOYD, selected and edited by **Martin Gardner.** 117 choice
puzzles by greatest American puzzle creator and innovator, from his famous "Cyclopedia
of Puzzles." All unique style, historical flavor of originals. Based on arithmetic, algebra,
probability, game theory, route tracing, topology, sliding block, operations research, geometrical dissection. Includes famous "14-15" puzzle which was national craze, "Horse of
a Different Color" which sold millions of copies. 120 line drawings, diagrams. Solutions.
xx + 167pp. 5⅜ x 8.   T498 Paperbound **$1.00**

SYMBOLIC LOGIC and THE GAME OF LOGIC, Lewis Carroll. "Symbolic Logic" is not concerned
with modern symbolic logic, but is instead a collection of over 380 problems posed with
charm and imagination, using the syllogism, and a fascinating diagrammatic method of
drawing conclusions. In "The Game of Logic" Carroll's whimsical imagination devises a
logical game played with 2 diagrams and counters (included) to manipulate hundreds of
tricky syllogisms. The final section, "Hit or Miss" is a lagniappe of 101 additional puzzles
in the delightful Carroll manner. Until this reprint edition, both of these books were rarities
costing up to $15 each. Symbolic Logic: Index. xxxi + 199pp. The Game of Logic: 96pp.
2 vols. bound as one. 5⅜ x 8.   T492 Paperbound **$1.50**

PILLOW PROBLEMS and A TANGLED TALE, Lewis Carroll. One of the rarest of all Carroll's
works, "Pillow Problems" contains 72 original math puzzles, all typically ingenious. Particularly fascinating are Carroll's answers which remain exactly as he thought them out,
reflecting his actual mental process. The problems in "A Tangled Tale" are in story form,
originally appearing as a monthly magazine serial. Carroll not only gives the solutions, but
uses answers sent in by readers to discuss wrong approaches and misleading paths, and
grades them for insight. Both of these books were rarities until this edition, "Pillow
Problems" costing up to $25, and "A Tangled Tale" $15. Pillow Problems: Preface and
Introduction by Lewis Carroll. xx + 109pp. A Tangled Tale: 6 illustrations. 152pp. Two vols.
bound as one. 5⅜ x 8.   T493 Paperbound **$1.50**

NEW WORD PUZZLES, G. L. Kaufman. 100 brand new challenging puzzles on words, combinations, never before published. Most are new types invented by author, for beginners
and experts both. Squares of letters follow chess moves to build words; symmetrical
designs made of synonyms; rhymed crostics; double word squares; syllable puzzles where
you fill in missing syllables instead of missing letter; many other types, all new. Solutions.
"Excellent," Recreation. 100 puzzles. 196 figures. vi + 122pp. 5⅜ x 8.
                                                                T344 Paperbound **$1.00**

MATHEMATICAL EXCURSIONS, H. A. Merrill. Fun, recreation, insights into elementary problem solving. Math expert guides you on by-paths not generally travelled in elementary math
courses—divide by inspection, Russian peasant multiplication; memory systems for pi; odd,
even magic squares; dyadic systems; square roots by geometry; Tchebichev's machine;
dozens more. Solutions to more difficult ones. "Brain stirring stuff . . . a classic," Genie.
50 illustrations. 145pp. 5⅜ x 8.   T350 Paperbound **$1.00**

THE BOOK OF MODERN PUZZLES, G. L. Kaufman. Over 150 puzzles, absolutely all new material based on same appeal as crosswords, deduction puzzles, but with different principles,
techniques. 2-minute teasers, word labyrinths, design, pattern, logic, observation puzzles,
puzzles testing ability to apply general knowledge to peculiar situations, many others.
Solutions. 116 illustrations. 192pp. 5⅜ x 8.   T143 Paperbound **$1.00**

MATHEMAGIC, MAGIC PUZZLES, AND GAMES WITH NUMBERS, R. V. Heath. Over 60 puzzles,
stunts, on properties of numbers. Easy techniques for multiplying large numbers mentally,
identifying unknown numbers, finding date of any day in any year. Includes The Lost Digit,
3 Acrobats, Psychic Bridge, magic squares, triangles, cubes, others not easily found elsewhere. Edited by J. S. Meyer. 76 illustrations. 128pp. 5⅜ x 8. T110 Paperbound **$1.00**

PUZZLE QUIZ AND STUNT FUN, J. Meyer. 238 high-priority puzzles, stunts, tricks—math puzzles like The Clever Carpenter, Atom Bomb, Please Help Alice; mysteries, deductions like The Bridge of Sighs, Secret Code; observation puzzlers like The American Flag, Playing Cards, Telephone Dial; over 200 others with magic squares, tongue twisters, puns, anagrams. Solutions. Revised, enlarged edition of "Fun-To-Do." Over 100 illustrations. 238 puzzles, stunts, tricks. 256pp. 5⅜ x 8. T337 Paperbound $1.00

101 PUZZLES IN THOUGHT AND LOGIC, C. R. Wylie, Jr. For readers who enjoy challenge, stimulation of logical puzzles without specialized math or scientific knowledge. Problems entirely new, range from relatively easy to brainteasers for hours of subtle entertainment. Detective puzzles, find the lying fisherman, how a blind man identifies color by logic, many more. Easy-to-understand introduction to logic of puzzle solving and general scientific method. 128pp. 5⅜ x 8. T367 Paperbound $1.00

CRYPTANALYSIS, H. F. Gaines. Standard elementary, intermediate text for serious students. Not just old material, but much not generally known, except to experts. Concealment, Transposition, Substitution ciphers; Vigenere, Kasiski, Playfair, multafid, dozens of other techniques. Formerly "Elementary Cryptanalysis." Appendix with sequence charts, letter frequencies in English, 5 other languages, English word frequencies. Bibliography. 167 codes. New to this edition: solutions to codes. vi + 230pp. 5⅜ x 8⅜. T97 Paperbound $1.95

CRYPTOGRAPHY, L. D. Smith. Excellent elementary introduction to enciphering, deciphering secret writing. Explains transposition, substitution ciphers; codes; solutions; geometrical patterns, route transcription, columnar transposition, other methods. Mixed cipher systems; single, polyalphabetical substitutions; mechanical devices; Vigenere; etc. Enciphering Japanese; explanation of Baconian biliteral cipher; frequency tables. Over 150 problems. Bibliography. Index. 164pp. 5⅜ x 8. T247 Paperbound $1.00

MATHEMATICS, MAGIC AND MYSTERY, M. Gardner. Card tricks, metal mathematics, stage mind-reading, other "magic" explained as applications of probability, sets, number theory, etc. Creative examination of laws, applications. Scores of new tricks, insights. 115 sections on cards, dice, coins; vanishing tricks, many others. No sleight of hand—math guarantees success. "Could hardly get more entertainment . . . easy to follow," Mathematics Teacher. 115 illustrations. xii + 174pp. 5⅜ x 8. T335 Paperbound $1.00

AMUSEMENTS IN MATHEMATICS, H. E. Dudeney. Foremost British originator of math puzzles, always witty, intriguing, paradoxical in this classic. One of largest collections. More than 430 puzzles, problems, paradoxes. Mazes, games, problems on number manipulations, unicursal, other route problems, puzzles on measuring, weighing, packing, age, kinship, chessboards, joiners', crossing river, plane figure dissection, many others. Solutions. More than 450 illustrations. viii + 258pp. 5⅜ x 8. T473 Paperbound $1.25

THE CANTERBURY PUZZLES H. E. Dudeney. Chaucer's pilgrims set one another problems in story form. Also Adventures of the Puzzle Club, the Strange Escape of the King's Jester, the Monks of Riddlewell, the Squire's Christmas Puzzle Party, others. All puzzles are original, based on dissecting plane figures, arithmetic, algebra, elementary calculus, other branches of mathematics, and purely logical ingenuity. "The limit of ingenuity and intricacy," The Observer. Over 110 puzzles, full solutions. 150 illustrations. viii + 225 pp. 5⅜ x 8. T474 Paperbound $1.25

MATHEMATICAL PUZZLES FOR BEGINNERS AND ENTHUSIASTS, G. Mott-Smith. 188 puzzles to test mental agility. Inference, interpretation, algebra, dissection of plane figures, geometry, properties of numbers, decimation, permutations, probability, all are in these delightful problems. Includes the Odic Force, How to Draw an Ellipse, Spider's Cousin, more than 180 others. Detailed solutions. Appendix with square roots, triangular numbers, primes, etc. 135 illustrations. 2nd revised edition. 248pp. 5⅜ x 8. T198 Paperbound $1.00

MATHEMATICAL RECREATIONS, M. Kraitchik. Some 250 puzzles, problems, demonstrations of recreation mathematics on relatively advanced level. Unusual historical problems from Greek, Medieval, Arabic, Hindu sources; modern problems on "mathematics without numbers," geometry, topology, arithmetic, etc. Pastimes derived from figurative, Mersenne, Fermat numbers: fairy chess; latruncles: reversi; etc. Full solutions. Excellent insights into special fields of math. "Strongly recommended to all who are interested in the lighter side of mathematics," Mathematical Gaz. 181 illustrations. 330pp. 5⅜ x 8. T163 Paperbound $1.75

FICTION

FLATLAND, E. A. Abbott. A perennially popular science-fiction classic about life in a 2-dimensional world, and the impingement of higher dimensions. Political, satiric, humorous, moral overtones. This land where women are straight lines and the lowest and most dangerous classes are isosceles triangles with 3° vertices conveys brilliantly a feeling for many concepts of modern science. 7th edition. New introduction by Banesh Hoffmann. 128pp. 5⅜ x 8. T1 Paperbound $1.00

SEVEN SCIENCE FICTION NOVELS OF H. G. WELLS. Complete texts, unabridged, of seven of Wells' greatest novels: The War of the Worlds, The Invisible Man, The Island of Dr. Moreau, The Food of the Gods, First Men in the Moon, In the Days of the Comet, The Time Machine. Still considered by many experts to be the best science-fiction ever written, they will offer amusements and instruction to the scientific minded reader. "The great master," Sky and Telescope. 1051pp. 5⅜ x 8.   T264 Clothbound **$3.95**

28 SCIENCE FICTION STORIES OF H. G. WELLS. Unabridged! This enormous omnibus contains 2 full length novels—Men Like Gods, Star Begotten—plus 26 short stories of space, time, invention, biology, etc. The Crystal Egg, The Country of the Blind, Empire of the Ants, The Man Who Could Work Miracles, Aepyornis Island, A Story of the Days to Come, and 20 others "A master . . . not surpassed by . . . writers of today," The English Journal. 915pp. 5⅜ x 8.   T265 Clothbound **$3.95**

FIVE ADVENTURE NOVELS OF H. RIDER HAGGARD. All the mystery and adventure of darkest Africa captured accurately by a man who lived among Zulus for years, who knew African ethnology, folkways as did few of his contemporaries. They have been regarded as examples of the very best high adventure by such critics as Orwell, Andrew Lang, Kipling. Contents: She, King Solomon's Mines, Allan Quatermain, Allan's Wife, Maiwa's Revenge. "Could spin a yarn so full of suspense and color that you couldn't put the story down," Sat. Review. 821pp. 5⅜ x 8.   T108 Clothbound **$3.95**

CHESS AND CHECKERS

LEARN CHESS FROM THE MASTERS, Fred Reinfeld. Easiest, most instructive way to improve your game—play 10 games against such masters as Marshall, Znosko-Borovsky, Bronstein, Najdorf, etc., with each move graded by easy system. Includes ratings for alternate moves possible. Games selected for interest, clarity, easily isolated principles. Covers Ruy Lopez, Dutch Defense, Vienna Game openings; subtle, intricate middle game variations; all-important end game. Full annotations. Formerly "Chess by Yourself." 91 diagrams. viii + 144pp. 5⅜ x 8.   T362 Paperbound **$1.00**

REINFELD ON THE END GAME IN CHESS, Fred Reinfeld. Analyzes 62 end games by Alekhine, Flohr, Tarrasch, Morphy, Capablanca, Rubinstein, Lasker, Reshevsky, other masters. Only 1st rate book with extensive coverage of error—tell exactly what is wrong with each move you might have made. Centers around transitions from middle play to end play. King and pawn, minor pieces, queen endings; blockage, weak, passed pawns, etc. "Excellent . . . a boon," Chess Life. Formerly "Practical End Play." 62 figures. vi + 177pp. 5⅜ x 8.   T417 Paperbound **$1.25**

HYPERMODERN CHESS as developed in the games of its greatest exponent, ARON NIMZO-VICH, edited by Fred Reinfeld. An intensely original player, analyst, Nimzovich's approaches startled, often angered the chess world. This volume, designed for the average player, shows how his iconoclastic methods won him victories over Alekhine, Lasker, Marshall, Rubinstein, Spielmann, others, and infused new life into the game. Use his methods to startle opponents, invigorate play. "Annotations and introductions to each game . . . are excellent," Times (London). 180 diagrams. viii + 220pp. 5⅜ x 8.   T448 Paperbound **$1.35**

THE ADVENTURE OF CHESS, Edward Lasker. Lively reader, by one of America's finest chess masters, including: history of chess, from ancient Indian 4-handed game of Chaturanga to great players of today; such delights and oddities as Maelzel's chess-playing automaton that beat Napoleon 3 times; etc. One of most valuable features is author's personal recollections of men he has played against—Nimzovich, Emanuel Lasker, Capablanca, Alekhine, etc. Discussion of chess-playing machines (newly revised). 5 page chess primer. 11 illustrations. 53 diagrams. 296pp. 5⅜ x 8.   S510 Paperbound **$1.45**

THE ART OF CHESS, James Mason. Unabridged reprinting of latest revised edition of most famous general study ever written. Mason, early 20th century master, teaches beginning, intermediate player over 90 openings; middle game, end game, to see more moves ahead, to plan purposefully, attack, sacrifice, defend, exchange, govern general strategy. "Classic . . . one of the clearest and best developed studies," Publishers Weekly. Also included, a complete supplement by F. Reinfeld, "How Do You Play Chess?", invaluable to beginners for its lively question-and-answer method. 448 diagrams. 1947 Reinfeld-Bernstein text. Bibliography. xvi + 340pp. 5⅜ x 8.   T463 Paperbound **$1.85**

MORPHY'S GAMES OF CHESS, edited by P. W. Sergeant. Put boldness into your game by flowing brilliant, forceful moves of the greatest chess player of all time. 300 of Morphy's best games, carefully annotated to reveal principles. 54 classics against masters like Anderssen, Harrwitz, Bird, Paulsen, and others. 52 games at odds; 54 blindfold games; plus over 100 others. Follow his interpretation of Dutch Defense, Evans Gambit, Giuoco Piano, Ruy Lopez, many more. Unabridged reissue of latest revised edition. New introduction by F. Reinfeld. Annotations, introduction by Sergeant. 235 diagrams. x + 352pp. 5⅜ x 8.   T386 Paperbound **$1.75**

WIN AT CHECKERS, M. Hopper. (Formerly "Checkers.") Former World's Unrestricted Checker Champion discusses principles of game, expert's shots, traps, problems for beginner, standard openings, locating best move, end game, opening "blitzkrieg" moves to draw when behind, etc. Over 100 detailed questions, answers anticipate problems. Appendix. 75 problems with solutions, diagrams. 79 figures. xi + 107pp. 5⅜ x 8. T363 Paperbound **$1.00**

HOW TO FORCE CHECKMATE, Fred Reinfeld. If you have trouble finishing off your opponent, here is a collection of lightning strokes and combinations from actual tournament play. Starts with 1-move checkmates, works up to 3-move mates. Develops ability to lock ahead, gain new insights into combinations, complex or deceptive positions; ways to estimate weaknesses, strengths of you and your opponent. "A good deal of amusement and instruction," Times, (London). 300 diagrams. Solutions to all positions. Formerly "Challenge to Chess Players." 111pp. 5⅜ x 8. T417 Paperbound **$1.25**

A TREASURY OF CHESS LORE, edited by Fred Reinfeld. Delightful collection of anecdotes, short stories, aphorisms by, about masters; poems, accounts of games, tournaments, photographs; hundreds of humorous, pithy, satirical, wise, historical episodes, comments, word portraits. Fascinating "must" for chess players; revealing and perhaps seductive to those who wonder what their friends see in game. 49 photographs (14 full page plates). 12 diagrams. xi + 306pp. 5⅜ x 8. T458 Paperbound **$1.75**

WIN AT CHESS, Fred Reinfeld. 300 practical chess situations, to sharpen your eye, test skill against masters. Start with simple examples, progress at own pace to complexities. This selected series of crucial moments in chess will stimulate imagination, develop stronger, more versatile game. Simple grading system enables you to judge progress. "Extensive use of diagrams is a great attraction," Chess. 300 diagrams. Notes, solutions to every situation. Formerly "Chess Quiz." vi + 120pp. 5⅜ x 8. T433 Paperbound **$1.00**

MATHEMATICS:
ELEMENTARY TO INTERMEDIATE

HOW TO CALCULATE QUICKLY, H. Sticker. Tried and true method to help mathematics of everyday life. Awakens "number sense"—ability to see relationships between numbers as whole quantities. A serious course of over 9000 problems and their solutions through techniques not taught in schools: left-to-right multiplications, new fast division, etc. 10 minutes a day will double or triple calculation speed. Excellent for scientist at home in higher math, but dissatisfied with speed and accuracy in lower math. 256pp. 5 x 7¼.
Paperbound **$1.00**

FAMOUS PROBLEMS OF ELEMENTARY GEOMETRY, Felix Klein. Expanded version of 1894 Easter lectures at Göttingen. 3 problems of classical geometry: squaring the circle, trisecting angle, doubling cube, considered with full modern implications: transcendental numbers, pi, etc. "A modern classic . . . no knowledge of higher mathematics is required," Scientia. Notes by R. Archibald. 16 figures. xi + 92pp. 5⅜ x 8. T298 Paperbound **$1.00**

HIGHER MATHEMATICS FOR STUDENTS OF CHEMISTRY AND PHYSICS, J. W. Mellor. Practical, not abstract, building problems out of familiar laboratory material. Covers differential calculus, coordinate, analytical geometry, functions, integral calculus, infinite series, numerical equations, differential equations, Fourier's theorem probability, theory of errors, calculus of variations, determinants. "If the reader is not familiar with this book, it will repay him to examine it," Chem. and Engineering News. 800 problems. 189 figures. xxi + 641pp. 5⅜ x 8. S193 Paperbound **$2.25**

TRIGONOMETRY REFRESHER FOR TECHNICAL MEN, A. A. Klaf. 913 detailed questions, answers cover most important aspects of plane, spherical trigonometry—particularly useful in clearing up difficulties in special areas. Part I: plane trig, angles, quadrants, functions, graphical representation, interpolation, equations, logs, solution of triangle, use of slide rule, etc. Next 188 pages discuss applications to navigation, surveying, elasticity, architecture, other special fields. Part 3: spherical trig, applications to terrestrial, astronomical problems. Methods of time-saving, simplification of principal angles, make book most useful. 913 questions answered. 1738 problems, answers to odd numbers. 494 figures. 24 pages of formulas, functions. x + 629pp. 5⅜ x 8. T371 Paperbound **$2.00**

CALCULUS REFRESHER FOR TECHNICAL MEN, A. A. Klaf. 756 questions examine most important aspects of integral, differential calculus. Part I: simple differential calculus, constants, variables, functions, increments, logs, curves, etc. Part 2: fundamental ideas of integrations, inspection, substitution, areas, volumes, mean value, double, triple integration, etc. Practical aspects stressed. 50 pages illustrate applications to specific problems of civil, nautical engineering, electricity, stress, strain, elasticity, similar fields. 756 questions answered. 566 problems, mostly answered. 36pp. of useful constants, formulas. v + 431pp. 5⅜ x 8. T370 Paperbound **$2.00**

MONOGRAPHS ON TOPICS OF MODERN MATHEMATICS, edited by J. W. A. Young. Advanced mathematics for persons who have forgotten, or not gone beyond, high school algebra. 9 monographs on foundation of geometry, modern pure geometry, non-Euclidean geometry, fundamental propositions of algebra, algebraic equations, functions, calculus, theory of numbers, etc. Each monograph gives proofs of important results, and descriptions of leading methods, to provide wide coverage. "Of high merit," Scientific American. New introduction by Prof. M. Kline, N.Y. Univ. 100 diagrams. xvi + 416pp. 6⅛ x 9¼.
S289 Paperbound **$2.00**

MATHEMATICS IN ACTION, O. G. Sutton. Excellent middle level application of mathematics to study of universe, demonstrates how math is applied to ballistics, theory of computing machines, waves, wave-like phenomena, theory of fluid flow, meteorological problems, statistics, flight, similar phenomena. No knowledge of advanced math required. Differential equations, Fourier series, group concepts, Eigenfunctions, Planck's constant, airfoil theory, and similar topics explained so clearly in everyday language that almost anyone can derive benefit from reading this even if much of high-school math is forgotten. 2nd edition. 88 figures. viii + 236pp. 5⅜ x 8.
T450 Clothbound **$3.50**

ELEMENTARY MATHEMATICS FROM AN ADVANCED STANDPOINT, Felix Klein. Classic text, an outgrowth of Klein's famous integration and survey course at Göttingen. Using one field to interpret, adjust another, it covers basic topics in each area, with extensive analysis. Especially valuable in areas of modern mathematics. "A great mathematician, inspiring teacher, . . . deep insight," Bul., Amer. Math Soc.

Vol. I. ARITHMETIC, ALGEBRA, ANALYSIS. Introduces concept of function immediately, enlivens discussion with graphical, geometric methods. Partial contents: natural numbers, special properties, complex numbers. Real equations with real unknowns, complex quantities. Logarithmic, exponential functions, infinitesimal calculus. Transcendence of e and pi, theory of assemblages. Index. 125 figures. ix + 274pp. 5⅜ x 8.
S151 Paperbound **$1.75**

Vol. II. GEOMETRY. Comprehensive view, accompanies space perception inherent in geometry with analytic formulas which facilitate precise formulation. Partial contents: Simplest geometric manifold; line segments, Grassman determinant principles, classication of configurations of space. Geometric transformations: affine, projective, higher point transformations, theory of the imaginary. Systematic discussion of geometry and its foundations. 141 illustrations. ix + 214pp. 5⅜ x 8.
S151 Paperbound **$1.75**

A TREATISE ON PLANE AND ADVANCED TRIGONOMETRY, E. W. Hobson. Extraordinarily wide coverage, going beyond usual college level, one of few works covering advanced trig in full detail. By a great expositor with unerring anticipation of potentially difficult points. Includes circular functions; expansion of functions of multiple angle; trig tables; relations between sides, angles of triangles; complex numbers; etc. Many problems fully solved. "The best work on the subject," Nature. Formerly entitled "A Treatise on Plane Trigonometry." 689 examples. 66 figures. xvi + 383pp. 5⅜ x 8.
S353 Paperbound **$1.95**

NON-EUCLIDEAN GEOMETRY, Roberto Bonola. The standard coverage of non-Euclidean geometry. Examines from both a historical and mathematical point of view geometries which have arisen from a study of Euclid's 5th postulate on parallel lines. Also included are complete texts, translated, of Bolyai's "Theory of Absolute Space," Lobachevsky's "Theory of Parallels." 180 diagrams. 431pp. 5⅜ x 8.
S27 Paperbound **$1.95**

GEOMETRY OF FOUR DIMENSIONS, H. P. Manning. Unique in English as a clear, concise introduction. Treatment is synthetic, mostly Euclidean, though in hyperplanes and hyperspheres at infinity, non-Euclidean geometry is used. Historical introduction. Foundations of 4-dimensional geometry. Perpendicularity, simple angles. Angles of planes, higher order. Symmetry, order, motion; hyperpyramids, hypercones, hyperspheres; figures with parallel elements; volume, hypervolume in space; regular polyhedroids. Glossary. 78 figures. ix + 348pp. 5⅜ x 8.
S182 Paperbound **$1.95**

MATHEMATICS: INTERMEDIATE TO ADVANCED

GEOMETRY (EUCLIDEAN AND NON-EUCLIDEAN)

THE GEOMETRY OF RENÉ DESCARTES. With this book, Descartes founded analytical geometry. Original French text, with Descartes's own diagrams, and excellent Smith-Latham translation. Contains: Problems the Construction of Which Requires only Straight Lines and Circles; On the Nature of Curved Lines; On the Construction of Solid or Supersolid Problems. Diagrams. 258pp. 5⅜ x 8.
S68 Paperbound **$1.50**

THE WORKS OF ARCHIMEDES, edited by T. L. Heath. All the known works of the great Greek mathematician, including the recently discovered Method of Archimedes. Contains: On Sphere and Cylinder, Measurement of a Circle, Spirals, Conoids, Spheroids, etc. Definitive edition of greatest mathematical intellect of ancient world. 186 page study by Heath discusses Archimedes and history of Greek mathematics. 563pp. 5⅜ x 8. S9 Paperbound **$2.00**

COLLECTED WORKS OF BERNARD RIEMANN. Important sourcebook, first to contain complete text of 1892 "Werke" and the 1902 supplement, unabridged. 31 monographs, 3 complete lecture courses, 15 miscellaneous papers which have been of enormous importance in relativity, topology, theory of complex variables, other areas of mathematics. Edited by R. Dedekind, H. Weber, M. Noether, W. Wirtinger. German text; English introduction by Hans Lewy. 690pp. 5⅜ x 8. S226 Paperbound **$2.85**

THE THIRTEEN BOOKS OF EUCLID'S ELEMENTS, edited by Sir Thomas Heath. Definitive edition of one of very greatest classics of Western world. Complete translation of Heiberg text, plus spurious Book XIV. 150 page introduction on Greek, Medieval mathematics, Euclid, texts, commentators, etc. Elaborate critical apparatus parallels text, analyzing each definition, postulate, proposition, covering textual matters, refutations, supports, extrapolations, etc. This is the full Euclid. Unabridged reproduction of Cambridge U. 2nd edition. 3 volumes. 995 figures. 1426pp. 5⅜ x 8. S88, 89, 90, 3 volume set, paperbound **$6.00**

AN INTRODUCTION TO GEOMETRY OF N DIMENSIONS, D. M. Y. Sommerville. Presupposes no previous knowledge of field. Only book in English devoted exclusively to higher dimensional geometry. Discusses fundamental ideas of incidence, parallelism, perpendicularity, angles between linear space, enumerative geometry, analytical geometry from projective and metric views, polytopes, elementary ideas in analysis situs, content of hyperspacial figures. 60 diagrams. 196pp. 5⅜ x 8. S494 Paperbound **$1.50**

ELEMENTS OF NON-EUCLIDEAN GEOMETRY, D. M. Y. Sommerville. Unique in proceeding step-by-step. Requires only good knowledge of high-school geometry and algebra, to grasp elementary hyperbolic, elliptic, analytic non-Euclidean Geometries; space curvature and its implications; radical axes; homopethic centres and systems of circles; parataxy and parallelism; Gauss' proof of defect area theorem; much more, with exceptional clarity. 126 problems at chapter ends. 133 figures. xvi + 274pp. 5⅜ x 8. S460 Paperbound **$1.50**

THE FOUNDATIONS OF EUCLIDEAN GEOMETRY, H. G. Forder. First connected, rigorous account in light of modern analysis, establishing propositions without recourse to empiricism, without multiplying hypotheses. Based on tools of 19th and 20th century mathematicians, who made it possible to remedy gaps and complexities, recognize problems not earlier discerned. Begins with important relationship of number systems in geometrical figures. Considers classes, relations, linear order, natural numbers, axioms for magnitudes, groups, quasi-fields, fields, non-Archimedian systems, the axiom system (at length), particular axioms (two chapters on the Parallel Axioms), constructions, congruence, similarity, etc. Lists: axioms employed, constructions, symbols in frequent use. 295pp. 5⅜ x 8.
S481 Paperbound **$2.00**

CALCULUS, FUNCTION THEORY (REAL AND COMPLEX), FOURIER THEORY

FIVE VOLUME "THEORY OF FUNCTIONS" SET BY KONRAD KNOPP. Provides complete, readily followed account of theory of functions. Proofs given concisely, yet without sacrifice of completeness or rigor. These volumes used as texts by such universities as M.I.T., Chicago, N.Y. City College, many others. "Excellent introduction . . . remarkably readable, concise, clear, rigorous," J. of the American Statistical Association.

ELEMENTS OF THE THEORY OF FUNCTIONS, Konrad Knopp. Provides background for further volumes in this set, or texts on similar level. Partial contents: Foundations, system of complex numbers and Gaussian plane of numbers, Riemann sphere of numbers, mapping by linear functions, normal forms, the logarithm, cyclometric functions, binomial series. "Not only for the young student, but also for the student who knows all about what is in it," Mathematical Journal. 140pp. 5⅜ x 8. S154 Paperbound **$1.35**

THEORY OF FUNCTIONS, PART I, Konrad Knopp. With volume II, provides coverage of basic concepts and theorems. Partial contents: numbers and points, functions of a complex variable, integral of a continuous function, Cauchy's intergral theorem, Cauchy's integral formulae, series with variable terms, expansion and analytic function in a power series, analytic continuation and complete definition of analytic functions, Laurent expansion, types of singularities. vii + 146pp. 5⅜ x 8. S156 Paperbound **$1.35**

THEORY OF FUNCTIONS, PART II, Konrad Knopp. Application and further development of general theory, special topics. Single valued functions, entire, Weierstrass. Meromorphic functions: Mittag-Leffler. Periodic functions. Multiple valued functions. Riemann surfaces. Algebraic functions. Analytical configurations, Riemann surface. x + 150pp. 5⅜ x 8.
S157 Paperbound **$1.35**

PROBLEM BOOK IN THE THEORY OF FUNCTIONS, VOLUME I, Konrad Knopp. Problems in elementary theory, for use with Knopp's "Theory of Functions," or any other text. Arranged according to increasing difficulty. Fundamental concepts, sequences of numbers and infinite series, complex variable, integral theorems, development in series, conformal mapping. Answers. viii + 126pp. 5⅜ x 8.
S 158 **Paperbound $1.35**

PROBLEM BOOK IN THE THEORY OF FUNCTIONS, VOLUME II, Konrad Knopp. Advanced theory of functions, to be used with Knopp's "Theory of Functions," or comparable text. Singularities, entire and meromorphic functions, periodic, analytic, continuation, multiple-valued functions, Riemann surfaces, conformal mapping. Includes section of elementary problems. "The difficult task of selecting . . . problems just within the reach of the beginner is here masterfully accomplished," AM. MATH. SOC. Answers. 138pp. 5⅜ x 8.
S159 Paperbound **$1.35**

ADVANCED CALCULUS, E. B. Wilson. Still recognized as one of most comprehensive, useful texts. Immense amount of well-represented, fundamental material, including chapters on vector functions, ordinary differential equations, special functions, calculus of variations, etc., which are excellent introductions to these areas. Requires only one year of calculus. Over 1300 exercises cover both pure math and applications to engineering and physical problems. Ideal reference, refresher. 54 page introductory review. ix + 566pp. 5⅜ x 8.
S504 Paperbound **$2.45**

LECTURES ON THE THEORY OF ELLIPTIC FUNCTIONS, H. Hancock. Reissue of only book in English with so extensive a coverage, especially of Abel, Jacobi, Legendre, Weierstrass, Hermite, Liouville, and Riemann. Unusual fullness of treatment, plus applications as well as theory in discussing universe of elliptic integrals, originating in works of Abel and Jacobi. Use is made of Riemann to provide most general theory. 40-page table of formulas. 76 figures. xxiii + 498pp. 5⅜ x 8.
S483 Paperbound **$2.55**

THEORY OF FUNCTIONALS AND OF INTEGRAL AND INTEGRO-DIFFERENTIAL EQUATIONS, Vito Volterra. Unabridged republication of only English translation. General theory of functions depending on continuous set of values of another function. Based on author's concept of transition from finite number of variables to a continually infinite number. Includes much material on calculus of variations. Begins with fundamentals, examines generalization of analytic functions, functional derivative equations, applications, other directions of theory, etc. New introduction by G. C. Evans. Biography, criticism of Volterra's work by E. Whittaker. xxxx + 226pp. 5⅜ x 8.
S502 Paperbound **$1.75**

AN INTRODUCTION TO FOURIER METHODS AND THE LAPLACE TRANSFORMATION, Philip Franklin. Concentrates on essentials, gives broad view, suitable for most applications. Requires only knowledge of calculus. Covers complex qualities with methods of computing elementary functions for complex values of argument and finding approximations by charts; Fourier series; harmonic anaylsis; much more. Methods are related to physical problems of heat flow, vibrations, electrical transmission, electromagnetic radiation, etc. 828 problems, answers. Formerly entitled "Fourier Methods." x + 289pp. 5⅜ x 8.
S452 Paperbound **$1.75**

THE ANALYTICAL THEORY OF HEAT, Joseph Fourier. This book, which revolutionized mathematical physics, has been used by generations of mathematicians and physicists interested in heat or application of Fourier integral. Covers cause and reflection of rays of heat, radiant heating, heating of closed spaces, use of trigonometric series in theory of heat, Fourier integral, etc. Translated by Alexander Freeman. 20 figures. xxii + 466pp. 5⅜ x 8.
S93 Paperbound **$2.00**

ELLIPTIC INTEGRALS, H. Hancock. Invaluable in work involving differential equations with cubics, quatrics under root sign, where elementary calculus methods are inadequate. Practical solutions to problems in mathematics, engineering, physics; differential equations requiring integration of Lamé's, Briot's, or Bouquet's equations; determination of arc of ellipse, hyperbola, lemsicate; solutions of problems in elastics; motion of a projectile under resistance varying as the cube of the velocity; pendulums; more. Exposition in accordance with Legendre-Jacobi theory. Rigorous discussion of Legendre transformations. 20 figures. 5 place table. 104pp. 5⅜ x 8.
S484 Paperbound **$1.25**

THE TAYLOR SERIES, AN INTRODUCTION TO THE THEORY OF FUNCTIONS OF A COMPLEX VARIABLE, P. Dienes. Uses Taylor series to approach theory of functions, using ordinary calculus only, except in last 2 chapters. Starts with introduction to real variable and complex algebra, derives properties of infinite series, complex differentiation, integration, etc. Covers biuniform mapping, overconvergence and gap theorems, Taylor series on its circle of convergence, etc. Unabridged corrected reissue of first edition. 186 examples, many fully worked out. 67 figures. xii + 555pp. 5⅜ x 8.
S391 Paperbound **$2.75**

LINEAR INTEGRAL EQUATIONS, W. V. Lovitt. Systematic survey of general theory, with some application to differential equations, calculus of variations, problems of math, physics. Includes: integral equation of 2nd kind by successive substitutions; Fredholm's equation as ratio of 2 integral series in lambda, applications of the Fredholm theory, Hilbert-Schmidt theory of symmetric kernels, application, etc. Neumann, Dirichlet, vibratory problems. ix + 253pp. 5⅜ x 8.
S175 Clothbound **$3.50**
S176 Paperbound **$1.60**

DOVER SCIENCE BOOKS

DICTIONARY OF CONFORMAL REPRESENTATIONS, H. Kober. Developed by British Admiralty to solve Laplace's equation in 2 dimensions. Scores of geometrical forms and transformations for electrical engineers, Joukowski aerofoil for aerodynamics, Schwartz-Christoffel transformations for hydro-dynamics, transcendental functions. Contents classified according to analytical functions describing transformations with corresponding regions. Glossary. Topological index. 447 diagrams. 6⅛ x 9¼.   ·S160 Paperbound **$2.00**

ELEMENTS OF THE THEORY OF REAL FUNCTIONS, J. E. Littlewood. Based on lectures at Trinity College, Cambridge, this book has proved extremely successful in introducing graduate students to modern theory of functions. Offers full and concise coverage of classes and cardinal numbers, well ordered series, other types of series, and elements of the theory of sets of points. 3rd revised edition. vii + 71pp. 5⅜ x 8.   S171 Clothbound **$2.85**
                                                                           S172 Paperbound **$1.25**

INFINITE SEQUENCES AND SERIES, Konrad Knopp. 1st publication in any language. Excellent introduction to 2 topics of modern mathematics, designed to give student background to penetrate further alone. Sequences and sets, real and complex numbers, etc. Functions of a real and complex variable. Sequences and series. Infinite series. Convergent power series. Expansion of elementary functions. Numerical evaluation of series. v + 186pp. 5⅜ x 8.
                                                                           S152 Clothbound **$3.50**
                                                                           S153 Paperbound **$1.75**

THE THEORY AND FUNCTIONS OF A REAL VARIABLE AND THE THEORY OF FOURIER'S SERIES, E. W .Hobson. One of the best introductions to set theory and various aspects of functions and Fourier's series. Requires only a good background in calculus. Exhaustive coverage of: metric and descriptive properties of sets of points; transfinite numbers and order types; functions of a real variable; the Riemann and Lebesgue integrals; sequences and series of numbers; power-series; functions representable by series sequences of continuous functions; trigonometrical series; representation of functions by Fourier's series; and much more. "The best possible guide," Nature. Vol. I: 88 detailed examples, 10 figures. Index. xv + 736pp. Vol. II: 117 detailed examples, 13 figures. x + 780pp. 6⅛ x 9¼.
                                                          Vol. I: S387 Paperbound **$3.00**
                                                          Vol. II: S388 Paperbound **$3.00**

ALMOST PERIODIC FUNCTIONS, A. S. Besicovitch. Unique and important summary by a well known mathematician covers in detail the two stages of development in Bohr's theory of almost periodic functions: (1) as a generalization of pure periodicity, with results and proofs; (2) the work done by Stepanof, Wiener, Weyl, and Bohr in generalizing the theory. xi + 180pp. 5⅜ x 8.   S18 Paperbound **$1.75**

INTRODUCTION TO THE THEORY OF FOURIER'S SERIES AND INTEGRALS, H. S. Carslaw. 3rd revised edition, an outgrowth of author's courses at Cambridge. Historical introduction, rational, irrational numbers, infinite sequences and series, functions of a single variable, definite integral, Fourier series, and similar topics. Appendices discuss practical harmonic analysis, periodogram analysis, Lebesgue's theory. 84 examples. xiii + 368pp. 5⅜ x 8.
                                                                           S48 Paperbound **$2.00**

SYMBOLIC LOGIC

THE ELEMENTS OF MATHEMATICAL LOGIC, Paul Rosenbloom. First publication in any language. For mathematically mature readers with no training in symbolic logic. Development of lectures given at Lund Univ., Sweden, 1948. Partial contents: Logic of classes, fundamental theorems, Boolean algebra, logic of propositions, of propositional functions, expressive languages, combinatory logics, development of math within an object language, paradoxes, theorems of Post, Goedel, Church, and similar topics. iv + 214pp. 5⅜ x 8.
                                                                           S227 Paperbound **$1.45**

INTRODUCTION TO SYMBOLIC LOGIC AND ITS APPLICATION, R. Carnap. Clear, comprehensive, rigorous, by perhaps greatest living master. Symbolic languages analyzed, one constructed. Applications to math (axiom systems for set theory, real, natural numbers), topology (Dedekind, Cantor continuity explanations), physics (general analysis of determination, causality, space-time topology), biology (axiom system for basic concepts). "A masterpiece," Zentralblatt für Mathematik und Ihre Grenzgebiete. Over 300 exercises. 5 figures. xvi + 241pp. 5⅜ x 8.   S453 Paperbound **$1.85**

AN INTRODUCTION TO SYMBOLIC LOGIC, Susanne K. Langer. Probably clearest book for the philosopher, scientist, layman—no special knowledge of math required. Starts with simplest symbols, goes on to give remarkable grasp of Boole-Schroeder, Russell-Whitehead systems, clearly, quickly. Partial Contents: Forms, Generalization, Classes, Deductive System of Classes, Algebra of Logic, Assumptions of Principia Mathematica, Logistics, Proofs of Theorems, etc. "Clearest . . . simplest introduction . . . the intelligent non-mathematician should have no difficulty," MATHEMATICS GAZETTE. Revised, expanded 2nd edition. Truth-value tables. 368pp. 5⅜ 8.   S164 Paperbound **$1.75**

TRIGONOMETRICAL SERIES, Antoni Zygmund. On modern advanced level. Contains carefully organized analyses of trigonometric, orthogonal, Fourier systems of functions, with clear adequate descriptions of summability of Fourier series, proximation theory, conjugate series, convergence, divergence of Fourier series. Especially valuable for Russian, Eastern European coverage. 329pp. 5⅜ x 8.   S290 Paperbound **$1.50**

THE LAWS OF THOUGHT, George Boole. This book founded symbolic logic some 100 years ago. It is the 1st significant attempt to apply logic to all aspects of human endeavour. Partial contents: derivation of laws, signs and laws, interpretations, eliminations, conditions of a perfect method, analysis, Aristotelian logic, probability, and similar topics. xvii + 424pp. 5⅜ x 8.   S28 Paperbound **$2.00**

SYMBOLIC LOGIC, C. I. Lewis, C. H. Langford. 2nd revised edition of probably most cited book in symbolic logic. Wide coverage of entire field; one of fullest treatments of paradoxes; plus much material not available elsewhere. Basic to volume is distinction between logic of extensions and intensions. Considerable emphasis on converse substitution, while matrix system presents supposition of variety of non-Aristotelian logics. Especially valuable sections on strict limitations, existence theorems. Partial contents: Boole-Schroeder algebra; truth value systems, the matrix method; implication and deductibility; general theory of propositions; etc. "Most valuable," Times, London. 506pp. 5⅜ x 8.   S170 Paperbound **$2.00**

GROUP THEORY AND LINEAR ALGEBRA, SETS, ETC.

LECTURES ON THE ICOSAHEDRON AND THE SOLUTION OF EQUATIONS OF THE FIFTH DEGREE, Felix Klein. Solution of quintics in terms of rotations of regular icosahedron around its axes of symmetry. A classic, indispensable source for those interested in higher algebra, geometry, crystallography. Considerable explanatory material included. 230 footnotes, mostly bibliography. "Classical monograph . . . detailed, readable book," Math. Gazette. 2nd edition. xvi + 289pp. 5⅜ x 8.   S314 Paperbound **$1.85**

INTRODUCTION TO THE THEORY OF GROUPS OF FINITE ORDER, R. Carmichael. Examines fundamental theorems and their applications. Beginning with sets, systems, permutations, etc., progresses in easy stages through important types of groups: Abelian, prime power, permutation, etc. Except 1 chapter where matrices are desirable, no higher math is needed. 783 exercises, problems. xvi + 447pp. 5⅜ x 8.   S299 Clothbound **$3.95**
                                                          S300 Paperbound **$2.00**

THEORY OF GROUPS OF FINITE ORDER, W. Burnside. First published some 40 years ago, still one of clearest introductions. Partial contents: permutations, groups independent of representation, composition series of a group, isomorphism of a group with itself, Abelian groups, prime power groups, permutation groups, invariants of groups of linear substitution, graphical representation, etc. "Clear and detailed discussion . . . numerous problems which are instructive," Design News. xxiv + 512pp. 5⅜ x 8.   S38 Paperbound **$2.45**

COMPUTATIONAL METHODS OF LINEAR ALGEBRA, V. N. Faddeeva, translated by C. D. Benster. 1st English translation of unique, valuable work, only one in English presenting systematic exposition of most important methods of linear algebra—classical, contemporary. Details of deriving numerical solutions of problems in mathematical physics. Theory and practice. Includes survey of necessary background, most important methods of solution, for exact, iterative groups. One of most valuable features is 23 tables, triple checked for accuracy, unavailable elsewhere. Translator's note. x + 252pp. 5⅜ x 8.   S424 Paperbound **$1.95**

THE CONTINUUM AND OTHER TYPES OF SERIAL ORDER, E. V. Huntington. This famous book gives a systematic elementary account of the modern theory of the continuum as a type of serial order. Based on the Cantor-Dedekind ordinal theory, which requires no technical knowledge of higher mathematics, it offers an easily followed analysis of ordered classes, discrete and dense series, continuous series, Cantor's transfinite numbers. "Admirable introduction to the rigorous theory of the continuum . . . reading easy," Science Progress. 2nd edition. viii + 82pp. 5⅜ x 8.   S129 Clothbound **$2.75**
                                                          S130 Paperbound **$1.00**

THEORY OF SETS, E. Kamke. Clearest, amplest introduction in English, well suited for independent study. Subdivisions of main theory, such as theory of sets of points, are discussed, but emphasis is on general theory. Partial contents: rudiments of set theory, arbitrary sets, their cardinal numbers, ordered sets, their order types, well-ordered sets, their cardinal numbers. vii + 144pp. 5⅜ x 8.   S141 Paperbound **$1.35**

CONTRIBUTIONS TO THE FOUNDING OF THE THEORY OF TRANSFINITE NUMBERS, Georg Cantor. These papers founded a new branch of mathematics. The famous articles of 1895-7 are translated, with an 82-page introduction by P. E. B. Jourdain dealing with Cantor, the background of his discoveries, their results, future possibiilties. ix + 211pp. 5⅜ x 8.
                                                          S45 Paperbound **$1.25**

NUMERICAL AND GRAPHICAL METHODS, TABLES

JACOBIAN ELLIPTIC FUNCTION TABLES, L. M. Milne-Thomson. Easy-to-follow, practical, not only useful numerical tables, but complete elementary sketch of application of elliptic functions. Covers description of principle properties; complete elliptic integrals; Fourier series, expansions; periods, zeros, poles, residues, formulas for special values of argument; cubic, quartic polynomials; pendulum problem; etc. Tables, graphs form body of book: Graph, 5 figure table of elliptic function sn (u m); cn (u m); dn (u m). 8 figure table of complete elliptic integrals K, K′, E, E′, nome q. 7 figure table of Jacobian zeta-function Z(u). 3 figures. xi + 123pp. 5⅜ x 8. **S194 Paperbound $1.35**

TABLES OF FUNCTIONS WITH FORMULAE AND CURVES, E. Jahnke, F. Emde. Most comprehensive 1-volume English text collection of tables, formulae, curves of transcendent functions. 4th corrected edition, new 76-page section giving tables, formulae for elementary functions not in other English editions. Partial contents: sine, cosine, logarithmic integral; error integral; elliptic integrals; theta functions; Legendre, Bessel, Riemann, Mathieu, hypergeometric functions; etc. "Out-of-the-way functions for which we know no other source." Scientific Computing Service, Ltd. 212 figures. 400pp. 5⅝ x 8⅜. **S133 Paperbound $2.00**

MATHEMATICAL TABLES, H. B. Dwight. Covers in one volume almost every function of importance in applied mathematics, engineering, physical sciences. Three extremely fine tables of the three trig functions, inverses, to 1000th of radian; natural, common logs; squares, cubes; hyperbolic functions, inverses; $(a^2 + b^2)$ exp: ½a; complete elliptical integrals of 1st, 2nd kind; sine, cosine integrals; exponential integrals; Ei(x) and Ei(−x); binomial coefficients; factorials to 250; surface zonal harmonics, first derivatives; Bernoulli, Euler numbers, their logs to base of 10; Gamma function; normal probability integral; over 60pp. Bessel functions; Riemann zeta function. Each table with formulae generally used, sources of more extensive tables, interpolation data, etc. Over half have columns of differences, to facilitate interpolation. viii + 231pp. 5⅜ x 8. **S445 Paperbound $1.75**

PRACTICAL ANALYSIS, GRAPHICAL AND NUMERICAL METHODS, F. A. Willers. Immensely practical hand-book for engineers. How to interpolate, use various methods of numerical differentiation and integration, determine roots of a single algebraic equation, system of linear equations, use empirical formulas, integrate differential equations, etc. Hundreds of short-cuts for arriving at numerical solutions. Special section on American calculating machines, by T. W. Simpson. Translation by R. T. Beyer. 132 illustrations. 422pp. 5⅜ x 8.
S273 Paperbound $2.00

NUMERICAL SOLUTIONS OF DIFFERENTIAL EQUATIONS, H. Levy, E. A. Baggott. Comprehensive collection of methods for solving ordinary differential equations of first and higher order. 2 requirements: practical, easy to grasp; more rapid than school methods. Partial contents: graphical integration of differential equations, graphical methods for detailed solution. Numerical solution. Simultaneous equations and equations of 2nd and higher orders. "Should be in the hands of all in research and applied mathematics, teaching," Nature. 21 figures. viii + 238pp. 5⅜ x 8. **S168 Paperbound $1.75**

NUMERICAL INTEGRATION OF DIFFERENTIAL EQUATIONS, Bennet, Milne, Bateman. Unabridged republication of original prepared for National Research Council. New methods of integration by 3 leading mathematicians: "The Interpolational Polynomial," "Successive Approximation," A. A. Bennett, "Step-by-step Methods of Integration," W. W. Milne. "Methods for Partial Differential Equations," H. Bateman. Methods for partial differential equations, solution of differential equations to non-integral values of a parameter will interest mathematicians, physicists. 288 footnotes, mostly bibliographical. 235 item classified bibliography. 108pp. 5⅜ x 8. **S305 Paperbound $1.35**

Write for free catalogs!

Indicate your field of interest. Dover publishes books on physics, earth sciences, mathematics, engineering, chemistry, astronomy, anthropology, biology, psychology, philosophy, religion, history, literature, mathematical recreations, languages, crafts, art, graphic arts, etc.

Write to Dept. catr
Dover Publications, Inc.
Science A   *180 Varick St., N. Y. 14, N. Y.*

4648